LABORATORY TEXT

IN

ORGANIC CHEMISTRY

Third Edition

LABORATORY TEXT
IN
ORGANIC CHEMISTRY

JAMES CASON

Professor of Chemistry
University of California at Berkeley

HENRY RAPOPORT

Professor of Chemistry
University of California at Berkeley

PRENTICE-HALL, INC., Englewood Cliffs, New Jersey

PRENTICE-HALL INTERNATIONAL, INC., London
PRENTICE-HALL OF AUSTRALIA, PTY. LTD., Sydney
PRENTICE-HALL OF CANADA, LTD., Toronto
PRENTICE-HALL OF INDIA PRIVATE LTD., New Delhi
PRENTICE-HALL OF JAPAN, INC., Tokyo

Preface

This edition of *Laboratory Text in Organic Chemistry* represents extensive revision; however, the basic concept of the book has not changed. The authors continue to feel that the prime function of laboratory work in general organic chemistry is the teaching of the techniques, skills, and philosophies involved in the synthesis, purification, and identification of organic compounds. Illustration of lecture material is delegated to a secondary position and is introduced only as a part of experiments designed primarily to contribute toward the accomplishment of the principal objective stated above. For these reasons, a majority of the experiments are concerned with a study of important techniques or a study of synthetic methods. "Test-tube experiments" are confined, for the most part, to brief tests made on compounds synthesized by the students, except for the introduction to separation and characterization of organic compounds offered in Chapter 30. Further, synthesis on a "semimicro" scale has been avoided, for the authors' experience with graduate students of varied undergraduate training indicates strongly that the type of "semimicro" synthetic work presented in undergraduate courses teaches the student very little about the handling of materials and equipment. Furthermore, in the modern-day undergraduate curriculum there is unlikely to be any course other than organic chemistry in which the student will learn to handle materials. As concerns the manipulation of the small amounts frequently involved in research in the day of the spectrometer, the student acquires an ideal introduction to this type of experimentation during the work involved in separation and identification of organic compounds (Chap. 30).

The inclusion in the elementary course of a scheme for separation and identification of organic compounds, which first appeared in the second edition, has proved quite successful in practice. Thus, this material (Chap. 30) has been expanded somewhat and substantially revised so that the Procedures are more reliable. This seems especially appropriate since the traditional advanced course on characterization of organic compounds is taught at fewer colleges. Where such a course is retained, it is appropriately devoted to extensive applications of spectroscopy, so that the student profits from having had previous training in the "wet chemistry" involved. A total of ten or twelve 3-hour laboratory periods at the end of the elementary course is recommended for the work on separation and identification.

In view of the truly great importance of separation procedures that are useful both for analysis and for supplying small samples for spectrometry, detailed chapters on gas phase chromatography and thin sheet chromatography are introduced at a rather early stage in the sequence (Chaps. 4 and 7). The latter chapter includes both paper chromatography and thin layer chromatography. In accord with the general philosophy of the book, emphasis is placed on both the experimental techniques and the principles behind the procedures.

As regards the study of spectra, the experimental determination of spectra is not described; however, applications of spectroscopy are included. In Chapter 10 is described the analysis of an alkene mixture by a combination of gas chromatography and nuclear magnetic resonance (NMR) spectroscopy. In appropriate chapters, especially Chapters 12 and 15, the infrared absorption characteristics of polar functional groups are described and spectra are included. As an illustration of more simple analytical techniques, an experiment on the solvolysis of *tert*-butyl bromide is included (Chap. 8).

As in earlier editions, several syntheses of heterocyclic compounds are included. This seems appropriate in view of the continuing importance of these compounds. Also continued is the avoidance of the lowest molecular weight compounds, which are quite atypical of the series as a whole.

The experiments described in the first thirty chapters may be performed with relatively simple equipment, while the final nine chapters are devoted to techniques and syntheses requiring more expensive equipment such as mechanical stirrers, relatively effective fractional distillation columns, three-necked flasks with ground joints, and equipment for vacuum distillation. In these final chapters are described a major percentage of the techniques and equipment utilized in carrying out research in organic chemistry. Also in these chapters are illustrations of the remarkable effectiveness as solvents of dimethyl sulfoxide (DMSO) and dimethoxyethane (DME or glyme).

Included in the less expensive equipment are certain items not usually found in elementary laboratory books, but which are quite convenient. These pieces of apparatus are illustrated in appropriate places, including Appendix I, in which is listed the equipment required for the experiments described. The additional items of equipment required for work in the final nine chapters are entered separately. As a part of the less expensive equipment are described pieces of glassware with ground joints which cost a total of about thirty-five dollars (only about twice the cost of alternate equipment it replaces). This relatively modest investment allows performance of most of the manipulations without boring of corks or stoppers; however, an alternate list of equipment without ground joints is presented. The experiments are described so that either type of equipment may be utilized.

In the Introduction, there are recommended specific procedures for the operation of an elementary laboratory course in organic chemistry. Although our hope is that these procedures may prove of interest to other instructors and to students, they are presented in full awareness that a teacher is likely to develop his own methods, based on his personal experience and local conditions. Our conditions involve relatively large classes, but with laboratories in small rooms accommodating a maximum of 24 students in one section, with a graduate teaching assistant for each room.

The authors gratefully acknowledge the substantial assistance received in preparation of this book from their many colleagues who have shared teaching the elementary course at Berkeley. Important contributions have been made also by many of the teaching assistants who have assisted with the courses, as well as several advanced undergraduate students who did the experimental work involved in developing new procedures. Worthy of specific note are the development of the solvolysis of *tert*-butyl bromide by Professor D. S. Noyce and Professor A. Streitwieser, the NMR analysis of methylcyclohexenes by Professor G. L. Kenyon, and the bromination of chlorobenzene by Professor C. H. Heathcock.

J. C.
H. R.

Contents

LABORATORY TEXT

IN

ORGANIC CHEMISTRY

Introduction

1

The experiments in this laboratory text are designed to accompany the lecture material in an elementary course in organic chemistry; however, illustration of lecture material should be regarded as a minor function of the experiments. The purpose is more concerned with expansion and extension of lecture material, and, above all, with teaching the techniques, skills, and philosophies involved in carrying out experimental work in organic chemistry. These objectives should be kept well in mind as the experiments are performed.

Since thoughtless performance of the experiments rapidly degenerates into routine following of a prescription, as from a cookbook, with the chemicals receiving more exercise than the student, study of the experiment prior to performance is of prime importance. Further, a discussion period in the laboratory before each experiment is of great utility. Such discussions are of value for emphasizing and clarifying the principles involved in the experiments, demonstrating any new techniques or apparatus, and pointing out any physical hazards that may be encountered. The manner in which a record of the experiment is recorded in a notebook is also of fundamental significance in connection with understanding the work that is done. Proper training in keeping a good notebook is of particular importance to anyone whose subsequent career brings him into the fascinating explorations involved in scientific research. A detailed procedure for the notebook record is described below.

Experiments are appropriately rated on the basis of the experimental skill displayed, the quality and quantity of the product, and the notebook write-up; hence, due attention should be directed to all these aspects of the work. In order that a student may have an indication of the rate at which it is reasonable to perform experiments, there may be issued at the beginning of a term a schedule on which due dates for the experiments are specified. Average times required for the experiments may be found in Appendix II.

The first several experiments consist of nonpreparative procedures designed to acquaint the student with apparatus and techniques used in carrying out the subsequent preparations and, especially, in isolating and purifying the products. Advanced experimental techniques are described in Chaps. 31–33. The remaining experiments are primarily of a preparative type, the making of organic compounds. In each of these chapters which is devoted to organic synthesis, a uniform pattern is followed which involves discussion of (1) the main reactions, (2) the side reactions, and (3) the purification procedure used for isolating the product. This approach has as its objective familiarizing the student with the principles involved so that he will be less prone to follow the directions without any conception of the significance of the operations; furthermore, it furnishes a background for the explanations of the ratios of reagents specified and the choice of synthetic method. Chapter 30 is devoted to an introduction to the study of methods of separating and characterizing organic compounds. These topics are of sufficient importance that an advanced course is frequently devoted entirely to their study; however, an introduction to the methods used is in order in the elementary course.

NOTEBOOKS AND REPORTS

For reporting experiments, a bound notebook of approximately 8½ × 11 inches is recommended. After an experiment has been performed and the notebook write-up is complete, the notebook is presented to the laboratory instructor, who checks it and may ask questions concerning the experiment. The form in which the notebook report is made will depend on whether the experiment is *preparative* or *nonpreparative*.

Nonpreparative Experiments

In this type of experiment, no prewrite-up is required; that is, no entries are made in the book before the experiment is performed. As the experiment is performed, a record of observations made, including any specified tables, is entered in the notebook. In case any tests involving chemical reactions are performed, balanced equations for these reactions must always be included in the write-up. When the experiment is reported, the instructor checks and initials the notebook.

Preparative Experiments

These experiments are reported in a formal manner as described below, and *all entries up to and including the calculation of theoretical yield* must be in the notebook before the experiment is begun. The experiments are written up in several sections. Of these sections, those numbered I–III appear on the *left-hand page*, and those numbered IV–VII appear on the *right-hand page*. Thus, the essential data pertaining to a given preparation are on a double page in the notebook.

Left-hand page:

 I. Main reactions
 II. Side reactions
 III. Other methods of preparation

Right-hand page:

 IV. Table of reactants and products (illustrated under ethyl iodide, Chap. 8)
 V. Yield data
    Theoretical yield
    Actual yield
    Percentage yield
 VI. Observed properties of product (melting point, boiling point, gas chromatography tracing, and so on)
 VII. Description of short experiments or tests (including equations for any reactions)

After the notebook has been written up as far as calculation of theoretical yield, it is presented to the laboratory instructor, who checks and initials it. The approved notebook must then be presented at the storeroom in order to obtain one of the starting materials for the experiment. After the preparation has been completed, appropriate entries are made in sections V, VI, and VII, then the experiment is reported to the laboratory instructor, who initials the notebook. At this time, the material prepared is also given to the instructor, in a labeled bottle (wide-mouthed bottle for solids, narrow-mouthed, glass-stoppered bottle for liquids). Small plastic bags are also satisfactory for solids. On the label is printed the name of the substance, its melting point or boiling point, the actual and percentage yields, and the student's name. An illustration of a properly prepared label follows.

```
ETHYL IODIDE
B.P. 69–72°
YIELD 27.6 g (75.2%)
FRANCISCO GOMEZ
```

SAFETY PRECAUTIONS

Although many things are involved in good technique in the organic laboratory, certain things are fundamentally important and should always be
borne in mind. These are listed below in two categories: *important points*
and *very important points.* Violation of the important points is likely to
lead to poor technical results and possibly to minor injury, whereas violation of the very important points may lead to permanent or fatal injury. In
order to encourage the student to respect these points, the instructors keep
a record of each student's violations, and this record is considered in determining the student's final grade for the course.

Very Important Points

1. Never heat inflammable solvents, even in small amounts, with *or
near* a flame unless the solvent is in a flask under reflux or attached to a
condenser for distillation. Do not pour inflammable solvents from one
vessel to another when a flame is near (within three feet).
2. When ether (diethyl ether) is being distilled, heat on a water bath
and use as a receiver an ice-cooled distilling flask attached to the condenser with a sound cork.
3. Never use carbon disulfide, diisopropyl ether, or tetrahydrofuran
except with specific authorization and instructions.
4. Never heat a closed system of any kind.
5. It is not regarded as discreet to heat or mix *anything* close to the face.
Keep the face as far back as possible during *all* heating or mixing operations. A *special alert* should be maintained against violation of this very
important point, for it is instinctive to hold a vessel directly in front of the
face when pouring into it, especially if a volume is being measured.
6. Never work in the laboratory except during a regular period when
an instructor is present. Any exceptions to this must be specifically authorized in writing by the *instructor in charge of the course.*
7. *Everyone* in the laboratory, including teachers, must wear some
type of eye glasses at all times, and this applies equally to those who are,
and those who are not, doing actual experimental work at a given moment.
Ordinary glasses are regarded as sufficient for routine wear, since they will
nearly always prevent damage to the eyes that might result unexpectedly in
elementary laboratory work. In case experiments involving known hazards, especially hazard of explosion, are being undertaken, either a complete face shield or goggles equipped with safety glasses and side shields
should be worn.

Important Points

1. Keep your working space neat at all times and clean when you leave for the day. Neatness is good technique, and technique is one of the things on which a student is graded.

2. Avoid unstable assemblies of apparatus, such as props consisting of books, pencils, matchboxes, and the like. Assemblies with a high center of gravity (as when a reagent is added through the top of a condenser) should be assembled and operated with extreme caution.

3. In boring corks, use the cork borer as a cutting instrument, not as a gouging instrument. Do not bore against a piece of wood, such as the top or sides of the desk.

4. In forcing glass tubing through a cork or stopper, do not use any part of the anatomy as a backstop for the tubing because it might break. When pushing the cork, hold the tubing very close to the cork. Whenever possible, *pull* the cork on. Never push a cork on the side arm of a distilling flask while holding the flask; hold the *side arm* close to the cork.

When forcing a rubber hose on a glass tube, always moisten the tube with glycerol or smear it very lightly with silicone grease. This makes the hose slip on easily.

5. A flexible metal spatula is usually recommended for breaking up caked solids in bottles. Do not use a glass stirring rod, for it is likely to break and cause injury. Do not use a tool sufficiently heavy and rigid to easily break the bottle, for this also may result in injury.

6. An Erlenmeyer flask is commonly used for crystallization. Never crystallize from a beaker unless specifically directed to do so.

7. Do not place volatile solvents in a beaker, even for short periods of time.

8. Taste nothing in the laboratory unless specifically directed to do so.

9. Never assemble apparatus over a sink or deliver distillate into a sink.

10. Do not evacuate a flat-bottomed flask unless it is a heavy-walled suction flask. Erlenmeyer flasks are especially likely to collapse.

11. Materials that give off noxious fumes should be handled in a forced-draft hood. Such materials include phosphorus trichloride, bromine, chlorosulfonic acid, benzenesulfonyl chloride, fuming nitric acid, acetyl chloride, and others.

12. Use care in disposing of hazardous chemicals, whether residual lots or unused lots. This applies especially to substances reacting violently with water, such as sodium metal, acetyl chloride, and chlorosulfonic acid. Poisonous, water-soluble substances, such as potassium cyanide, should be put

directly into a drain and washed down thoroughly. Concentrated sulfuric acid should be added to water, not vice versa.

If the above points are ignored, it is wise to read the following paragraphs with particular care.

IN CASE OF ACCIDENT

The most common minor accident is that of cutting the hand with glass tubing. Such a cut is ordinarily treated by applying an antiseptic and bandaging. However, this kind of cut may need special attention. If the rate of blood flow indicates that an artery or vein has been cut, a tourniquet should be put on the arm at once and a physician consulted. If the forearm or hand has been seriously cut, and control of one or more fingers has been lost, a tendon has probably been cut and a physician should be consulted at once. It is best to have a physician examine any deep cut for glass, but this is especially indicated if the cut is sensitive to pressure, or if the piece of glass was shattered.

In case of *fire, the student's first concern should be to remove himself from danger.* In no case should a hasty effort be made to extinguish the fire before it is noticed by an instructor. This is a good way to get the clothing on fire. Only after one's own safety is assured should the matter of extinguishing the fire be considered. Since all laboratories should be adequately equipped for fighting fire, the only hazard is to the people in the vicinity of the fire. If the clothing does catch fire, it is imperative that the person not run, but that he lie on the floor and smother the flames. Among other things, this keeps the flames away from the head. When a person's clothes are on fire, he usually needs help from his neighbors or the instructors in smothering the flames with a fire blanket, a coat, or anything that can be seized instantly. Because a few seconds' delay can result in very serious injury, every person in the laboratory should plan in advance what he will do in case of such an emergency to himself or his neighbor.

If corrosive or hot reagents get into the eyes, the most important thing is to flood the eyes *immediately* with water. As soon as the outsides of the eyes are well washed, the eyes should be forced open and irrigated with plenty of water. This should be continued for at least two or three minutes. Then a bland oil should be put into the eyes, and a physician consulted as quickly as possible. Delay at this point is especially hazardous. Each student should locate the water outlet nearest his desk which is suitable for eye washing and fix its position so well in mind that he can find it with his eyes shut.

The general treatment for corrosive reagents on the skin is immediate, thorough scrubbing with soap and water, followed by massage with glycerine. For most chemical burns, it is very poor policy to apply a burn ointment. Such preparations usually contain grease, and this helps the reagent to penetrate the tissue.

The Melting Point

2

The physical properties of a substance, such as crystalline form, melting point, boiling point, gas chromatographic behavior, and spectral properties, are useful characteristics for recognizing and identifying organic compounds. For solid substances, a useful property is the melting point. It may be determined rapidly and accurately, using simple apparatus and small samples of material, yet it furnishes valuable information as to the compound's identity and purity. This combination of ease and significance makes a melting-point determination of wide applicability for recognizing a known compound as well as characterizing a new one. For rigorous confirmation of identity, the melting point is supplemented by determination of gas chromatographic behavior and spectral properties.

The manner in which a melting point indicates a compound's purity and identity is an important consideration which should be well understood by a student of organic chemistry. The *melting point of a substance is defined* as the temperature at which liquid and solid may exist in equilibrium with each other. In other words, at this temperature the escaping tendency of molecules from the solid phase is just equal to the escaping tendency from the liquid phase. When the solid and liquid are in contact, molecules are constantly passing from solid to liquid phase and vice versa, but there is no net change in the amount of each phase unless heat is added to or taken from the system. When molecules pass from the solid state to the liquid state, heat is absorbed (heat of fusion); therefore, if heat is put into the system some of the solid melts, and if enough heat is added all the solid will melt. Conversely, if heat is removed from the system some of the liquid crystallizes, or freezes, and if enough heat is removed all the liquid

8

will freeze. Thus, the melting point and freezing point are the same temperature. Finally, it should be pointed out that, as heat is slowly removed from the system, the temperature of the system will not drop until all the liquid freezes, for heat is evolved by the crystallization. Only after all the liquid has crystallized does the temperature begin to drop, unless heat is removed so rapidly that crystallization cannot occur sufficiently rapidly to supply enough heat to balance the loss. Thus, a *characteristic of a pure compound* is that a mixture of solid and melt remains at a constant temperature (the melting point of the compound) unless enough heat is supplied to melt all the solid or enough heat is withdrawn to crystallize all the liquid.

Let us now refer to Fig. 1 and consider a sample of substance A, melting at 130°, to which has been added a small amount of substance B. If this mixture is melted and then allowed to cool, the substance which crystallizes out is A, so long as the amount of substance B present is less than that at the composition (40% of B) giving the lowest point, E, on the curve in Fig. 1. The escaping tendency of molecules from this solid substance A naturally remains the same at a given temperature as if it were in contact with pure liquid A, but the escaping tendency of A from the liquid is now less because it is diluted with some B in the liquid. It follows that A cannot be in equilibrium at 130° (the melting point of A) with a melt which is a

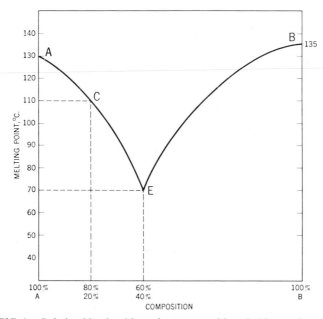

FIG. 1.   Relationship of melting point to composition of a binary mixture.

mixture of A and B; the solid A will melt into the mixture. As the temperature is lowered, however, the escaping tendency from a solid proves to decrease more rapidly than is the case in a liquid; therefore, as the temperature is lowered below 130° there is eventually reached a temperature at which solid A and the liquid mixture become in equilibrium. *In other words, the mixture of A and B has a lower melting point than does pure A*. This commonly observed phenomenon is responsible for the fact that the freezing point of water is lowered by the addition of salt. Similarly, addition of "antifreeze" to the water in an automobile radiator lowers the temperature at which freezing (crystallization of water) will occur.

As the amount of substance B in a mixture of A and B is increased, the equilibrium temperature at which A begins to crystallize becomes lower and lower, following curve ACE until finally the low point in the curve, E, is reached. As the amount of B is increased still further, beyond 40%, then B begins to crystallize as the melt is cooled; and as the amount of B is increased the equilibrium temperature now becomes higher, for there is a lower concentration of A in the melt. Increasing amounts of B (thus lower concentrations of A) in the mixture cause higher and higher equilibrium temperatures, following along curve EB, until finally there is reached the point where pure B has the melting point of 135°.

Thus, a mixture of A and B will exhibit a lower melting point than a pure component; furthermore, there is another behavior characteristic of mixtures which readily distinguishes them from pure substances, and which should be discussed next. As mentioned above, the curve in Fig. 1 represents the temperatures for various compositions where solid begins to appear in equilibrium with the liquid. From this it follows that the compositions plotted on the x axis are liquid compositions in equilibrium with solid A or B at the respective temperatures. Thus, solid A is in equilibrium at 110° with a melt containing 80% of A and 20% of B. Let us now consider further cooling of this melt of a mixture containing 20% of B which, according to Fig. 1, begins to deposit crystals of A at 110°. As heat is removed from the mixture, more of A crystallizes from the melt; therefore, the concentration of A in the melt becomes less. Since the melt now has a lower concentration of A, it is in equilibrium with solid A at a lower temperature. As crystallization of A continues, its concentration in the melt becomes progressively lower, and equilibrium between solid and melt occurs at a lower and lower temperature until finally point E is reached, at which point both A and B will begin to crystallize together. This will continue until all of the remaining melt has solidified at the temperature of 70°. If withdrawal of heat is continued, the solid will merely cool down.

From the discussion above, it follows that if a solid mixture containing 20% of B and 80% of A is heated, it will begin to melt at point E. As more heat is put into the mixture, A and B will melt together in the ratio of 60% *A* and 40% *B*, for this composition of liquid is in equilibrium with both *A* and *B*. When all of *B* has melted, as more heat is put in, the remaining *A* will begin to melt and thus increase the concentration of *A* in the melt, and raise the equilibrium temperature, following along curve *EC* until point *C* is reached, at which point the last of *A* will melt. Thus, *a mixture not only has a lower melting point than one of the pure components, but it has a broad melting range.*

The lowest point in a binary melting point curve, such as point *E* in Fig. 1, is known as the *eutectic point.* This is a very important point for at least two reasons. First, it is the dividing point in composition between crystallization of *A* from the melt or crystallization of *B*. Secondly, it is the only point at which both *A* and *B* can crystallize together. Thus, a *eutectic mixture* of two compounds (in Fig. 1, the mixture of 60% *A* and 40 % *B*) will melt "sharply," that is, at a constant temperature, just as a pure compound does. For this reason, a eutectic mixture is sometimes mistaken for a pure compound. If either of the two components is added to this mixture, however, the melting point will be raised.

Attention should also be called to the fact that the *eutectic point may occur at any composition*, even 99% of one component. The eutectic point may even occur at a 50% mixture of two components, so that the binary curve is entirely symmetrical; however, this is statistically unlikely except in the case of two compounds that are nearly identical. In case two components, which may be termed *X* and *Y*, have a eutectic containing only a few percent of one, say 3% of *Y*, a behavior is encountered which may puzzle one unaware of this possibility, especially if *Y* melts considerably above *X*. In such a situation, the melting point of the eutectic is likely to lie only a very few degrees below the true melting point of pure *X*. In this instance, if one adds a relatively small amount of *Y* to *X*, say 10%, he has passed beyond the eutectic and up the curve on the side where *Y* crystallizes. The "lowered melting point" usually expected for an impure compound is not observed; instead, the impure sample of *X* will melt higher than the pure sample (one is actually observing the melting point of impure *Y*). This behavior is uncommon, however, and purification of a compound, as by crystallization, which is discussed in the next chapter, is normally expected to give a higher and "sharper" (narrower range) melting point.

A very pure substance has a very sharp melting point which is not raised by further purification, and this is a very commonly accepted criterion for purity of a solid compound. Not only the location (temperature) of the melting point is important, therefore, but also the *range* of melting; and the range should always be reported, not just the temperature at which the last of the solid melts. The term "melting point," m.p., as used by the organic chemist, refers to the melting *range*. The point at which the last of the solid fuses is termed the "top" of the melting range.

The "bottom" of the melting range is taken as the point at which liquid may first be *seen*. It is apparent, from the discussion above, that any impure substance will first start to melt at the eutectic point; however, it is ordinarily not possible actually to see liquid until some higher temperature is reached, and the melting point is determined by visual observation. Thus, as a compound is purified, the bottom of the observed melting range nearly always rises as does the top of the range; and the range usually becomes "narrower" as the top of the range approaches the melting point of the pure substance. The best melting points ordinarily obtainable rarely have a range of less than 0.5°, and a substance with a range of one or two degrees is usually regarded as pure enough for most purposes.

The significance of melting-point behavior, as has been discussed, may be summarized as follows. If a substance is relatively pure, its melting range is very narrow and the top of this range is very near the true melting point. If a substance is impure, not only is the melting range broad, but the top of the range is below that of the true melting point. Thus the purification of an impure substance may be followed by the determination of the melting point, and, when this becomes sharp and reaches the correct temperature, the substance may be considered pure.

Also, the identity of a compound may be established by the use of the melting point, even if one is confronted with two or more substances having nearly identical melting points. Suppose a substance melting at 125° is isolated from a reaction. A study of its chemical properties and a search in the literature reveal several compounds melting at or very near 125° that might be identical with the unknown compound. To prove or disprove the identity, a sample of the unknown compound is mixed with a sample of the known compound and the melting point of the mixture is determined. This procedure is known as a *mixed melting-point* determination. If the compounds are the same, the mixture will melt at the same temperature as each compound separately. If the compounds are different, the melting point of the mixture will be lower and have a broad range. This comparison of melting-point behavior is most effectively accomplished by placing three melting-point tubes in the same heated bath. One tube contains the compound of known identity, another contains the compound of unknown identity, and the third contains the mixture of the two. As a precaution against substances giving a eutectic point occurring at a composition containing only a few per cent of one component, as discussed above, the range should be noted with care. In doubtful cases, melting points should be determined for mixtures of more than one composition.

The great majority of solid substances behave as has been described; however, there are significant numbers of compounds whose behavior in melting is more complex. Two types of unusual behavior will be described briefly. Some compounds are polymorphic, that is, they crystallize in more than one crystal form. The crystal form which develops is normally a function of conditions of crystallization, especially temperature. If a compound does exist in more than one crystal form, the polymorphs nearly always exhibit different melting points. In some instances, polymorphs differ in melting point by 25° or more. Furthermore, a mixture of two polymorphs behaves like any other mixture of different crystals; there is a broad melting-point range. In case one polymorph changes to the other as the mixture is melting, this further complicates interpretation of the melting-point behavior. It often becomes necessary to resort to absorption spectroscopy in order to characterize compounds exhibiting polymorphism.

Compounds which are not polymorphic sometimes give abnormal melting-point diagrams; the curve may not slope regularly down to the eutectic, as in Fig. 1. For example, addition of several per cent of compound B to compound A may not lower the melting point of compound B; that is, the part of the curve represented by AC in Fig. 1 could be flat (parallel to the x axis). Other compounds give double eutectic curves, with compositions between the two eutectics having higher melting points than either of the eutectic mixtures. Such situations are not commonplace, but neither are they extremely rare. The student of organic chemistry should be aware of their existence.

A simple apparatus for determining melting points is illustrated in Fig. 2, and the method of using this apparatus is described in the next section. The sample is placed in the bottom of a capillary tube, sealed at the lower end, which is then attached to a 360° partial-immersion thermometer. The thermometer is supported in a cork stopper in which has been drilled a hole of suitable size to receive the thermometer. The cork is slotted (cf. Fig. 2) so as to allow visibility of the entire scale and at the same time provide a vent for the expanding air during heating. A 30-ml Kjeldahl flask is used as the containing vessel, because the shape of the bulb promotes a good degree of mixing by the convection currents set up in the liquid during heating. A satisfactory, cheap liquid for the bath is cottonseed oil,[1] which may be heated safely to about 250°. At higher tem-

---

[1]Cottonseed oil becomes discolored sufficiently to interfere with visibility after prolonged heating, especially above 200°, but it may be heated as high as 250° before smoking and danger of catching fire become excessive. A mineral oil, such as Nujol, remains clear longer than cottonseed oil, but is a much greater fire hazard above 200°, especially if a heated flask should be broken. Concentrated sulfuric acid is an ideal bath liquid in most respects, for it may be heated to about 290°, and if it becomes darkened it may be clarified by heating with a few crystals of potassium nitrate. A serious objection to sulfuric acid is its corrosive nature. When the thermometer is removed from the bath, in order to attach a capillary tube, a drop of acid from the thermometer is likely to get on the skin or clothes. Particular caution must be exercised to avoid breakage of a heated flask of sulfuric acid.

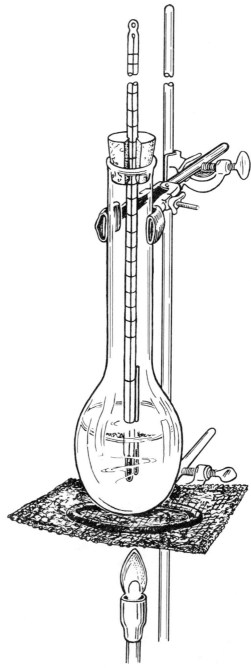

FIG. 2. Apparatus for determination of melting point by the capillary-tube method.

peratures than safely attainable with the liquid being used as a bath, an apparatus fabricated by suitable machining of a metal block is recommended.[2] For precision work, a useful type of apparatus[3] is one arranged so that the heated liquid is circulated by a mechanical stirrer. Material may be conserved by observing melting points under a microscope;[4] however, the melting point determined on a microscope hot stage is not strictly comparable with that determined in a capillary tube. For higher melting points, the discrepancy becomes greater between a capillary melting point and a hot-stage melting point; however, either is reproducible if proper techniques are used.

For research work to be reported in the chemical literature, melting points should be determined with use of calibrated thermometers. Calibration may be accomplished either by comparison with thermometers calibrated by the Federal Bureau of Standards, or by taking melting points of pure compounds whose melting points are accurately known.

STUDY OF MELTING POINTS

The Preparation of Melting-Point Capillaries

The capillary tubes are made from a piece of 9-mm soft glass tubing[5] by rotating the tubing lengthwise slowly and continuously in the hottest part of the flame from a Bunsen burner fitted with a wing-tip. When the

[2]A rather satisfactory commercially available apparatus is known as the Electrothermal Melting Point Apparatus, and is marketed by several laboratory supply houses. In 1969, prices for the same apparatus ranged from $193.50 to $265.00. This is one of numerous illustrations of the virtues of shopping around for scientific laboratory apparatus. Another satisfactory device, called Mel-Temp, is sold by Laboratory Devices, P. O. Box 68, Cambridge, Mass. 02139.

[3]An apparatus which may be built in the laboratory (using the piece of glassware obtainable from laboratory supply houses) has been described by E. B. Hershberg, *Ind. Eng. Chem.*, *Anal. Ed.*, **8**, 312 (1936). A commercial apparatus, manufactured in Switzerland, and known as the Dr. M. Tottoli Model of melting-point apparatus, is available from LaPine Scientific Co. at a price of more than $300.

[4]For observing melting points under a microscope, it is necessary to attach a "hot stage" to the instrument for heating the sample. The recommended device is the Kofler Micro Hot Stage, which is available commercially and was originally described by L. Kofler, *Mikrochemie*, **15**, 242 (1934).

[5]Actually, it is an advantage to prepare melting-point capillaries from Pyrex tubing, for the melting points of some compounds are affected by soft glass; however, Pyrex glass (or other brands of hard glass) cannot be worked in the flame from a Bunsen burner. Pyrex capillaries of 1.5-mm diameter, in 12-inch lengths, may be purchased for a nominal sum from Corning Glass Works, catalog No. 9530. If these tubes are scratched in the center and broken, each 6-inch length may be sealed in the center to give two 3-inch capillaries. The thin capillary tubing of hard glass may be sealed in the flame from a good Bunsen burner.

glass begins to sag, it is withdrawn from the flame; after a moment's hesitation, it is drawn out steadily, but not too rapidly, to about arms' span. After it has been allowed to cool, the resulting capillary section of 1–1.5-mm diameter is cut into suitable lengths (see below). Several trials will probably be necessary in order to learn just how much to heat the tubing and how fast to draw it out. Capillaries that are smaller should not be used because of the difficulty of inserting and seeing the sample; larger capillaries require too much sample and result in inaccurate melting points. The tubes are cut by scratching with the edge of a piece of broken clay plate[6] and broken into sections about 6 inches long. Each 6-inch section[5] is sealed in the middle by holding the center portion in a narrow flame (crosswise in the flame from a wing-tip) with rotation until the tube is melted through. The sealed tip of each 3-inch tube so obtained is touched to the edge of the flame until the sealed tip has become a tiny solid bead. It is important that tubes be sealed by heating away from an open end, as described. If sealing of an open end is attempted, two difficulties arise. First, complete sealing is difficult; there is likely to be left a tiny capillary opening through which the liquid from the melting-point bath will seep. Secondly, water from the flame is likely to condense in the tubing and remain to become an impurity in the sample placed in the tube for determination of melting point.

Since many melting points will be determined, the art of making capillary melting-point tubes should be practiced,[5] and a supply of about twenty-five tubes should be prepared. Since cleanliness of the tubes is imperative, if contamination of samples is to be avoided, they should be stored in a stoppered test tube.

Filling the Melting-Point Tube

The melting-point tube is filled by dipping its open end gently into a pile of previously powdered sample. A suitable small amount of sample may be powdered by grinding on a watch glass with a spatula. The material scooped into the open end of the tube is shaken down toward the closed end by gently tapping the tube on the bench top and is then packed tightly by repeatedly dropping the capillary through a vertical 6-mm glass tube about two feet long onto a hard surface. This operation, essential for packing the sample into the bottom of the capillary, makes apparent the importance of a solid seal at the bottom of the capillary. Not only is a light fragile tip likely to break, but it does not give a sudden shock when dropped on the bench, so the sample will not pack well.

---

[6]For scratching glass tubing, especially light capillary tubing, a convenient and cheap device is the small glass cutter used by the medical profession and others for opening small vials.

Determining Melting Points

The capillary is attached by touching it to the drop of liquid on the bulb of the partially withdrawn thermometer, and spreading this liquid along the side of the thermometer. The capillary is then placed against this wetted portion so that the sample is opposite the center of the thermometer bulb and is held there by capillary action. The thermometer, with attached capillary, is carefully placed in the heating bath so that its position is as shown in Fig. 2.

The bath is heated rapidly to about 15° below the melting point, after which the rate of heating is slowed down so that the temperature increase is about one to two degrees per minute at the melting point. If the melting point of a substance is completely unknown, much time can be saved by first making a rapid estimation, omitting the slower heating period, to ascertain the approximate melting point and then following this with a slower, more accurate determination. It must be remembered that the temperature of melting is recorded on the thermometer in the bath. If heating near the melting point is too rapid, the contents of the tube, even though it is a thin capillary tube, will not become thermally equilibrated with the bath; so too high a melting point will be recorded.

EXPERIMENTAL PROCEDURES

1. A small sample, (0.1–0.2 g) of cinnamic acid is pulverized on a watch glass by grinding with a spatula or a rounded glass rod, and its melting point is determined by the capillary-tube method. Similarly, the melting point of urea is determined.

2. A mixture of about 90% cinnamic acid and 10% urea is prepared. This mixture is made up by roughly estimating the sizes of long thin piles of the two substances. The substances are mixed by thorough grinding, and the melting point of the mixture is determined.

3. Similarly, the melting point of a mixture containing 10% cinnamic acid and 90% urea is determined.

4. In a similar manner, melting points are determined for the following mixtures of cinnamic acid and urea: 75:25, 50:50, and 25:75.

5. A table is made containing the melting points determined as above, and a melting-point composition diagram for urea-cinnamic acid is constructed. Since the eutectic for this mixture is rather far from a composition of 50%, it may prove necessary to determine one or two additional points in order to approximately locate the eutectic. It should also be remembered that the mixtures were prepared rather qualitatively; so some scatter of the points from a best line should be expected.

6. From the observations made in the experiments above, write a short, concise statement setting forth the differences in melting-point behavior of a pure substance and a mixture of two substances. If you were given two solids having the same melting point, how could you determine whether the two samples are the same substance or different substances?

7. The melting point of an unknown, obtained from the storeroom, is determined and reported.

Crystallization

3

A useful and frequently employed method for purification of solids is *crystallization*, a procedure which involves the conversion of a substance from some other form into the form of crystals. The process by which a substance forms crystals is extremely delicate and, in most cases, we find that molecules of only one species will fit readily into the spaces of the crystal lattice. In a few instances different substances will crystallize within the same lattice, but, except for solvent molecules, this is quite rare. This discriminating selectivity, plus several other properties discussed below, makes crystallization an excellent purification method.

Crystallization may be accomplished either from the fused state or from solution, but the latter is by far the best and most common method. When an impure substance is cooled below its melting point, it may crystallize. However, if cooling is continued until the entire material is solid, obviously no purification has taken place; the substance has been merely changed in state from a liquid to a solid. If the substance is only partly frozen, the crystals formed probably will be pure (see Chap. 2) but will be wet with liquid containing the impurity. By decanting the liquid, melting the solid, and then only partly freezing it again, an increased degree of purification can be obtained. Continued repetition of this process, called "fractional freezing," will ultimately give pure material. This method is only occasionally used, however, because a large amount of material must be wasted to eliminate a small amount of impurity. Another disadvantage to this method is that many organic substances are not stable to the melting and remelting required.

Crystallization from solution is the best and most generally applied method. The procedure consists of preparing a saturated solution of the substance to be purified at the boiling point of the solvent, filtering this hot solution, cooling the filtrate to effect crystallization, then filtering and drying the crystals. Every step in the process has a definite purpose in the purification procedure and involves rather exact techniques; both aspects will be discussed in detail below.

Selection of a Solvent

The first step, selection of a suitable solvent, is quite important. If the substance is known, a solvent for crystallization has usually been reported, and the best procedure is to turn to the literature for this information. However, if the substance is new, a solvent must be found, and, in many cases, it is difficult to predict what the solvent will be. In general, we may say that "like dissolves like"—that is, a substance will dissolve in a solvent containing similar groups—or better, that polar solvents will dissolve polar molecules and nonpolar solvents will dissolve nonpolar molecules. Frequently, a substance will dissolve in a solvent but will not crystallize on cooling; a second solvent, miscible with the first, in which the original substance is insoluble, must be added to cause crystallization. Even with these generalizations, it is very difficult to predict the best solvent for a new substance; frequently the method of trial and error may be used to advantage.

In searching for a suitable solvent, there are certain desirable features that should be kept in mind. The solvent should have a good temperature coefficient; that is, it should dissolve a large amount of the substance when hot and a very small amount when cold. The impurities should be either insoluble in the hot solvent or moderately soluble in the cold. The solvent should have a moderate boiling point so that it can be easily removed when drying the crystals, and it should not react chemically with the substance being purified. These last two characteristics may be evaluated from a knowledge of the chemical and physical properties of common solvents and of the substance being crystallized. It should also be mentioned that a solvent which is rather high-boiling, but otherwise satisfactory, may be washed off the crystals with some low-boiling solvent in which the substance being crystallized is relatively insoluble.

The trial-and-error method is especially widely used in determining the solubility characteristics of the substance. For this purpose, several small test tubes or centrifuge tubes are used to contain about 0.5-ml portions of any solvents whose properties are otherwise satisfactory. A few milligrams of the substance is added to each solvent, and any tubes in which the substance does not dissolve in the cold are heated. A choice is made on the basis stated above—the best solvent dissolves the most of the substance when hot and the least when cold; in other words, the recovery on crystallization is maximum. In order to determine whether the impurities are removed by the crystallization (either by very low solubility when hot, or sufficient solubility when cold to remain in solution), it is usually necessary to actually crystallize a small sample and follow the rate of purification. The purity may be evaluated by observing the melting point, as discussed in the preceding chapter.

Preparing the Solution

After the solvent has been selected, there is then prepared a solution that is saturated[1] with the substance at the boiling point of the solvent. The solid material is added to an Erlenmeyer flask (not a beaker), and the solvent is added in portions as boiling is maintained. It is important to wait between additions of portions of solvent, since solution takes time and the solid must be given a chance to dissolve. Also, too much solvent should be avoided, because, even if the solvent is very favorable, it will still dissolve some of the substance when it is cold. Excess solvent will mean greater losses. Before heating the solvent to a boil, a boiling chip should be added. This is a small piece of porous tile. The escaping gas bubbles from this boiling chip will break the surface of the liquid and thus prevent superheating, which might be very dangerous. Whenever heating is resumed after boiling has been interrupted, it is essential to add a fresh boiling chip, for liquid will have entered the pores of the previous one on cooling. If an organic solvent that is inflammable is used, the solution must be heated on a steam bath, or under reflux (see Fig. 8-1) if there are any flames present. Toxic solvents (including benzene) must be heated under reflux or in a fume hood, even though they may not be inflammable.

When a mixture of two solvents is to be used in preparing the hot solution, the solid is first dissolved in the solvent in which it is readily soluble; to this boiling solution, the second solvent (in which the solid is relatively insoluble) is added slowly until the solution just becomes cloudy. More of the first solvent is then added until the solution is again clear. In the case of mixed solvent, filtration of the hot solution may be carried out either before or after addition of the second solvent, depending on whether addition of this solvent precipitates impurities that could be filtered from the hot solution. It is, of course, easier to filter before addition of the second solvent, on account of the greater solubility of the substance in the first solvent.

[1]In special situations, a less concentrated solution may be prepared. This matter is discussed in the section on "Cooling," and there is later encountered a preparation in which this technique is used (nitrophenols, Chap. 18).

Filtering the Hot Solution

The purpose of filtering the hot solution is to remove insoluble impurities. *If no insoluble impurities are present, this step may be omitted.* The chief difficulty in this operation is that of keeping the solution hot enough that crystallization does not take place during the process. For this purpose a short-stem funnel is used to prevent crystallization in the stem, and a fluted filter paper (Fig. 1) is used to increase the rate of filtration. The filter paper should not extend above the rim of the funnel, as shown in Fig. 1. The filter paper and funnel are preheated or, if water is the solvent or facilities are available for heating without flames, they are heated by

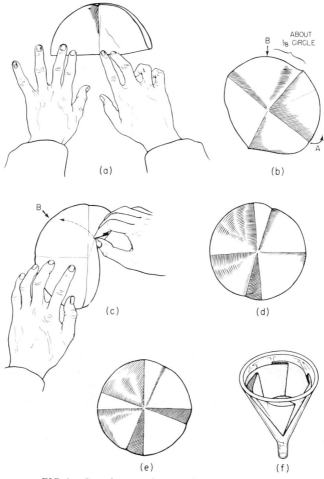

FIG. 1. Steps in preparing a semi-fluted filter paper.

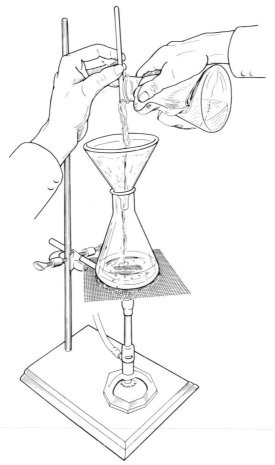

FIG. 2. Filtration of a hot solution by gravity. If an inflammable solvent
is used, a flame is not permissable. Heating must be done with steam, an
electric hot plate, or a bath of previously heated water.

the vapors of a small amount of boiling solvent previously placed in the
flask used to receive the filtrate. A satisfactory setup is shown in Fig. 2;
however, the open flame shown in this illustration must *never* be used
with inflammable solvents. When such a setup is used with inflammable
solvents, heat must be supplied by a steam bath or by an electric hot plate.
Of course a boiling chip must be included in the receiving flask to promote
smooth boiling of the solvent.

Before the hot solution is poured on the filter, a small amount of excess
solvent is usually added to the solution as an aid in preventing crystallization in the funnel during filtration. Furthermore, while the solution is in

the filter, it is covered with a watch glass except when more solution is being added. This prevents evaporation and the resultant cooling of the hot solution. The flask, which is kept over the heater except when solution is being poured into the funnel, is conveniently handled with a towel or a canvas glove.[2] If significant crystallization should begin to occur in the filter, this may sometimes be controlled by addition of fresh hot solvent to the funnel; however, it is frequently best not to try to complete the filtration in this way. It is usually easiest and fastest to allow most of the liquid to drain from the funnel into the receiving flask, return the filter and its contents to the flask containing the unfiltered solution, and add additional solvent. The solution is then reheated and filtration is completed through a fresh paper.

It should be emphasized that the hot filtration is done with gravity, as illustrated in Fig. 2, *not* by suction filtration as described later for collection of the crystallized product. The use of suction for filtering a hot, nearly saturated solution is nearly always highly unsatisfactory, for the reduced pressure causes rapid evaporation of the hot solvent. This results not only in concentration of the solution but in its being cooled by the heat of vaporization; so crystallization in the funnel is almost inevitable, and usually the funnel will be completely plugged by the deposited crystals.

After all the solution has been filtered, a few milliliters of solvent are added to the flask from which the solution was filtered, the solvent is heated, and then it is used to rinse down the filter paper and walls of the funnel. In this way, a few crystals which may form on the filter paper can be washed into the filtrate. Before the filtrate is cooled as described in the next step, it is concentrated by distillation to about the volume which was required initially to dissolve the substance.

Cooling

Crystallization is accomplished by allowing the hot filtrate to cool slowly to whatever temperature is desired. During this process, the objective is that the desired substance be deposited as pure crystals and any soluble impurities remain dissolved. The lower the temperature to which the solution is cooled, the more of the desired substance will crystallize; however, at some point the impurities may also begin to separate from solution. In purifying a substance for the first time, it is usually necessary to determine how much the solution may be cooled without causing separation of impurities. Frequently, the solution is cooled to room temperature, and a so-called "crop" of crystals is collected as described in the next

[2]A pair of cheap canvas work gloves is a very useful adjunct to one's laboratory equipment. Such gloves are useful for handling the many hot flasks and heating baths used in the laboratory. They also offer significant protection against cuts from broken glassware.

section. The filtrate may then be cooled to a lower temperature, in an ice-bath or ice and salt bath, so that a "second crop" of crystals may be collected. On some occasions, the filtrate from the first or second crop of crystals may be profitably concentrated to a smaller volume and cooled to yield an additional crop of crystals (the second or third crop). A determination of the melting points of the respective crops of crystals will reveal their purity. In favorable cases, the lower crops of crystals may prove to be pure. In such instances, if the procedure is repeated, then the solution will be either concentrated or cooled, or both, before any crystals are collected so that all the product may be collected in a single filtration. In instances where the lower crops prove to be impure, they may usually be purified by *recrystallization* from fresh solvent. Such a procedure, designed to recover as much product as possible, is sometimes termed "systematically working up the filtrates." It is always applied to valuable compounds prepared by a long or expensive procedure.

The size of the crystals which separate will vary with the rate of cooling and the amount that the solution is agitated. Rapid cooling and stirring tend to give smaller crystals, while slow cooling of an undisturbed solution tends to give larger crystals. Generally speaking, either very large or very small crystals are undesirable. Very large crystals will *occlude* considerable amounts of solution; so when the crystals are dried by evaporation of the solvent the impurities present in the solution will remain behind with the crystals. On the other hand, if the crystals are too small, significant amounts of impurities may be *adsorbed* on the large surface resulting from such small crystals. It is difficult to state just how large a crystal size is optimum, but in an approximate manner one can state that they should be large enough for the crystal form to be seen easily with the naked eye but not more than about 2 mm in diameter. In the case of slender needles, a length of 10–15 mm is satisfactory. In most instances, organic compounds tend to give rather small crystals, so the most frequently used procedure is slow cooling without agitation. The slow cooling is accomplished by allowing the flask to stand in air rather than in a cooling liquid such as water.

In some instances, a solution will become surprisingly supersaturated before crystallization sets in; then crystal formation will shoot rapidly through the solution. In other cases, crystallization is very stubborn about starting; the solution may stand for days without any crystals forming. If crystallization does not start readily, it may often be induced by scratching the surface of the inside of the flask with a glass rod, preferably just at or just above the surface of the solution. In case crystals of the substance are available, crystallization may always be induced by "seeding," which is accomplished by adding a tiny speck of crystals to the supersaturated solution. Sometimes, seed crystals may be obtained by putting a glass rod in the solution, withdrawing it, and allowing the solution on the rod to evaporate. In the case of low-melting substances, the material which separates may dissolve enough impurities or solvent to become an oil rather than crystals. Such an occurrence is known as "oiling out." Since such oils are usually excellent solvents for impurities, if a substance first separates as an oil which later crystallizes, the impurities will be concentrated in the crystals. Thus, it is imperative that the substance not separate first as an oil, then crystallize from the oil. In such situations, crystallization must be initiated at lower temperature, usually by using a more dilute solution (for example, see Chap. 18).

As a final point concerned with the actual crystallization procedure, it should be mentioned that crystallization may occur slowly, even after it begins; therefore, the solution should be allowed to stand sufficiently long in the cold to allow completion of crystallization. For many substances, crystallization is complete after half an hour at the lower temperature, but sometimes more than an hour is required. In a few instances, twenty-four to forty-eight hours are needed (for example, refer to lactose, Chap. 16).

Filtering the Cold Solution

Separation of the crystals from the supernatant solution is best achieved by suction filtration, using an apparatus as illustrated in Fig. 3. This apparatus consists of a filter flask fitted with a Büchner funnel and a trap bottle. All connections should be made with heavy-walled (pressure) rubber tubing. The trap bottle has very important functions and *should be included in every suction filtration assembly.* A major function of the trap is to prevent any contamination of the filtrate that might be caused by a drop in the water pressure and the resulting backflow of water from the aspirator. In many buildings, it is unwise to leave such an evacuated system unattended for a long period, even with a trap in the line, for the pressure may remain low sufficiently long to allow the trap to fill up and additional water to flow into the filter flask. The third outlet on the trap, closed with a screw clamp, is very convenient for letting air into the system when the pressure is to be released. If the screw clamp is almost closed, this outlet may also be used to bleed a small amount of air into the system in order to prevent the pressure from becoming low enough to boil volatile solvents. A good water pump will reduce the pressure below 20 mm of mercury, which places a pressure of about 15 pounds per square inch on the flask; therefore, *under no circumstances should any type of flask except a round-bottomed flask or a heavy-walled suction flask be evacuated.* An imploding flask can cause serious injury. When this pressure is considered, it also becomes clear why most of the crystals are likely to be blown out of a funnel if it is suddenly disconnected from an evacuated flask. The screw clamp is used to let air into the system cautiously.

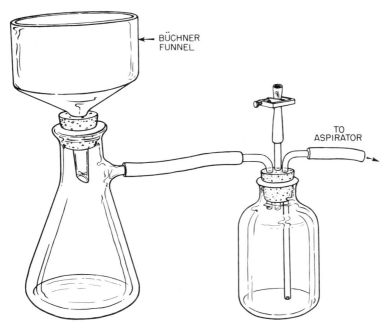

FIG. 3.   Apparatus for collection of crystals by suction filtration.

The Büchner funnel is prepared for filtration by placing it on the suction flask, applying a piece of filter paper of slightly smaller diameter than the filter plate, wetting the paper with the solvent being used, then smoothing the paper snugly against the filter plate as suction is applied with a water pump. The screw clamp is not quite closed unless a solvent as high-boiling as water is being used. With the suction on, and before the filter paper becomes dried out by the air passing through it, the solution is poured into the funnel. As the solution is poured, the bulk of the crystals are scraped into the funnel with a glass rod, or preferably with a long spatula of nickel or stainless steel. Any remaining crystals are transferred to the funnel by means of the filtrate. This could also be done by using fresh solvent, but fresh solvent, even if cold, would dissolve some of the crystals. It is more efficient to pour the filtrate, already saturated with the substance, back into the crystallizing flask and to use this to transfer the remaining solid.

It is important to remove all adhering solution ("mother liquor") from the crystals, for this solution contains the soluble impurities. This is done by pressing the crystals on the filter with a spatula or the bottom of a small beaker, as suction is applied, then releasing the suction (by opening the screw clamp) and covering the crystals with a small amount of fresh, cold solvent. After this wash portion has thoroughly wetted the crystals, suction is again appli⸱ ⸱⸱d the crystals pressed dry as before. For complete removal of the mother liquor from the crystals, two or three such washes are recommended; however, in order to keep loss of product to a minimum, the wash portions should be small in volume and the solvent should be cold.

Drying the Crystals

The crystals now on the filter must be dried from the small amount of adhering solvent, and this is effected by removing them from the filter to a clean watch glass, using a spatula. They are covered with another watch glass, supported on cork stoppers, so that air can circulate above the crystals but falling dust particles are kept out. In many cases, this air-drying is sufficient, but, frequently, the drying process may be accomplished more rapidly and thoroughly by heating the crystals above a radiator or in an oven. Care must be exercised not to melt the crystals.

Another aspect of purification by crystallization may be profitably mentioned here. It is the *use of decolorizing carbon to remove colored or colloidal impurities*. This specially prepared, finely divided carbon is added to the hot solution and mixed thoroughly by swirling. Hot gravity filtration then removes the carbon, which, in turn, has adsorbed the impurities. Before the carbon is added to the hot solution, the source of heat must be removed and the boiling allowed to cease; otherwise, the addition of the carbon particles might cause a very rapid increase in bubbling and the boiling over of the solution. Although colored substances are adsorbed preferentially by carbon, most organic molecules will also be adsorbed to some extent; therefore, only small portions of carbon should be used. Since very finely divided carbon is used, in order that it may have a large surface for adsorption, traces of the carbon may pass through the filter paper and thus contaminate the filtrate. In case this happens, the carbon is best removed by adding a small amount of "filter aid" (finely divided silica) to the filtrate and refiltering.

In purification by crystallization, one must always keep in mind that soluble impurities are to remain behind in the mother liquor; thus, sufficient solvent must be used to keep them in solution in the cold. Since the substance being purified will also have a slight solubility in the cold solvent, a certain loss of material is inevitable if purification is to be achieved by crystallization. These losses may be kept to a minimum, however, by skillful manipulation.

EXPERIMENTAL PROCEDURE

Selection of a Solvent

In research work on new compounds, it is necessary to find a suitable solvent for crystallization by testing the solubility of the substance in various solvents, as described in the discussion; however, when a known compound is being crystallized, it is usually possible to select an appropriate solvent by consulting solubility data available in a handbook of chemistry or in other literature. For example, if we wish to purify acetanilide by crystallization, we may find by consulting a handbook that 100 ml of water will dissolve 3.5 g at 80° and 0.53 g at 6°. On the other hand, 100 ml of ethyl alcohol will dissolve 46 g of this substance at 60° and 21 g at 20°. Thus, we conclude that water is a much better solvent for the crystallization. Further, we can determine about how much water will be necessary for the crystallization, and can decide whether it will be profitable to concentrate the filtrate from the first crystallization in order to obtain a second crop of crystals.

Purification of Acetanilide

A 10-g sample of impure acetanilide[3] is placed in a 500-ml Erlenmeyer flask and dissolved in the minimum amount of boiling water. (There are impurities insoluble in water, but the dark oil formed in the hot solution is a solution of water in acetanilide.) The hot solution is filtered by gravity into a 500-ml Erlenmeyer flask, with the aid of a short-stem funnel, and the filtrate (which should be clear) is cooled by being allowed to stand undisturbed in a water bath (Note 1). After the cooled solution has stood for about 30 minutes, the crystals are collected by suction filtration, washed with a few milliliters of cold water, and pressed on the funnel with a spatula or small beaker. The crystals, after drying overnight on a watch glass or filter paper, are weighed and their melting point is determined.

The total filtrate from the above crystals is transferred to an Erlenmeyer flask and concentrated by boiling to about one-fourth of the original volume. A second crop of crystals is obtained by cooling the concentrate. If the concentrated solution is discolored appreciably, the crystals separating from it will also be discolored unless the solution is first clarified. For this purpose, the boiling solution is allowed to cool slightly, and a "pinch" of decolorizing charcoal is added (if this is added to the boiling solution it usually causes the solution to boil over the top of the flask). Next, the solution is heated again to boiling, then filtered while hot by gravity. The clear filtrate is cooled in order to induce crystallization of the second crop, which is collected and dried as before. The melting point of the second crop, which should be determined, is likely to be below that of the first crop. This illustrates the effectiveness of the crystallization process. In instances where maximum recovery of a valuable compound is desired, pure material is recovered from the second crop by recrystallization from a suitable amount of solvent.

Unless the two crops of crystals have the same melting point, they

---

[3]A suitable mixture consists of 8.9 g of acetanilide, 1.0 g of oxalic acid, and 0.1 g of carbon.

should be turned in separately, and each should be properly labeled (cf. Chap. 1, under "Notebooks and Reports"). In this instance, the per cent yield is the per cent of crude material recovered in each crop.

NOTE

1. Since acetanilide tends to form relatively large crystals, it is satisfactory, in fact desirable, to accelerate cooling with a water bath. The crystals will be sufficiently large even if the flask is occasionally swirled, but the beautiful crystal formations will be broken up.

Gas Phase Chromatography

4

The procedure originally designated as chromatography involved adsorption of colored substances from a solution passed through a column of solid adsorbent contained in a glass tube. The colored substances were adsorbed by the solid adsorbent near the top of the column, but as more solvent was passed through the tube, the substances separated into zones as they migrated down the column at different rates dependent on their relative strengths of adsorption. The development of colored bands gave rise to the name chromatography, based on the Greek word meaning color. This method of separation, which is very effective and remains in wide use, depends on *distribution* of a material between a solution and a solid adsorbent. Several other highly effective methods for separation of compounds depend on distribution processes; and the practice has developed of calling any procedure chromatography if it depends on some type of distribution between two phases. The overwhelming majority of substances that are separated by chromatography are colorless, so the use of a word meaning colored to describe the process is of historical significance only.

Although the several varieties of chromatography are basically processes for separation of compounds, this capability for separation also allows application of the methods to both qualitative and quantitative analysis. Indeed, analytical applications constitute the most widely applied uses of chromatography, and our present considerations will be focussed on these aspects. Liquid phase chromatography on thin sheets is the subject of Chapter 7. The present chapter is concerned with gas phase chromatography, which has truly revolutionized the methods of laboratory practice which are applied in chemistry, biochemistry, and some aspects of biological science. This development becomes all the more impressive when it is recalled that the first practical application of gas phase chromatography occurred after 1950, and the technique was widely applied first during the period 1956 to 1960. In gas phase chromatography, the distribution of material is effected between the gas phase and solution in a liquid,[1] so a more specifically descriptive term is *gas liquid partition chromatography*, frequently abbreviated glpc.[2]

The principal limitation to glpc is the requirement of some vapor pressure in the compounds being used. A vapor pressure less than 1 mm suffices, however, and temperatures above 300° may be employed if the compounds are stable at such temperatures; therefore, a minimum volatility is required. Anything that may be distilled, even at a pressure of 0.01 mm, may be gas chromatographed, and glpc is a vastly more effective method of separation than is distillation. Compounds boiling two degrees apart, scarcely separable by distillation with the best equipment, may be separated by glpc so easily that they will come out of the column a minute or more apart. Indeed, compounds with identical boiling points are usually separable by glpc. Furthermore, azeotropes, which so frequently interfere with separations by fractional distillation (see Chap. 5), do not apply in gas chromatography, for separations are accomplished at a given temperature, not at the boiling point of a mixture. Finally, glpc may be applied to very small amounts; 1 mg is a normal sample used for analysis, and quantities of 1 microgram (μg, 0.001 mg) or less can be utilized. Separation of large quantities (more than about 50 mg) by glpc becomes rather laborious or requires costly equipment; however, modern spectroscopic methods for examining compounds often eliminate the need for large quantities.

Procedure and Equipment Used for Gas Phase Chromatography

For application of glpc, a substance or a mixture is injected from a small syringe[3] into a stream of inert gas, preheated to a suitable temperature, and is swept by this gas stream through a tube containing the *partitioning agent*. The partitioning agent is dispersed in a very thin film over the sur-

[1]Occasionally, the distribution has been between the gas phase and adsorption on a solid; however, this application is relatively uncommon with organic compounds.

[2]The abbreviation glpc has become accepted usage in *The Journal of Organic Chemistry* and *The Journal of the American Chemical Society*. Since these are probably the most prestigious journals publishing research in organic chemistry, use of abbreviations recommended by them is likely to be understood; therefore, glpc will be used in this book to refer to gas liquid partition chromatography.

[3]Total volume of the syringe is rarely more than 0.1 ml [100 microliters, abbreviated μl; use of the term lambda (λ) instead of μl is vigorously opposed by microchemists]. Syringes most commonly use are of 1- to 10-μl capacity, so that injections of 1.0 μl can be measured with reasonable accuracy.

face of some porous material, such as finely ground firebrick, so that a large surface is available for rapid solution of gas and loss of gas from solution. As the zone of vapor encounters the first of the partitioning agent, the amount of the gas which dissolves in a given amount of partitioning agent will be a function of two major factors: the vapor pressure of the substance at the temperature of the chromatography, and the solubility of the substance in the partitioning agent. As the undissolved portion of the vapor is swept further down the tube and encounters fresh partitioning agent, more of it is dissolved and the concentration remaining in the vapor phase is reduced. Thus, if the quantity of material injected is sufficiently small, essentially all the vapor will quickly become dissolved in a relatively short zone of partitioning agent. However, fresh carrier gas, continuing to enter the tube after the substance was injected, follows through the tube and encounters the zone of dissolved substance. Naturally, the substance becomes partitioned between the solution and the gas phase according to the distribution determined by its vapor pressure and solubility. As carrier gas continues to sweep through the tube, the material is moved along by a continual repetition of the process of solution in the partitioning agent, re-extraction by the carrier gas, re-solution, and so on. It follows that *the distribution ratio between liquid and gas phase determines the rate at which the substance passes through the tube.* The more favorable the distribution ratio is to the liquid phase, the more slowly the substance will pass through the tube. Furthermore, *substances with different distribution ratios will pass through the tube at different rates and will therefore be separated.*

In order to use the glpc process for either analytical purposes or separation, it is necessary to be able to determine when an organic substance is passing out of the tube. Various devices have been used as *detectors*, but the most widely used and most generally satisfactory device is the thermal conductivity detector. For this purpose, a fine wire or thermistor,[4] heated by an electric current passed through it, is inserted into the effluent gas stream, and this heated element is included in one arm of a Wheatstone bridge. An identical heated element, located in the inert gas stream before it enters the column, is included in the other arm on the same side of the bridge, and the two elements are included in a thermostated zone (usually a metal block). The carrier gas for the chromatography is chosen to have

---

[4]The thermistor has a much greater change of resistance with temperature than does an ordinary resistance wire. This great temperature coefficient of resistance (3–5% per degree) gives a much larger signal than is received from a wire, so a less sensitive recorder is required to deliver the same response. The smaller bridge current which is effective with thermistors, as compared with hot wires, is also an advantage in terms of the power supply required. A mercury cell is practical for use with a thermistor circuit, in contrast with the bulky storage battery or expensive electronic power supply required for hot-wire bridges.

a high thermal conductivity,[5] considerably higher than organic gases; and the heated element in the effluent gas stream is arranged so that its heat loss occurs through the effluent gas. When the organic material, of lower thermal conductivity, appears in the effluent, heat is dissipated to the metal block at a slower rate than when pure helium is passing the element. Thus, the element in the effluent gas becomes hotter than the one in the other arm of the bridge, its resistance changes, and the electrical potential at the take-off of the bridge is changed. This electrical signal is sent to a suitable recorder which traces a line as a function of the magnitude of this signal. A recording such as shown in Fig. 1 is obtained.

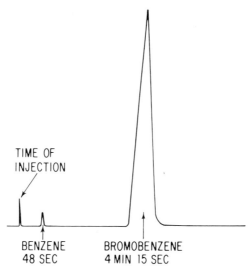

TIME OF INJECTION

BENZENE
48 SEC

BROMOBENZENE
4 MIN 15 SEC

FIG. 1.   Gas chromatography of 0.5 μl of bromobenzene containing 0.6% of benzene as impurity. Carle Basic Chromatograph Model 6500, Heath 10 mv span recorder, 5-ft silicone column, B temperature settings (about 85°), attenuation 1.

When ⅛-inch columns are used, even 0.5 μl of material tends to overload the column if most of the material injected is in a single band. This is the reason that the bromobenzene peak is "pushed over" so that the tip of the peak is not in the center of the band. In such instances, the midway point at the base of the peak is taken as the retention time, as is marked on the tracing.

---

[5]The most satisfactory gas, on account of its high thermal conductivity and inertness to chemical reaction, is helium, and this gas is usually used for glpc in the United States. The United States has a virtual world monopoly on helium, which is obtained from helium wells in Texas or by extraction from natural gas wells in that region. Since helium remains in rather short supply, its export is severely restricted, so that helium is not widely used for glpc in other countries.

The recorder tracing, of the type shown in Fig. 1, is at the heart of utilization of glpc for either analytical purposes or separation of a mixture. For *separation of a mixture*, the effluent is collected by attachment of a suitable receiver to the outlet from the column during the time that a "peak" is appearing on the recorder. As soon as the peak passes, the receiver is removed and a second receiver is attached when the next peak appears. For *analytical purposes*, the important factor is that the area under the peak is proportional to the amount of material passing from the column. The area may be determined by use of a recorder which includes a mechanical or electronic integrator, or the area may be measured with a planimeter; however, if the peaks are reasonably symmetrical, as is usually the case, the area is measured easily and with satisfactory accuracy by considering the peak as a combination of two right triangles. Since the area of a right triangle is given by one-half the product of the length of the two arms, the area of the peak is one-half the product of the height and the width of the base. For comparison of peaks, there is no object in dividing by one-half—this merely changes the units of area. Details of quantitative analysis are included in the next section.

Quantitative Analysis

Since different organic molecules have different thermal conductivities, an accurate quantitative analysis is accomplished only if there is determined the ratio of peak area to weight for the specific substance under investigation. For this purpose, a known weight of substance is injected (usually in 5-10% solution in a low-boiling solvent, for greater accuracy of injection), and the area under the resultant recorder tracing is measured. Dividing the area by the weight yields a value for area per unit of weight. So long as the same settings are retained on the chromatograph, this value may be used for quantitative determination of that substance. Thus, per cent of impurities may be determined with ease and precision, or the yield in a reaction may be determined without ever isolating the product. For the latter purpose, a reaction mixture is worked up according to whatever method is appropriate for the reaction, then a solution of the total products is diluted to some known volume, and a small aliquot (e.g., 50 μl) of the solution is injected in gas chromatography. The total yield of the desired product, as well as yields of impurities, may be determined from the single injection.

Substances of similar structure, especially isomeric compounds, usually have rather similar thermal conductivities; therefore, a direct comparison of area under peaks in the glpc tracing gives a ratio of the amounts of the respective products in the mixture chromatographed. Even for different structures, therefore different conductivities, relative ratios of two products in different lots of the mixture may be determined from comparison of areas. For example, the relative amount of impurity in several lots of a product (such as student yields in a laboratory synthesis) may be determined by simple comparison of areas under the peaks for the desired product and the impurity.

Retention Time

The time elapsing between injection of a compound into the gas chromatograph and its appearance in the effluent from the column is the retention time for the substance in that particular column under the specific conditions of chromatography used. This time is usually measured to the top of the peak on the glpc tracing. The retention time is a very valuable physical constant that can be used for recognizing a compound, in spite of the fact that the various conditions of the chromatography (temperature, helium flow rate, exact length of column, denseness of packing in the column, etc.) are not reproducible at a later time, especially in another chromatograph. This is only a minor handicap, for a sample of the compound of known identity can be injected just before or after the unknown, and the two retention times checked for identity. Carrying out two gas chromatographies in this manner is likely to consume less time than determining a melting point, and the identification is far more reliable, because different partitioning agents may be used to give a multiple check on identity.

Of course the time consumed in accomplishing a gas chromatography depends on the length of time required for the material to pass through the column, i.e., the retention time. The retention time is a function of the temperature of the chromatography, the rate of helium flow through the tube, the length of the tube, and the amount of partitioning agent dispersed on the solid support. In order to strike a balance between capacity of the column and rapid equilibration in solution in the film of liquid, the partitioning agent is usually 5–15% of the weight of the support. With this amount of partitioning agent, a column of about 5 feet in length gives satisfactory separations in all but the most difficult situations. Under these conditions, and with an applied helium pressure of about 15 psi. (pounds per square inch), a compound will usually give a retention time between 1 minute and 10 minutes at a temperature 50° below its boiling point. In order to double the retention time, at a constant rate of gas flow, it is necessary to lower the temperature between 10° and 30°. Usually, chromatography is carried out at the highest temperature that gives satisfactory separation, for this shortens the time consumed. This practice is limited by the fact that separation becomes poorer as the temperature is raised and retention times are shortened. Of course other possible limitations are the temperature limit of the instrument, thermal stability of the partitioning agent, and thermal stability of the compounds being chromatographed.

Partitioning Agents

A host of different partitioning agents have been examined and evaluated for use in glpc. A useful partitioning agent must have a very low vapor pressure at the temperature at which it is used, otherwise it will slowly pass out of the column. For this reason, many of the more useful partitioning agents are polymers, which may be used for glpc at relatively high temperatures. Of course, the partitioning agent must also be thermally stable at the temperature of utilization, as well as inert to chemical reaction with the compounds chromatographed. The various *silicone fluids* are particularly stable at high temperatures and have been widely used as partitioning agents. Most of the silicones give separation in glpc predominantly on the basis of the different vapor pressures of the respective compounds. Differences in solubility in this type of partitioning agent are usually minor. Such a partitioning agent is known as a *nonpolar agent*. In general, lengths of retention times observed with the nonpolar agents will fall in the same order as temperatures of boiling points. In other words, a higher-boiling compound will have a longer retention time.

Partitioning agents in which solubilities of different compounds tend to differ are known as *polar* partitioning agents. By use of partitioning agents of this type, it is possible to separate compounds with identical boiling points, sometimes with great ease. Common partitioning agents of the polar type are Carbowax (a polymeric ether) and DEGS (diethylene glycol succinate, a polymeric ester). Relative retention times on polar and nonpolar partitioning agents nearly always differ, and this allows a reliable check on the identity of two samples of a compound. It also greatly expands the capability of glpc for separating compounds. Extremely complex mixtures may be either analyzed or separated by successive chromatographies on a polar and a nonpolar partitioning agent, or on two different polar partitioning agents. In difficult situations, such as separation of the remarkably complex mixtures often encountered in natural products, a sequence of four gas chromatographies has been used. In these instances, a peak from the first chromatography is collected and re-injected into a column of a different partitioning agent. Instances have been encountered where the second injection of material, from what appeared to be a single peak, revealed as many as eight peaks on the second partitioning agent.

Separation of Mixtures

In order for the zones in the chromatography tube to remain sharp, when the fluid has the high mobility of a gas, the tube must be of relatively small diameter. For analytical purposes, tubes of either $\frac{1}{8}$- or $\frac{1}{4}$-inch internal diameter (i.d.) are used. The former is too small to be of any value for separation, on account of the small capacity, but it is the best size for analytical work. A $\frac{1}{4}$-inch tube remains quite good for analysis, and can accommodate samples of 1–5 mg; therefore, a tube of this size is often used in a multipurpose chromatograph. The largest tube that can be used in the form of a spiral (4–8 inches in diameter), without serious damage to the sharpness of the separation, is $\frac{3}{8}$-inch i.d. Use of straight tubes is quite inconvenient, for a minimum length of 5 feet is usually required for satisfactory separation, and columns of 20 feet in length are not uncommon. The $\frac{3}{8}$-inch columns will usually accommodate at least 10 mg per injection, and retention times longer than 30 minutes are not common, so several injections can be made in a few hours (the time required for a fractional distillation). Thus, collection of as much as 50 mg of material is not excessively laborious unless the desired component is only a minor constituent of the mixture. In case larger amounts of material must be collected by gas chromatography, straight columns of larger diameter (up to one inch) may be used, but the best solution is likely to be the automatic gas chromatograph. This instrument injects a sample, changes receivers whenever a peak appears on the recorder, and then makes another injection after the last peak in the sequence has been collected. The same fractions are placed in the same receivers for each injection. Getting this instrument in operation is likely to require 10–20 hours of time, in order to get all the variables properly evaluated and set on the machine, but once the instrument is in operation the separation will continue day and night until the desired amount of material is collected—or a mechanical or electrical defect develops. With such an instrument, which is less expensive than the cheapest spectrometer, it is feasible to collect 100 g or more by glpc.

Shape and size of receivers for collection of samples vary according to the instrument used and quantity being collected. For a 1–5-mg sample, as required for ultraviolet, infrared, or mass spectra, it is frequently practical to insert in the outlet a capillary such as used for determining melting points, but with both ends open and with a wet cloth looped over the center of the tube.

EXPERIMENTAL TECHNIQUES

Specific experimental procedures are not included in this chapter, for the most meaningful use of glpc will be application of the process as an analytical device[6] to assess the purity of compounds synthesized in future experi-

---

[6]Numerous books on gas phase chromatography have appeared, some dealing with instrumentation, others focussing on the theoretical basis of gas chromatography, and still others emphasizing advanced consideration of techniques useful in the practice of gas chromatography. A useful book of the latter type is *The Practice of Gas Chromatography*, eds., L. S. Ettre and A. Zlatkis (New York: Interscience, 1967).

ments. The effectiveness, ease, and speed of the method may be visualized by examination of the recorder tracing reproduced in Fig. 1, which was generated after injection in glpc of a sample of bromobenzene prepared by bromination of benzene as described in Chap. 17. It is apparent that, with use of 2 μl (0.002 ml) of the product and expenditure of about five minutes of time, as little as 0.1% of starting material in the product may be detected reliably. Most liquid products may be analyzed quantitatively, as may solid products that have any volatility at all. Solids are injected in solution.

The gc Syringe and Its Manipulation

For analytical purposes, where a $\frac{1}{8}$-inch column is used, a sample of 0.5–2 μl is usually injected; so a syringe no larger than 10-μl capacity is required in order to secure even an approximate measure of the amount injected. Such a syringe should be handled with care so that it will not be broken. In particular, dirt must be kept off the slender plunger, else it will stick and likely cause breaking of the barrel. If the tip of the needle should become bent, it must be sharpened, before use, on a fine stone such as used for sharpening knives; otherwise, the septum through which injection is made will be torn so that helium rushes out and defeats the chromatography.

Since traces of impurities are readily revealed in glpc, a scrupulously clean syringe is important. A small syringe is best cleaned by flushing it several times with acetone, then carefully "pumping" the plunger several times to clear out most of the solvent. Traces of such a low-boiling solvent may show in the chromatograph, but will cause no difficulty.

For filling the syringe, the tip of the needle is inserted into the liquid, the plunger is withdrawn above the full mark, and sufficient time is allowed to permit liquid to pass through the narrow needle and reach the maximum height to which it will rise. This will leave a large vapor pocket above the liquid, which must be eliminated (or very nearly eliminated) before injection is made. Since there is about 15 psi. pressure inside the chromatography tube, attempting to inject liquid with gas between the plunger and liquid will result principally in compressing the gas. To get rid of the gas pocket, fully depress the plunger, then withdraw it again, and allow liquid to rise as far as it will. After four or five repetitions of this procedure, enough of the gas will usually have been eliminated. A very tiny bubble will not seriously alter the volume injected. After most of the gas has been eliminated, the plunger is carefully depressed until its bottom is opposite the proper mark to give the desired injection when the syringe is emptied. For example, if a 1-μl injection is desired the tip of the plunger is placed opposite 1 μl on the scale.

If the 2.5-μl syringe known as a Student Injector (manufactured by the

Hamilton Co.) is used, difficulty with an air pocket in the syringe is eliminated. The Student Injector has a plunger which goes to the very tip of the needle, and the volume is measured in the needle although the calibration scale is in a glass barrel. Since the tip of the plunger is actually in contact with the liquid being drawn into the needle, there can be no air pocket. Additional advantages of the Student Injector are low cost (about two-thirds that of the traditional microliter syringe) and ruggedness. Average lifetime of a Student Injector in the undergraduate laboratory approximates ten times that of syringes available previously. Chief objection to the Student Injector is that it cuts a larger hole in the septum through which injection is made; however, septums are inexpensive and easily replaced.

Preparing the Chromatograph for Injection

In practice, this step is necessarily carried out before the syringe is filled for injection, except that settings on the chromatograph are frequently left unchanged for a series of injections of similar materials. For the Basic Gas Chromatograph, Model 6500, manufactured by Carle Instrument Co., directions for putting the equipment in operation are printed on the inside of its cover. Since similar operational procedure applies to other gas chromatographs, instructions for operation of the Carle instrument will be outlined.

Since the gas chromatograph and recorder are separate units, any of the multitude of recorders available on the market may be used. The Carle Basic Gas Chromatograph utilizes a thermistor as detector, so a recorder of 10-mv span is quite adequate (refer to Fig. 1) for use in undergraduate laboratory courses. This point is likely to be of importance to most laboratories, for the cheapest recorder of 1-mv span will cost at least 50% more than the Basic Gas Chromatograph, whereas an excellent recorder of 10-mv span costs slightly more than one-half as much as the Basic Gas Chromatograph. In the authors' laboratories, the recorder of 10-mv span manufactured by the Heath Co., Benton Harbor, Michigan, has proved to be highly versatile, rugged, and relatively inexpensive. This recorder has an adjustment by which the span can be extended to 3.3 mv. At this span, the dead band becomes significant. The chart-drive motor sold with this recorder moves the paper at 2 inches per minute, which is excessively fast. A chart-drive motor giving a speed of $\frac{1}{2}$ inch per minute may be purchased (price $< \$15.00$) and is recommended. This drive speed not only gives sharper peaks on the recording; it reduces the cost of chart paper by one-fourth. Slower chart drives are not recommended, for rather long retention times become required in order to give a peak whose area may be measured with reasonable accuracy. The following procedure refers to the Heath recorder.

Operating Procedure

1. *After checking to make sure that the reducing valve is completely closed* (cf. "Close-Down Instructions"), open the valve on the helium cylinder, raise the output pressure on the two-stage reducing valve to about 15 lbs, and open the valve admitting the gas to the instrument being used (several instruments may be connected to the same helium cylinder).

2. Plug the power cord of the instrument into a 120-volt 3-wire grounded electric outlet. Set the switch controlling column temperature to the desired contact (A, B, C, or D), selected by referring to the temperature corresponding to these settings and choosing a temperature appropriate to the material being chromatographed. Retention times less than 10 minutes will usually be desirable for your present work. Set the inlet temperature switch to the same letter setting as used for the column temperature. Allow at least 20 minutes for the oven to heat. A longer time may be required, but can be checked by examining the baseline given by the recorder; a small slope is acceptable. When the oven is cooled or heated from its previous setting, a similar time interval is usually required.

3. Set the attenuator switch to TEST and insert the plug in the single jack that connects the battery to the bridge. Since about 5 minutes is required for the thermistors in the bridge to heat, the bridge should be connected after the oven has been heating for about 15 minutes. Insert the plug on the wire from the recorder into the double jack labeled RECORDER, with the side where the wires enter the plug facing to your right for use of the right-hand gas chromatography column, to the left for use of the left-hand chromatography column. This orientation should make the recorder pen travel from right to left on the chart as a peak is being recorded, so that the chart will read forward in the direction that people read in this country—from left to right. In case the instrument should be wired in a reverse manner, it would become necessary to reverse the direction in which the double jack is inserted.

4. For the Heath recorder, move the recorder switch to SERVO and wait about 15 minutes unless the recorder was already on STANDBY. Move the zero knob on the recorder to place the pen (which should be in the lifted position) over a point near the right edge of the chart paper at the level of the first heavy line parallel to the sides of the paper. This allows the baseline to drift down somewhat without pinning the pen off-scale. Now shift the attenuator switch on the gc to 100 (after the oven has heated to equilibrium), and use the zero adjust on the gc to bring the pen back to its original position, if necessary. Move the attenuator switch to 1, and again bring the pen back to the original zero position.

You are now ready to make an injection.

5. Move the recorder switch to CHART, then lower the pen onto the chart paper. The paper will advance at a steady rate determined by the

speed of the chart-drive motor (1 inch in 2 minutes is recommended); so retention times can be read from the chart if the point of injection is marked. Grasp the syringe with the left hand (if your are right-handed) near the front and with one finger supporting the needle to prevent it from bending. Place the right hand in position to manipulate the plunger. *The plunger must be held when the needle is inserted into the septum;* otherwise, pressure in the chromatography tube will blow out the plunger. The needle is inserted full length through the septum of the desired column (left-hand or right-hand), and the plunger is immediately depressed so as to inject the entire contents of the syringe. A slow injection will spread the peaks on the chart. As soon as the injection has been made, the needle is withdrawn and the zero knob *on the recorder* is turned enough to displace the pen and thus mark the time of injection. The knob is then turned back in order to return the pen to the baseline.

6. Write on the chart paper, near the point where injection is marked, data related to the chromatography. This should consist at least of the following: (1) volume injected, (2) identity of material injected, (3) column used, as designated on the instrument, (4) temperature settings, (5) attenuation used. In case attentuation is changed during the run, as is often practiced in order to keep the tracing on scale, this is marked at the time it is done.

At this point, you wait and watch the pen trace out your results. Clean the syringe while you are waiting; a dirty syringe may stick, and syringes are expensive.

7. When you feel that everything is through the column, as judged from knowledge of what was injected, lift the pen, turn the recorder switch to STANDBY (which conserves the chopper and battery, but keeps the tubes hot for immediate use if desired), turn the attenuator switch to CHECK, and finally turn the recorder paper beyond your tracing so that you can tear it off.

The equipment is now ready for the next person to use. If you are the last to use it for a time, especially if it is at the end of the day, *observe the close-down instructions below.*

8. Measure retention times to the peaks, and write them on the tracing. If you know the identity of the substances giving the peaks, mark that on the paper also. Place your name and the date on the tracing, and attach the tracing to your notebook as a part of the record of the experiment. This tracing constitutes a precise record of the identity and purity of your product.

The tracing is conveniently attached to a notebook with either rubber cement or scotch tape. In case of a tracing longer than the width of the notebook, it is best attached only at one end and folded like an accordion —this gives ready access to the tracing. Each tracing should be attached to a separate page of the notebook, and such pages should not be used for other purposes, such as recording data.

Close-down instructions. When the gc (gas chromatography) equipment is not to be used soon, and especially if it is to stand overnight, the following steps are followed.

1. Adjust the reducing valve to the helium tank so that output pressure reads zero, then close the cylinder valve to the helium tank so that helium will not be wasted. *IMPORTANT:* Do not cut off the helium tank valve without closing the reducing valve, as just directed. Opening a high pressure tank into an open reducing valve sometimes breaks the diaphragm in the reducing valve and thus delivers full tank pressure into the system. Of course this may cause explosion of the system.

2. Pull out the single plug which connects the battery to the bridge; otherwise, this battery will be discharged.

3. Unplug the gc from the electric power outlet.

4. Turn the recorder switch to OFF.

Reference Data

As a general guide in choosing conditions for gas chromatography, a few data are assembled in Table I. Even for the same column and same instrument, retention times will vary somewhat; however, such data as included in Table I are useful in choosing temperatures that will best fit the characteristics of the material being chromatographed. The columns supplied with the Basic Chromatograph have a very low percentage of partitioning agent dispersed on the support. If higher percentages of partitioning agent are utilized, retention time becomes longer, separation becomes poorer, and capacity of the column becomes greater. Since the principal function of the Basic Chromatograph is for analysis, low percentage of partitioning agent is desirable. Of course columns containing different

Table I

Data for Chromatography on a Five-Foot Silicone Column
Carle Basic Gas Chromatograph

Compound (b.p.)	Temperature Setting	Retention Time
Benzene (80°)	D (145°)	26 sec
Bromobenzene (156°)	D	1 min
Bromobenzene	C (110°)	3 min
Dinitrobenzene (291°)	D	7 min, 40 sec
Nitrobenzene (211°)	D	2 min, 10 sec
Toluene (111°)	B (85°)	2 min, 24 sec
Toluene	C	1 min, 30 sec

partitioning agents may give quite different retention times; however, silicone fluid has a very wide range of applicability. Occasionally, a polar partitioning agent is needed for mixtures of compounds with similar boiling points but with functional groups of different polarity.

A few data on magnitude of recorder response are of use in determining amount of material required, or desirable, for an analysis. The following data were obtained on the Heath recorder set at 10-mv span:

1. Injection of 0.8 μl of toluene on the c setting at an attenuation of 5 gave a peak height of 19% on the chart. This injection was slightly off-scale at an attenuation of 1.

2. At the D setting, injection of 1 μl of bromobenzene containing about 5% of benzene gave a peak height of 47% for benzene at attenuation of 5 and a peak height of 45% for bromobenzene at attenuation of 25. In this chromatography, retention times were excessively short for accurate measurement of areas under the tracings. In case accurate measurement of areas should be desired, longer retention times would be secured by use of lower temperatures, as illustrated in Fig. 1.

Distillation

5

Gas chromatography has become the most effective method, by a wide margin, for separation of liquid mixtures; however, this technique is conveniently applicable only on a rather small scale (cf. Chap. 4). For quantities of material normally handled in organic synthesis, distillation remains the most important and versatile method for separation and purification of liquid compounds. It may be used for separating volatile liquids from nonvolatile substances, and may also be used for separating two or more volatile liquids, provided that their boiling points are not too close together. Substances whose boiling points differ by 30° or more may be separated by the use of simple laboratory equipment, while substances whose boiling points differ by no more than 3° may be separated by the use of elaborate fractional distillation equipment. Simple efficient fractionating equipment is discussed in Chap. 32.

In general, crystallization of a solid is able to yield a more nearly pure compound than is distillation of a liquid; however, a more complex mixture may be separated by distillation than is usually separable by crystallization. Separation of liquids is sometimes handicapped, however, by formation of azeotropes or by the fact that liquids of the same boiling point are not separable. These matters will be discussed in this chapter.

During distillation, the boiling point of the substance may be observed; this is a physical constant that may be used for the identification of liquids and the estimation of their purity. As will be developed shortly, this property of liquids is less useful and reliable than the melting point of solids.

Simple Distillation and Determination of Boiling Point

Simple distillation refers to the distillation of an essentially pure substance or a substance in a homogeneous mixture with nonvolatile material. It is commonly carried out in such an apparatus as shown in Fig. 1.

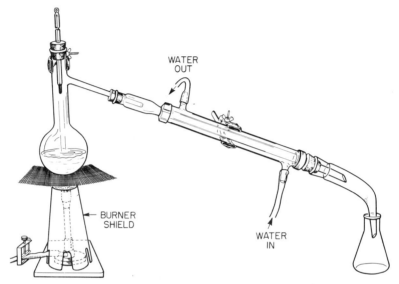

FIG. 1.   Apparatus for simple distillation.

All liquid substances have a vapor pressure that is constant at a constant temperature. The vapor pressure is caused by the tendency of molecules to escape from the surface of a liquid, and this escaping tendency is different for different liquids. If water or gasoline is left in an open vessel at room temperature, it evaporates; but, if lubricating oil is left in an open vessel, it does not evaporate at an appreciable rate, for its vapor pressure is very low. The vapor pressure of a substance is a function of the temperature, and the vapor pressure increases as the temperature is raised. If the temperature is raised sufficiently, the vapor pressure of the substance becomes equal to atmospheric pressure, and the substance boils. The *boiling point* of a substance may be defined as the temperature at which the vapor pressure of the substance is equal to the external pressure.

If the substance is placed in an outfit such as shown in Fig. 1, and heated, it will eventually become sufficiently hot to boil, and additional heat applied to the flask will not further raise the temperature of the liquid (cf. *superheating*, below), but will supply the *heat of vaporization* necessary to convert a liquid to a gas. The vapor will pass up the neck of the flask, be condensed by the cold neck, and then run back into the flask; but this process will rapidly heat the neck of the flask and allow the ring of condensing liquid (boiling ring) to rise in the neck until vapors reach the thermometer, pass into the side tube (or delivery tube) of the flask, and thence into the condenser. Since cold water is circulated through the jacket of the condenser, all the vapor is condensed (the heat of vaporization is transferred to the water) and the liquid *distillate* flows into the flask (receiver) placed to collect it. Any nonvolatile material (such as ionic substances or the tarry material often encountered in chemical reactions) will be left behind in the distilling flask, and the distillate will be separated from such materials.

In addition to any purification that may be effected by such a distillation, the boiling point is determined by reading the thermometer placed in the vapor. If the thermometer were placed in the boiling liquid, a temperature above the boiling point might be recorded, for the liquid can be *superheated* by feeding in heat faster than it can be dissipated by vaporization of the liquid. If the thermometer is placed in the vapor path, however, liquid condenses on the upper part of the thermometer and flows back down over the bulb, where it is in contact with the vapors passing the bulb. Thus, liquid and vapor are in equilibrium and the true boiling point is recorded. If the vapor drops below the true boiling point, it will condense; thus, it will not reach the sidearm and appear as liquid distillate. This can be observed, and is a signal that more heat input is indicated. On the other hand, if so much heat is supplied that the vapors coming off the liquid are so overheated that they do not cool to the true boiling point by the time they reach the bulb of the thermometer, all the liquid will be evaporated from the bulb of the thermometer, and too high a boiling point may be registered. This nonequilibrium condition will be evidenced by the disappearance of the droplet of liquid normally hanging from the thermometer bulb. This is a signal that the heat input should be decreased. If these precautions are observed, an accurate boiling point may be obtained.

If the liquid being distilled contains nonvolatile material in solution, the escaping tendency of the molecules of volatile liquid at a given temperature will be reduced because they are diluted with molecules of the nonvolatile substance. This means that a higher temperature will be required to boil the liquid, as will be discussed in more detail below. It follows that the temperature at which this solution boils will be higher than the true boiling point of the volatile liquid; hence, this is another reason for not recording the temperature of the boiling liquid by placing the thermometer in it. Nonvolatile material will not reach the thermometer placed in the vapor, as shown in Fig. 1, however; hence, equilibrium will be between pure liquid (drop on thermometer) and pure vapor. Since the vapor becomes distillate, the thermometer registers the boiling point of the material being collected as distillate. Thus, if water containing a quantity of sodium chloride were placed in the distilling flask, the boiling point of the liquid would be above that of water, but the boiling point registered by the thermometer in the vapor would be that of water, and pure water would be collected in the distillate. Since sodium chloride is not volatile in the ordinary sense, pure water would continue to vaporize and the thermometer would continue to register the temperature at which water liquid and vapor are in equilibrium, that is, the boiling point of water. Similarly, if any pure liquid is distilled, the temperature registered by the thermometer will remain constant at the boiling point of this liquid, the temperature at which its vapor pressure is equal to atmospheric pressure.

Distillation of a Homogeneous Mixture of Two Substances

Distillation of a homogeneous mixture of two substances involves the same principles as distillation of a homogeneous mixture of more than two substances, but the discussion is simplified by considering a mixture of only two.

Let us consider two liquids, A of b.p. 60° and B of b.p. 90°, each in a separate container as shown in Fig. 2(a) and (b). Only one kind of molecule

(a)   (b)   (c)

FIG. 2.

is present at the surface of each liquid, so the escaping tendency, or vapor pressure, is that characteristic of that kind of molecule. Next, let us consider a homogeneous mixture of the two liquids, as shown in Fig. 2(c). In this instance, each kind of molecule is diluted by the other kind, and the escaping tendency of A at the surface is reduced because not all the molecules at the surface are A. The same argument applies to B. The amount by which the escaping tendency, or vapor pressure, of A is reduced is clearly proportional to the amount by which the concentration of molecules of A is reduced by the presence of B. This principle is known as Raoult's law, and is most clearly presented by the mathematical expression

$$P_A = P_A^\circ N_A \qquad (5\text{-}1)$$

where P_A is the partial pressure of A from the solution,
P_A° is the vapor pressure of pure A,
N_A is the mole fraction of A in the liquid.

P_A remains constant for a given N_A so long as the temperature is constant. Obviously, we must use the mole fraction, N_A, in this expression, rather than the weight per cent, for the significant factor is the number of molecules, not their weight. It should be noted[1] in Eq. 1 that the vapor pressure of A from the solution depends only on its mole fraction and its vapor pressure when pure, *not* on the vapor pressure of the other component, B. If the other component should be nonvolatile, as is salt, for example, then the total vapor pressure of the solution would equal the partial pressure of component A. On the other hand, if component B is volatile, then it exerts a partial pressure from the solution and an expression similar to Eq. 1 gives the partial pressure of B:

$$P_B = P_B^\circ N_B \qquad (5\text{-}2)$$

If we term P_t the total vapor pressure of the solution, and the solution contains only the two components, A and B, it follows that $P_t = P_A + P_B$. For a given temperature, P_t for the mixture remains constant, and, as the temperature is raised, P_t increases. If the temperature is raised until P_t is equal to atmospheric pressure, the liquid boils. The boiling point can be determined experimentally, or it may be calculated if P_A° and P_B° are known over a sufficient range of temperature.

Although the above expressions are simple and follow from logical reasoning, they may be used to deduce a principle of fundamental importance in the separation of two volatile liquids by distillation. If we define A as the lower-boiling component of the mixture, then the principle may be stated as follows: *The concentration of the lower-boiling component, A, in the vapor in equilibrium with a liquid mixture of A and B is greater than is the concentration of A in the liquid mixture.* From this, it follows that if such a mixture is heated to boiling and the vapor is condensed as distillate, the distillate is richer in the lower-boiling component than is the mixture from which it was distilled. Note carefully that no statement has been

---

[1]For the sake of brevity, the chapter number will be omitted in text references to equations within the same chapter. The present reference is, for example, to Eq. 5-1.

made to the effect that the distillate is richer in A than it is in B, but it was stated that the distillate is richer in A than was the liquid mixture from which it was distilled. The extension of this principle to the essentially complete separation of liquid mixtures will be developed after the truth of the principle has been demonstrated by the use of Raoult's law.

Since the vapor pressure is a measure of the escaping tendency at the surface, if X is used to indicate mole fraction in the vapor, it follows that the ratio of X_A to X_B is equal to the ratio of the partial pressures of A and B from the liquid. This may be expressed as follows:

$$\frac{X_A}{X_B} = \frac{P_A}{P_B} \tag{5-3}$$

If we substitute in this expression the values of P_A and P_B from Raoult's law (Eqs. 1, 2), we obtain

$$\frac{X_A}{X_B} = \frac{P_A^\circ N_A}{P_B^\circ N_B} = \frac{P_A^\circ}{P_B^\circ} \left(\frac{N_A}{N_B}\right) \tag{5-4}$$

If we recall that A is the lower-boiling substance, then for a given temperature $P_A^\circ > P_B^\circ$; therefore, $P_A^\circ / P_B^\circ > 1$. If this is considered in connection with the equation immediately above, it follows that

$$\frac{X_A}{X_B} > \frac{N_A}{N_B} \tag{5-5}$$

This will become clear if one considers the simple equation, $y = kx$. If k is greater than unity, it is clear that x must be less than y. Thus, it has been demonstrated that when A is the lower-boiling substance, the molar ratio of A to B in the vapor is greater than the ratio of A to B in the liquid.

Since the vapor has a higher concentration of A than has the liquid in equilibrium with it, if a plot is made which shows the boiling point of the mixture at various concentrations, a diagram such as shown in Fig. 3 results. The vapor composition is that in equilibrium with the liquid. According to this diagram, a mixture that is 80% B (and 20% A) boils at 78°, and the vapor in equilibrium with the liquid at the boiling point contains only 45% B (and 55% A). Thus, the first drop of distillate obtained on distilling this mixture would contain 55% A, whereas the liquid from which it was distilled contained only 20% A. If it were possible to redistill this first drop of distillate, it would boil at 67° and the first distillate would be quite rich in A. Another redistillation of the first distillate would give essentially pure A. In practice, such rapid enrichment in A cannot be accomplished with the simple distilling outfit such as shown in Fig. 1, for a finite amount of distillate must be collected each time.

Since it has been shown that the vapor is much richer in A than is the liquid from which the vapor was distilled, it follows that A is being re-

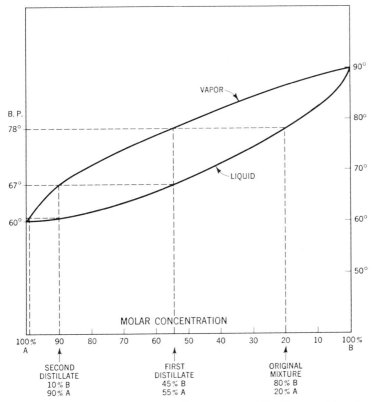

FIG. 3. Relationship of mole fraction to vapor and liquid composition at the boiling point.

moved from the distilling flask faster than *B*, and, as distillation progresses, the *liquid left in the flask* becomes less rich in *A*, the lower-boiling constituent. Thus, the concentration moves to the right and the boiling point rises. Although the vapor continues to be richer in *A* than is the liquid, the vapor becomes progressively less rich in *A* as distillation progresses. This will become evident if coordinates are drawn for a mixture containing 90% *B*. Finally, the material left in the flask will be pure *B* and the boiling point will be 90°. The boiling point will remain at 90° as *B* distills, for only one kind of molecule is left in the flask; hence, the composition cannot change as distillation proceeds. Thus, it has been shown that *when a mixture containing two liquids of different boiling points is distilled, the initial boiling point of the mixture is between the boiling points of the constituents of the mixture, and, as distillation proceeds, the boiling point rises.* The boiling point may or may not eventually reach the boiling point of the higher-boiling constituent. This depends on the composition of the original mixture. Furthermore, it should be noted that the approximate composition of the distillate may be estimated from the boiling point. For example, if the mixture should boil at 62°, the distillate would be nearly pure A; if the boiling point were 70°, the distillate would be a mixture consisting of substantial amounts of both A and B; and, if the boiling point were 89°, the distillate would be essentially pure B. Such information is used in deciding where to "cut" fractions during fractional distillation.

During the experiment on distillation, the behavior of a pure liquid and of a mixture should be carefully observed and well understood. The distillation process is of wide utility and much significance. The behavior of liquids on distillation should be contrasted with the behavior of solids on melting, and the types of behavior should not be confused.

It will be recalled, for example, that a mixture of two different substances of the same melting point will show a melting point below that of each pure component of the mixture. In contrast, a mixture of two liquids of the same boiling point will have the *same boiling point* as each constituent taken separately. This important conclusion may be readily deduced from Raoult's law. Thus, the boiling point is far less useful for identification than is the melting point. Furthermore, two liquids of the same boiling point (or nearly the same boiling point) cannot be separated by fractional distillation.

It should be mentioned at this point that the above discussion of the behavior of liquids on distillation applies to all homogeneous liquid mixtures that form "ideal solutions." An "ideal solution" is sometimes defined as one which obeys Raoult's law! Although one normally assumes that a given liquid mixture will obey Raoult's law, there are actually a rather significant number[2] of liquid mixtures that do not obey Raoult's law but form *azeotropes*. An *azeotrope*, or an *azeotropic mixture*, is a mixture of definite composition that distills at a constant temperature as if it were a pure compound. The boiling point of an azeotrope is never between the boiling points of the constituents, but is above the boiling point of the highest-boiling constituent, or below the boiling point of the lowest-boiling constituent. These are known, respectively, as *maximum-boiling* and *minimum-boiling* azeotropes. In some instances, the boiling point of an azeotrope differs only slightly from the boiling point of one

[2]There has been published a 328-page book in which are tabulated the boiling points and compositions of known azeotropes: L. H. Horsley, *Azeotropic Data* (Washington: American Chemical Society, 1952). A part of the tabulated material was also published in *Analytical Chemistry*, **19**, 508 (1947), and **21**, 831 (1949). A 92-page second volume of tables of azeotropes has also been published: L. H. Horsley and W. S. Tamplin, *Azeotropic Data—II* (Washington: American Chemical Society, 1962). Numerous other azeotropes have been reported in research papers, while many others which exist have not been recognized and reported.

component of the azeotropic mixture. For example, the minimum-boiling azeotrope of water and ethyl alcohol, containing about 95.5% (by weight) ethyl alcohol and 4.5% water, boils at 78.15°, while pure ethyl alcohol boils at 78.3°. An example of a maximum-boiling azeotrope is the mixture containing 20.2% hydrogen chloride gas (b.p. −85°) and 79.8% water. This azeotrope boils at 108.6°. In addition to binary azeotropic mixtures, a few ternary azeotropes are known. An example is the minimum-boiling mixture of water, benzene, and ethyl alcohol, which boils at 64.9°. Obviously, azeotropic mixtures cannot be separated by simple fractional distillation. *Azeotropic mixtures can be separated by gas phase chromatography* (cf. Chap. 4), where the separation depends on principles different from those which apply in distillation. In research on new compounds, gas chromatography of liquid distillates is a wise precaution. This will reveal any unexpected occurrences of azeotropes.

Fractional Distillation

As already mentioned, a mixture of two components boiling 30° apart, such as substances A and B, can be separated by use of the simple distillation equipment if a large number of fractions are collected and intermediate fractions are repeatedly redistilled. This procedure is so laborious as to be impractical, however, unless the two components of the mixture differ in boiling point by 70° or more. This situation is greatly improved if a fractionating column is used. The simple design shown in Fig. 4 is suitable for separating substances boiling 30° or more apart. Note that the column amounts to an elongation and elaboration of the neck of the distilling flask.

When vapor leaves the boiling flask and starts up the column, it will be partially condensed while passing up the column, and the liquid that condenses will be richer in the higher-boiling constituent than will be the vapor remaining uncondensed. The equilibrium is the same as when liquid is partially vaporized as discussed above. Thus, the vapor has been enriched in the lower-boiling component. Furthermore, liquid running back down the column encounters hot vapors rising and the liquid is partly revaporized, again giving vapor richer in the lower-boiling component. These two processes go on continually as the vapor rises in the column, so that vapor reaching the takeoff at the top of the column has been effectively redistilled several times, and an essentially pure lower-boiling component may be obtained at the top of the column even though its mole fraction in the pot is relatively small (refer to Fig. 3). As this lower-boiling substance is removed, however, its mole fraction in the pot continually goes down, the composition moves to the right (see Fig. 3), and eventually the number of redistillations that the column can accom-

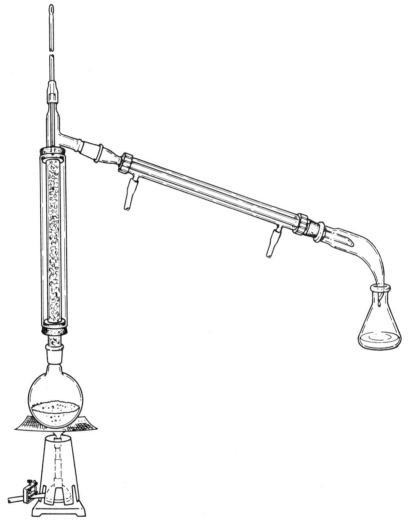

FIG. 4. Apparatus for simple fractional distillation, equipped with ground-glass joints. A similar fractionating column, without ground joints, should have a 10-mm tube at bottom with beveled tip and an 8-mm side tube.

plish is not enough to furnish essentially pure *A* at the top of the column. At this point, the temperature at the top of the column begins to rise, indicating that a mixture is being collected in the distillate, so receivers are changed and the intermediate fraction is collected. When the temperature reaches a value near that of the higher-boiling component, receivers are changed again, and the higher-boiling component is collected. The yield of the two nearly pure components may be increased by redistilling the intermediate fraction.

For the efficient operation of a fractionating column, there should be intimate contact of the returning liquid and the rising vapor, so a column usually has some provision for spreading the liquid over a large surface. This is accomplished in the column shown in Fig. 4 by packing the column with short sections of glass tubing. Such a column is known as a "randomly packed" column, in contrast with columns containing orientated packing. The efficiency of a column is reduced if distillation is too rapid, for this reduces the time of contact between the liquid and the vapor, and also tends to overheat the column and reduce the amount of reflux. Other factors are involved, but these are more appropriately discussed in Chap. 32. In any case, it should be remembered that a given separation is accomplished in less time if the rate of distillation is not too fast; a rate of 10–15 drops per minute is recommended.

EXPERIMENTAL PROCEDURES

Simple Distillation

A simple distillation outfit is assembled as illustrated in Fig. 1. All apparatus must be *dry*. In simple distillation, it is not necessary that the distilling flask be vertical, and the apparatus should be arranged in such a way that the burner and the receiving flask rest on the desk. Several of the details illustrated in Fig. 1 are of such importance as to deserve special comment. Of prime importance is the location of the thermometer, with the top of the bulb just below the outlet to the condenser, so that the bulb is fully immersed in the vapor stream. It is highly desirable that the delivery tube of the distilling flask and the delivery end of the condenser extend through the cork by one or two inches, as shown, for this reduces the contact of vapor or liquid with the cork. Furthermore the burner must be close to the distilling flask and protected from air currents by a shield. A very small, even flame is needed for distillation; if the heat input varies, distillation may be intermittent and the boiling point inaccurate. Correct heat input should always be obtained by adjusting the flame to an appropriate size, *not* by moving the flame back and forth. The use of a screw clamp on the rubber tubing to the burner gives much better adjustment than does control with the gas-cock. Since the outfit must be gas-tight (escaping vapors may be ignited), all corks should be bored carefully and the apparatus should be checked by an instructor before distillation is begun. The ideal way to quickly assemble a vapor-tight apparatus is by use of interchangeable ground joints.

If there is available glassware equipped with ground joints, as described in Appendix I, there may be used a distillation flask assembled as illustrated in Fig. 5. The head and joints are too large for assembly of small distillation flasks in this manner, but such an assemblage is quite convenient for flasks of 250 ml or larger, and avoids boring of corks. There may be used either the flask with side tubes, closed as shown, or a simple round-bottomed flask with ground joint, depending on the type of flask available in the desired size. The side tubes may also be plugged by use of a glass rod in a rubber connection such as used for attaching the thermometer

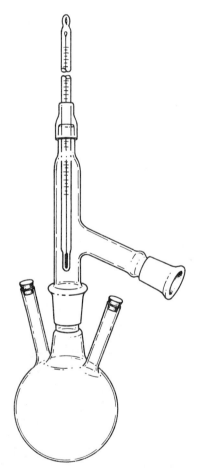

FIG. 5. Distillation flask assembled from distillation head and round-bottomed flask with side tubes. A simple round-bottomed flask with ground joint is equally suitable, unless there is desired insertion of a thermometer, separatory funnel, or other equipment in the side tubes.

in Fig. 5. A trace of glycerol or silicone grease is used to lubricate tubes being slipped into the rubber connection. The rubber tubing is slipped over the outer tube first, then the inner tube is inserted.

The rubber slip joint illustrated in Fig. 5, for attaching a thermometer or glass tube, is satisfactory if there is used a piece of heavy gum rubber tubing of such size as to give a vapor-tight fit around the small tube but allow stretching over the larger outer tube. There is, however, danger of breaking the glassware and injury to the experimenter if he is a bit clumsy about forcing the gum rubber over the larger tube, or if he is not provided with a proper piece of gum rubber tubing. A rubber adapter which eliminates hazard of breakage is illustrated [3] in Fig. 6.

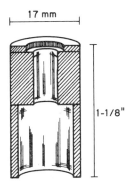

FIG. 6. Cross section of rubber adapter used for attachment of tube inserted inside tube of flask or top of distilling head.

Distillation of 75 ml of benzene is carried out, using a 250-ml distilling flask in the apparatus. For this distillation, as well as for *all other distillations*, or when liquids are heated under reflux, one or two boiling chips (small pieces of porous clay plate) should be put into the distilling flask. Bubbles arising from the boiling chips promote smooth boiling and minimize superheating. A liquid heated without boiling chips may become so superheated that, when the surface finally breaks, the entire contents of the flask are blown out. This is a *common cause of serious accidents*, ranging from fires to corrosive or hot reagents in the eyes. *A boiling chip should never be dropped into a superheated liquid*—the liquid is first cooled below the boiling point. A discussion of other devices for controlling "bumping" will be found in Chap. 31.

After the liquid has been heated to boiling, the size of the flame is reduced until the liquid distills at a moderate rate (20–30 drops per minute).

[3]This adapter, designed by Mr. Ernest Hee, manager of the organic stockrooms at Berkeley, is commercially available (Kontes Glass Co., No. 773900).

For a substance boiling as low as benzene, this rate of distillation requires a very small flame. Shielding of the flame from drafts and regulation of gas flow with the screw clamp (Fig. 1) are essential.

Note the distillation temperature (boiling point, b.p.) 2 minutes after distillation has begun (a little time is allowed for the thermometer to heat up) and thereafter at intervals of a few minutes until all but about 10 ml of liquid has been distilled. These values are recorded in a table, and the boiling *range* (such as b.p. 78.5–80.0°) is recorded. A boiling point should never be recorded as a single temperature, unless there was *no* range, and there always is some range unless exceedingly pure material and very elaborate equipment are used.

Return the distilled and undistilled benzene to the bottle marked "Recovered Benzene."

Fractional Distillation

A mixture of 150 ml of carbon tetrachloride and toluene is distilled from the simple distillation outfit (*BOILING CHIP IN FLASK!*), and the distillate is collected in three flasks marked "A," "I" (for intermediate), and "B." In flask A is collected material distilling at 77–79°, if any; in flask I, the material distilling at 79–109°; and in flask B, the material distilling at 109–111°. If the boiling point of benzene, as determined in simple distillation, differed from 80° by more than one degree, your thermometer is inaccurate by this amount, or atmospheric pressure in your location differs significantly from 760 mm; therefore, an appropriate correction should be applied to the above temperature ranges. Measure the volumes of fractions A, I, and B in a graduated cylinder and record in tabular form.

Next, a fractional distillation apparatus is constructed as shown in Fig. 4, using a round-bottomed flask of 200–300 ml capacity. The column is packed with short sections of 5-mm tubing. The packing is supported at the bottom of the column by a ring of indentations at that point. A small piece of glass wool may be used to help support the packing, but it should not be packed tightly enough to obstruct the flow of returning liquid and thus cause flooding of the column. No glass wool is recommended. In order to break off a short (1–1.5 cm) section of tubing, the tube is scratched with a file or glass cutter at the proper distance from the end; then a cork borer of the correct size is slipped over the tube to the scratch. Gentle pressure breaks off the end without danger to the experimenter. A short section of the correct size of brass tubing may be substituted for the cork borer. Enough glass tubing to pack the column may be broken off in 15–20 minutes. The fractionating column should be set up in an *approximately vertical position* so that reflux will be evenly distributed. The glass insulating shield is necessary to prevent large fluctuations in rate of distillation and reflux, from air currents in the room.

The three fractions obtained from simple distillation are recombined and distilled (*BOILING CHIP IN FLASK!*) again through the fractionating column at a suitable slow rate (10–15 drops per minute). The three fractions, A, I, and B, are collected over the same temperature ranges as before. Measure the volumes of the three fractions, record in tabular form, and compare with the volumes obtained when no column was used.

Fraction I is redistilled and the material boiling at 77–79° is collected in the flask already containing fraction A from the first fractionation. Similarly, fraction I is collected, and fraction B is added to the original fraction B. Thus, fractions A and B now contain the material from the first fractionation and refractionation of fraction I. Tabulate the final volumes of A, I, and B. Fraction I should contain less than one-third of the total.

Each of your fractions (A, I, and B) is gas chromatographed according to the procedure which has been described in Chap. 4. Select a temperature for the glpc, after consulting the data in Chap. 4, which will give retention times of suitable length that the areas under the peaks in the tracing may be measured with reasonable accuracy. Note that in gas chromatography, separation of the two components is *complete*; that is, significant time elapses with the *recorder tracing at baseline* between the two components. The contrast with fractional distillation is rather striking.

Determine the percentage content of carbon tetrachloride and of toluene in each fraction, assuming that each substance gives the same "response factor" (same area under the tracing for a given weight of each). Record these data on the glpc tracings, along with the usual data recorded on the tracings. Also enter the compositions of the fractions in your table in which the volumes and boiling points of the fractions are recorded. Attach the recorder tracings in your notebook, preferably with rubber cement.

Turn in fractions A and B, properly labeled, and place fraction I in the bottle marked "Fraction I, Recovered."

Be prepared to explain why redistillation of fraction I yielded material boiling in the A and B ranges, as well as in the I range.

More Precise Quantitative Analysis by glpc

Actually, glpc response factors are likely to be rather different for substances as different in structure as carbon tetrachloride and toluene. Thus, accurate determination of the composition of your distillation fractions becomes possible only if the response factor for each substance is determined. For this purpose, 1 μl of each *pure* substance (not your distillation fraction) is injected under the same conditions (including helium pressure) used for analysis of the distillation fractions, and the area under the tracing is determined. If necessary to keep the tracing on scale, a higher attenuation may be used, and an appropriate ratio applied to the area measured. For example, at attenuation of 1 the area is five times that recorded at attenuation of 5.

Each injection is repeated twice, for a total of three measurements, and a response factor for each compound is calculated as the average of the three values. One can also note the deviation from the average for each injection, and thus gain a measure of the precision of his measurements with the particular apparatus he is using. The response factors so obtained may be used directly to calculate the *volume per cent* composition of the distilled fractions; however, weight per cent is more meaningful for substances of such differing densities. The *weight per cent* can be determined by looking up the specific gravities of the two components in a handbook of chemistry: carbon tetrachloride, 1.594 g/ml (or mg/μl); toluene, 0.866 g/ml. Dividing by these factors converts *area per μl* to *area per mg*. Without knowing the specific gravity of the mixture injected, one can calculate its composition in weight per cent by using the response factors to determine *weight* of each component corresponding to area under the peak for that component. For example, for one of the injections of a distillation fraction, if W_c is mg of carbon tetrachloride determined as just described, and W_t is mg of toluene, then total weight (W_{to}) is $W_c + W_t$. It follows that weight per cent of carbon tetrachloride in the mixture is calculated as $W_c / W_{to} \times 100$. A similar calculation gives weight per cent of toluene.

Using the response factors determined for carbon tetrachloride and toluene, determine the weight per cent composition of your three distilled fractions. How does this compare with the approximate values that were based on the assumption of the same response factor?

It is worthwhile noting, at this point, that after the response factor for a substance has been determined, the weight of that substance in any volume of solution injected may be readily calculated. Thus, the yield in a synthesis may be calculated without actually isolating the product. A solution of the reaction products is diluted to a known volume, an aliquot (10–50 μl, depending on concentration) is injected in glpc, weight of product is calculated from area under its peak in the tracing, then total yield in the entire volume of solution is calculated. This calculation of yield is successful, even if the desired product is accompanied by many by-products, provided that the by-products are separable by glpc—a condition that can be met on nearly all occasions.

Steam Distillation

6

Steam distillation is very useful for the separation of slightly volatile, water-insoluble substances from nonvolatile materials. It is especially useful in cases where a relatively small amount of volatile material is to be separated from a relatively large amount of tarry or voluminous nonvolatile material. Thus, it is often used in the isolation of natural products. Steam distillation may be *direct* (a mixture of water and the substance distilled directly) or *indirect* (steam generated in a separate flask or obtained from a steam line). In many instances, the mixture being steam-distilled contains precipitates or tarry materials that cause bumping or charring if direct steam distillation is attempted; therefore, indirect steam distillation is most widely used. It is *important to remember* that the principles of steam distillation apply only if the organic substance to be distilled is insoluble in water. If the substance is soluble in water, the principles of fractional distillation apply (cf. Chap. 5). The principles of steam distillation will be developed next.

In Chap. 5, it was pointed out that the partial pressure of a substance from a homogeneous mixture with another substance is a function of the molar concentration of the substance. The quantitative relationship is known as Raoult's law. If two substances are immiscible in each other (or nearly so) their mixture is heterogeneous; that is, two phases are present. Distillation of such a mixture is known as *heterogeneous distillation;* if one of the phases is water, the term *steam distillation* is applied. The principles of steam distillation may be developed by consideration of a mixture of bromobenzene (b.p. 156°) and water (b.p. 100°). These two substances are almost entirely insoluble in each other.

61

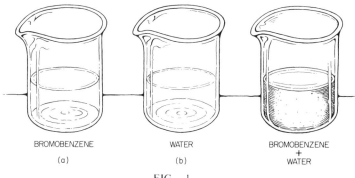

BROMOBENZENE   WATER   BROMOBENZENE
+
WATER

(a)   (b)

FIG. 1.

If these substances are considered at a temperature of 30°, then the vapor pressure of bromobenzene in a vessel alone [cf. Fig. 1 (a)] may be measured, and is found to be 6 mm. Similarly, the vapor pressure of water is 32 mm. If the two substances are now placed in the same vessel and stirred well [Fig. 1 (c)], the surface will consist partly of droplets of bromobenzene and partly of droplets of water, for the two substances are immiscible. If it be recalled that "vapor pressure" is force per unit area, it is apparent that the vapor pressure of a substance is not a function of the size of the surface. To express this in another way, the vapor pressure of a substance at a given temperature is constant, no matter whether the substance be contained in a 10-ml flask or a 500-ml flask. Further, the vapor pressure of water at 30° is 32 mm of mercury no matter whether it be in a vessel alone [Fig. 1 (b)] or in a droplet surrounded by droplets of bromobenzene [Fig. 1 (c)]. Thus, the vapor pressure of the mixture in Fig. 1 (c) is the *sum* of the vapor pressures of water and bromobenzene. This radical difference from the behavior of a homogeneous mixture is caused by the fact that the molecules of water in a water droplet are not diluted with molecules of bromobenzene. On a molecular scale, the droplets of bromobenzene might as well be in another container. Since the same consideration applies to the bromobenzene, the vapor pressures of the substances are additive.

Let us now consider a temperature of 95°, where the vapor pressures are approximately as follows:

$$P_{\text{bromobenzene}} = 120 \text{ mm} \qquad P_{\text{water}} = 640 \text{ mm} \qquad P_{\text{mixture}} = 760 \text{ mm}$$

Thus, the total vapor pressure of the well-stirred mixture is 760 mm, which is atmospheric pressure; *therefore, the mixture boils*, and bromobenzene and water distill together. This is steam distillation. Several important features of this type of distillation should be emphasized.

1. Although water boils at 100° and bromobenzene boils at 156°, the

mixture of the two boils at 95°, *below* the boiling point of either component of the mixture.

2. Since the vapor pressure of each substance and of the mixture is entirely independent of concentration, it follows that the boiling point will remain constant so long as there is *some* of each constituent present. If either constituent becomes exhausted, the boiling point will *suddenly* (not gradually) rise to that of the remaining constituent.

3. Since the vapor pressure of each substance remains constant so long as any of it is present, and since the molar concentration of each substance in the vapor is proportional to its vapor pressure, it follows that the molar ratio of the two substances in the distillate remains constant so long as the mixture being distilled contains some of each. For the distillate, the composition is determined according to the following ratio:

$$\frac{\text{Moles of bromobenzene}}{\text{Moles of water}} = \frac{P_{\text{bromobenzene}}}{P_{\text{water}}} \qquad (6\text{-}1)$$

Since there are no concentration factors in this expression, it holds throughout the distillation. We cannot separate water and bromobenzene by distillation, but we can separate bromobenzene and water from other nonvolatile (or high-boiling water-soluble) substances. The water may then be very simply separated from the bromobenzene by the use of a separatory funnel.

The above equation is most useful if the molar ratio is replaced by a weight ratio. Since

$$\text{Moles} = \frac{\text{Grams}}{\text{Gram M. W.}} \quad \text{or} \quad \frac{\text{Wt}}{\text{M. W.}} \qquad (6\text{-}2)$$

we may substitute this expression in Eq. 1, transpose, and obtain

$$\frac{\text{Wt}_{\text{bromobenzene}}}{\text{Wt}_{\text{water}}} = \frac{(P_{\text{bromobenzene}})(\text{M. W. of bromobenzene})}{(P_{\text{water}})(\text{M. W. of water})} \qquad (6\text{-}3)$$

Various things may be calculated from this expression, depending on what is known (cf. "Experimental Procedures," page 68).

It is interesting to note that, since the molecular weight of water is only 18 and that of bromobenzene is 157, in spite of the much lower vapor pressure of bromobenzene it distills faster than water on a weight basis. The low molecular weight of water is very convenient for the rapid steam distillation of organic materials.

It is instructive to consider now a substance, which will be termed *y*, that has the same boiling point as bromobenzene but is *soluble* in water. If this substance were in a mixture with water where the mole fraction of *y* was

0.01, the mixture would boil slightly *above* 100°. The vapor pressure of pure y at a temperature slightly above 100° would be about 145 mm; thus, the partial pressure of y from the solution would be given by

$$P_y = P_y^\circ N_y = (145)(0.01) = 1.45 \text{ mm} \qquad (6-4)$$

Since the partial pressure of water from the solution would then be about 758.5 mm, the concentration of y in the distillate would be exceedingly small; the first distillate would be nearly pure water. In contrast, as shown before, bromobenzene would distill even faster than water, on a weight basis; the only difference is that substance y is soluble in water and bromobenzene is insoluble in water.

The more complicated, but widely used, *fractional steam distillation* may now be considered. For this purpose, we may consider two organic compounds, C and D, which are miscible with each other but mutually insoluble in water. Let us suppose that C is lower boiling than D. If a mixture of these two substances is distilled with steam, then at the boiling point

$$P_{\text{total}} = P_{\text{organic phase}} + P_{\text{water}} = 760 \text{ mm} \qquad (6-5)$$
and
$$P_{\text{organic phase}} = P_C + P_D = P_C^\circ N_C + P_D^\circ N_D \qquad (6-6)$$

As this mixture is distilled, the principles of steam distillation apply to the mixture as a whole; that is, the two phases distill together and the molar ratio of the two phases in the distillate is the ratio of their vapor pressures. However, the organic phase is distilling according to the principles of fractional distillation. Thus, C and D are both distilling, but the distillate is richer in C than is the residue, for C is the lower-boiling component (cf. Chap. 5). As distillation progresses, the proportion of D in the undistilled portion increases as C decreases; that is, N_C is decreasing as N_D increases. Of course $N_C + N_D$ is always unity for the organic phase, since these are the only two components present. Because C is the lower-boiling substance, for a given temperature, the numerical value of P_C° must be greater than that of P_D°. Thus, as N_C becomes smaller and N_D becomes larger during distillation, an inspection of Eq. 6 will show that $P_{\text{organic phase}}$ must decrease. This follows from the fact that the multiplier of N_C is a larger number than is the multiplier of N_D. Perhaps the easiest clarification of this behavior will follow from substitution of simple numbers in Eq. 6. Any numbers will suffice for demonstration so long as P_C° is greater than P_D°, and N_C plus N_D is equal to unity (these requirements follow from our definition that the organic phase contains only two components, of which C is the lower-boiling).

Since the partial pressure of the organic phase in a fractional steam distillation is decreasing, the temperature of the mixture must rise slightly if the total pressure is to continue to equal 760 mm. This temperature rise will be small, however. The most striking evidence of fractional steam distillation is that the relative amount of organic phase in the distillate decreases as distillation progresses. This follows logically from the facts that (1) the vapor pressure of the organic phase is decreasing, and (2) the ratio of each phase in the distillate is proportional to its vapor pressure. If a fractionating column is used for the fractional steam distillation, of course the components of the organic phase may be separated. The effectiveness of such a separation is similar to that which would be obtained in a homogeneous distillation, without the addition of steam; but the use of steam lowers the distillation temperature of higher-boiling components below the boiling point of water. Herein lies the explanation of the widespread use of fractional steam distillation in industrial operations.

If the student can obtain a clear understanding of fractional steam distillation, it is safe to say that he understands the principles of both fractional distillation and steam distillation.

EXPERIMENTAL PROCEDURES

Apparatus and Manipulation

A steam-distillation apparatus like the one illustrated in Fig. 2 is assembled, unless steam lines are available on the workbenches. If live steam is available, connection is not made directly to the steam-distillation flask, but by way of a steam trap, such as illustrated in Fig. 3. This allows draining of the condensate from the steam line and prevents excessive accumulation of water in the steam-distillation flask.

If the steam generator is used, according to Fig. 2, a 1-liter flask is used as the steam boiler, and a 500-ml flask as the distilling flask. All connections are made as short as possible, and the glass tubing should be no smaller than 7 mm. This keeps condensation at a minimum, and this is desirable. In contrast to ordinary distillation, there is no objection to carrying out a steam distillation rapidly; in fact, it is desirable to distill as rapidly as permitted by the capacity of the condenser, for this saves time. It is usual to put two burners under the steam generator. A small flame may be put under the distilling flask to prevent excessive condensation in this flask. In no case should the distilling flask be allowed to become more than half full, for too full a flask encourages splashing into the steam outlet. The most effective means of preventing bumping in the steam generator is to add a small pinch of zinc dust to the water. The slow evolution of hydrogen promotes very smooth boiling.

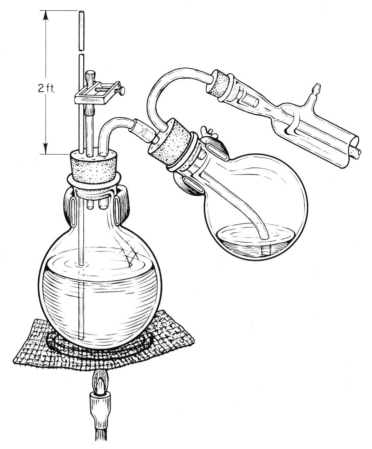

FIG. 2. Apparatus for indirect steam distillation including steam generator.

It should be noted that the steam-inlet tube is so bent as to extend to the bottom of the flask in a tilted position. *Unless this steam inlet reaches to the bottom of the flask*, a two-phase solution may not be stirred sufficiently to allow both phases to exert their equilibrium vapor pressures. The steam-outlet tube passes just through the cork. This reduces the likelihood of non-volatile material splashing into the steam outlet and thus getting into the distillate. Tilting the flask also reduces this likelihood.

The two-foot upright tube in the steam generator, which should extend to the bottom of the flask, is a safety tube. If the apparatus becomes plugged at any point, water will rise in this tube and warn the operator to remove the heat. Even if boiling water is driven out of this tube, as a result of insufficient attention, this is far less hazardous than the explosion of the apparatus that would result from absence of the safety tube. When steam dis-

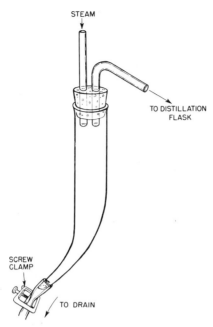

FIG. 3.   Simple trap for steam distillation, utilizing steam from a line. Connection to the steam distillation flask should be kept as short as possible. A longer tube to the steam outlet is usually required, but this should be no longer than necessary.

tillation is stopped or interrupted, the sucking of the contents of the distilling flask into the steam generator is avoided by opening the third outlet from the steam generator by loosening the screw clamp. (*CAUTION! Steam rushes out at first.*) If a live steam line is being utilized, in conjunction with the steam trap shown in Fig. 3, suck-back from the distilling flask is prevented by *fully* opening the screw clamp at the bottom of the adapter. This screw clamp is only partly opened when draining of condensate becomes necessary.

If ground-jointed equipment is available, a *superior steam-distillation flask* may be constructed from a round-bottomed flask and the distilling head, as is illustrated in Fig. 4. The large diameter of the distilling head is a great help in preventing splashover into the distillate.

Whatever steam-distillation assembly is used, it should be saved, for it is utilized in later experiments.

Distillation Experiments

1. Forty ml of bromobenzene and 20 ml of water are placed in the distillation flask and indirectly steam-distilled. The distillate is collected in a

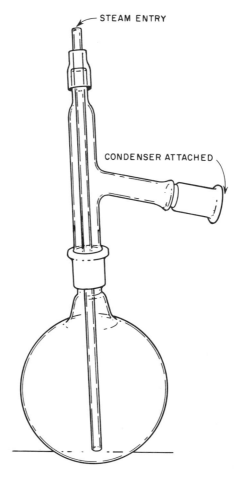

FIG. 4. Utilization of head with ground joint for steam distillation. The large diameter of this head alleviates difficulty due to splashing of material into the distillate, so that a large tilt to the flask becomes unnecessary. Connection to the steam source should be kept as short as possible.

graduated cylinder until 25 ml have been obtained. Note the volume of water and the volume of bromobenzene (lower layer). A second 25-ml portion of distillate is collected and the volumes of the layers noted.

Compare the volumes of bromobenzene in the first and second portions of distillate. Using the density of bromobenzene (1.5), calculate the weight ratio of water to bromobenzene. Also calculate the theoretical ratio of water to bromobenzene if the vapor pressure of water at 95° (the boiling point of the mixture) is 640 mm (these data do not apply if atmospheric pressure differs significantly from 760 mm).

The distilled and undistilled bromobenzene are separated from the water in a separatory funnel, and the bromobenzene is returned to the bottle provided.

2. A mixture of 25 ml of benzene (b.p. 80°) and 25 ml of xylene (b.p. 135°; xylene is a hydrocarbon of higher molecular weight than benzene) is steam-distilled. Collect two 25-ml portions of distillate and note the volumes of the water layer and of the hydrocarbon layer (upper layer) in each sample. Be prepared to explain any difference from the behavior of bromobenzene.

The distilled and undistilled hydrocarbons are returned to the bottle provided.

3. The melting point of a mixture of 1 g of naphthalene and 3 g of salicylic acid is determined (the melting-point sample should be well mixed). This mixture and 20 ml of water are placed in the steam-distillation flask and indirectly steam-distilled. In order to *prevent the solid from plugging the condenser*, water is not circulated through the condenser jacket, but a small amount of water is allowed to stand in it. As this warms up so that the steam is not condensed, a little more cold water is allowed to run in at intervals. *If the water level in the safety tube begins to rise, this is a sign that the condenser is plugged*, so the jacket should be drained immediately, and the spurting of boiling water from the safety tube should be anticipated. In such an emergency, it may become advisable to vent steam by opening the screw clamp, stop distillation, and remove the plug from the condenser. The distillation is continued until the distillate runs clear. The solid distillate is separated from the water, pressed between absorbent paper for the removal of most of the water, and allowed to dry (Note 1). The weight and the melting point of the solid distillate are determined. Which compound distilled?

The hot residual liquid in the steam-distillation flask is poured into a small Erlenmeyer flask (filtering hot by gravity if not clear) and cooled in water. After standing 20–30 minutes in cold water, the separated crystals are collected by suction filtration, dried, and weighed. The melting point is also determined.

These two products, properly bottled and labeled, are turned in when the experiment is reported. Be prepared to explain why one substance distilled with steam and the other did not.

NOTE

1. This solid proves to be rather volatile, and significant loss by evaporation will occur if it is dried overnight. If the material that has been pressed as dry as possible with paper is spread on a watch glass it will dry in one or two hours. A small sample for melting point, ground on a watch glass, will dry in 10–15 minutes.

It may be added that high volatility is not the principal reason that this compound steam distilled and the other did not.

Thin Sheet Chromatography

7

Chromatography on thin sheets—either of paper or of some adsorbent material such as silica gel or alumina deposited on a glass plate—is one of the most common procedures used for the separation of mixtures. In this chapter will be discussed its application to the separation of plant pigments and amino acids. The attractiveness of these processes lies in their simplicity and extreme sensitivity. Thus minute amounts of materials are used, and separations are rapidly effected. Complex mixtures of closely similar compounds are frequently easily separated, making this technique particularly useful in natural products chemistry. Since the process involves solution and partition phenomena in the liquid phase, volatility is not a requirement, and, in contrast to gas chromatography, nonvolatile, high molecular weight, and unstable molecules may be separated.

The procedures described below are analytical in that a qualitative or semiquantitative knowledge of the nature and components of a mixture is sought. The same results, however, can be translated to a preparative scale, for example, by using thicker layers and larger sheets. With many complex mixtures this is actually the process followed: analytical chromatography is performed to determine the best system of adsorbent and developing solvent and these results are then applied on many larger sheets to separate large amounts (up to grams) of the mixture.

In paper chromatography a small amount of the material to be separated is applied about an inch from the bottom of a paper strip. The material becomes adsorbed on the strip. The strip is then placed into a test tube so that only the tip of the strip extends into the solvent at the bottom of the tube. By means of capillary action the solvent slowly moves up the paper strip. When the solvent reaches the spot where the material has been applied, an equilibrium is established between the material adsorbed to the paper strip and material dissolved in the solvent. Let us consider the material to be separated as made up of equal amounts of two kinds of substances, A and B. If A is more soluble in the solvent or has less of an attraction to the paper on which it is adsorbed, more A molecules will be in the solvent than B molecules. The solvent then moves upward slightly, and a new equilibrium is reached between material in the solvent and material adsorbed to the paper strip. Since the probability of an A molecule being present in the solvent is greater than a B molecule, and since the solvent is moving because of capillary action, substance A will move faster than substance B. Eventually, substances A and B will be separated into two distinct bands. This process is illustrated in Fig. 1.

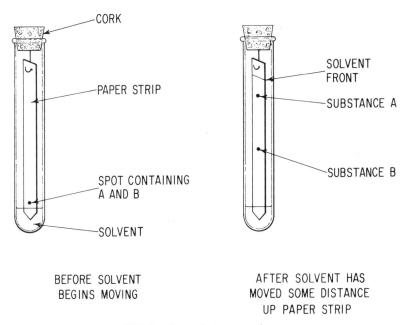

CORK

SOLVENT FRONT

PAPER STRIP

SUBSTANCE A

SPOT CONTAINING A AND B

SUBSTANCE B

SOLVENT

BEFORE SOLVENT
BEGINS MOVING

AFTER SOLVENT HAS
MOVED SOME DISTANCE
UP PAPER STRIP

FIG. 1. Paper chromatography.

Essentially, paper chromatography is a partitioning process in which each substance distributes itself, according to its partition coefficient, between the water phase adsorbed on the paper surface and the solvent phase moving up the paper. Since two substances would not be expected to have exactly the same partition coefficient, and since the number of distributions for each substance between the two phases is practically infinite, even extremely similar compounds would move at different rates and be separated. In addition there is some, but a minor, interaction between each compound and the hydroxyl groups of the cellulose of the paper.

Thin layer chromatography (tlc) was invented in 1938 by Izmailov and Schraiber, Russian workers who employed it for the analysis of plant extracts; it enjoyed only sporadic use by other chemists until 1956–58 when E. Stahl, a German scientist, perfected it for analysis of the constituents of stinging nettles. Since 1960, tlc has played an expanding role in chemical research largely because of its capability of analyzing microgram and even nanogram amounts of complex mixtures. In fact, tlc has often permitted the completion of hitherto unsolvable research problems, particularly in natural products organic chemistry. In practice, tlc is accomplished by applying a very small amount of compound or mixture (*ca.* 0.1 mg) to a thin layer of adsorbent deposited on a glass plate. The adsorbent usually contains some binder (such as calcium sulfate) which assures its adherence to the plate. The plate is placed in an enclosed vessel containing the solvent, and as the developing solvent moves up the adsorbent layer, the various substances will also move up, but to different extents. The distance each compound moves, divided by the distance covered by the solvent (that is, the distance from the starting spot or origin to the solvent (front) is called the R_f value for that compound. By using different developing solvents and various adsorbents, the R_f's can be varied and in some cases even reversed. Thus the R_f is characteristic for each individual compound with a given specific adsorbent and solvent system.

Here again we are observing a partitioning process, and the migration of each compound is a function of its tendency to adhere to the surface of the adsorbent and to dissolve in and move with the solvent. This behavior is usually termed *adsorption chromatography* in contrast to the primarily partition chromatography taking place on paper sheets. However, in some instances where a significant water layer remains on the adsorbent or when a mixed solvent is used, one of which adheres very strongly to the adsorbent, tlc may also be partition chromatography. The almost infinite number of solute distribution events—between adsorbent surface and solvent or between adsorbed, immobile solvent and mobile solvent—results in different R_f's and separation.

The next step in thin sheet chromatography is to detect the various compounds and their positions on the sheet. If the substances are colored, this is easily accomplished by visual inspection. For colorless compounds, a large variety of visualizing procedures have been devised. Mostly these consist in spraying the sheet with a reagent that gives a color with the compounds under study. This may be a general type of reagent reacting with organic compounds in general (not applicable to paper chromatography) or a specific reagent for a certain functionality. Also detection by ultraviolet fluorescence is frequently used.

Finally, in some analytical chromatograms and in all preparative work, the various compounds are removed from the adsorbent sheet. This is accomplished by cutting out the appropriate strips of paper or scraping off the appropriate portions of thin layer adsorbent. The fractions then are digested with suitable solvents for removing the adhering compound.

In summary then, thin sheet chromatography consists in:

1. *Placing the material on the chromatographic sheet.* Precaution must be exercised not to overload the sheet and not to spread the applied spot over too large an area.

2. *Developing the chromatogram by having solvent move up the sheet.* Here it is very important that the solvent phase and vapor phase be in equilibrium so that evaporation from the chromatogram surface does not occur during the development. This is particularly important when mixed solvents are used. The choice of solvent is crucial, and use of mixed solvents greatly extends the possibilities. In choosing a developing solvent, polarity is of primary importance. For example, the more polar the solvent, the greater the R_f for a polar compound, whereas less polar compounds will move less rapidly in such a solvent. Thus the developing solvent can be adjusted to fit the mixture being chromatographed. A series of solvents in order of increasing polarity is:

Aliphatic hydrocarbons: petroleum ether, hexane, cyclohexane
Carbon tetrachloride
Aromatic hydrocarbons: toluene, benzene
Methylene dichloride
Chloroform
Ethers: diethyl ether, tetrahydrofuran, dioxan
Ethyl acetate
Acetone
Alcohols: isopropanol, ethanol, methanol
Water

3. *Detecting the spots.* Colored compounds, of course, are easily detected by visual inspection. Colorless compounds require visualization, usually accomplished by specific and extremely sensitive (in some cases, to less than 0.1 μg) color reactions. Frequently, a general test for any organic material is used, such as exposure to iodine vapor or spraying with ceric sulphate. The latter general reagents can be used with inert thin layer adsorbents but are unusable with paper. Keep in mind that detection with such reagents in most cases causes structural changes in the compounds. For polyunsaturated compounds, ultraviolet fluorescence is frequently a very sensitive detection method.

4. *Elution.* This requires separation of the fractions by cutting the paper or scraping the proper portion of the thin layer adsorbent from the

plate, followed by digestion with a good solvent. Filtration through a fine filter then removes the adsorbent.

EXPERIMENTAL PROCEDURES

Materials

Tomato paste; carrot paste; frozen, chopped spinach
Wire hooks made from paper clips
Whatman No. 1 filter paper
Capillary tubes
Microscope slides, 25 × 75 mm
Silica gel G suspension
Standard solutions of histidine, glycine, proline, tryptophan, valine (1% solutions in 80% water, 20% isopropanol)
Ninhydrin reagent: 0.3% ninhydrin in 95% ethanol
Ehrlich reagent: 5 g of *p*-dimethylaminobenzaldehyde in 100 ml concentrated HCl
Unknown amino acid

Preparation of Capillary Tubes

Syringes capable of applying microliter ($1 \ \mu l = 1 \ mm^3$) amounts of solution to the thin layer are commonly used in tlc for quantitative work, but fine glass capillaries are adequate for semiquantitative and qualitative purposes. Fine capillaries can be made by pulling them from melting point capillaries using a burner (cf. Chap. 2 for technique). The melting-point capillary is rotated in the hot portion of the burner flame, removed when soft, and pulled, deliberately, to about twice its original length. A capillary of outside diameter somewhat smaller than standard paper clip wire is acceptable. Scratch the center of the capillary section and break by bending away from the scratch, taking care that the fine end of the applicator is broken off squarely to insure an even flow of solution out of the capillary onto the layer. Make several capillaries.

Paper Chromatography

Preparation of extract.   Place approximately one-third of a scoopulafull of tomato paste or carrot paste, or ½ oz (~15 g) of frozen, chopped spinach in a test tube. Add 10 ml of acetone and warm gently in the warm water bath or steam bath with mixing. Pour the solution carefully into a clean 50-ml Erlenmeyer flask. Repeat this digestion two more times, combining the three portions of acetone solution. Add a boiling chip and concentrate the acetone solution to about 5 ml, using the warm water bath or steam bath. Carry out this operation in the hood, or carry the acetone vapors away with a tube attached to an aspirator. The concentrated acetone extract of the spinach is used directly for the chromatography experiments. To the concentrated carrot and tomato extracts are added 5-ml portions of hexane, the contents are swirled moderately, and only the hexane (upper) phase is used for spotting the chromatograms as directed below.

Preparation of chromatogram. Attach a strip of chromatography paper to a cork by means of a wire hook and place in a test tube (Fig. 2). Make sure that the strip reaches almost to the bottom of the test tube, and that the paper hangs straight in the tube. Cut the bottom of the paper into a V shape.

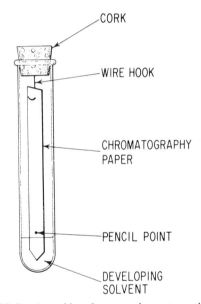

CORK

WIRE HOOK

CHROMATOGRAPHY PAPER

PENCIL POINT

DEVELOPING SOLVENT

FIG. 2. Assemblage for paper chromatography.

Take the cork and paper out and pour enough developing solvent into the test tube so that the bottom of the paper strip will dip into the liquid. For spinach extract, use 1% propanol in petroleum ether as developing solvent; for carrot or tomato extract, use butanol:water, 5:1.

In pencil, not ink, draw a point on the paper strip about an inch from the bottom. Place a drop of a pigment extract on the pencil point with a capillary tube. Allow the paper to dry. Then place another drop onto the point, and allow it to dry. Repeat a few times until the color of the spot is dark.

Place the paper into the test tube. Make sure that the bottom of the paper dips into the developing solvent, but try to keep the paper from touching the sides of the test tube. Allow the developing solvent to rise almost to the top of the paper strip. Remove the strip, mark the solvent front with a pencilled line, circle the colored spots, attach a paper clip to the bottom (to prevent curling), and allow to dry. Note the position of pigments on the paper strip, and calculate the R_f for each using the center of the spot.

Thin Layer Chromatography

Developing chamber. Place a piece of filter paper, about 100 × 150 mm, in a 150-ml beaker or 250-ml wide-mouthed Erlenmeyer flask as shown in Fig. 3. Sufficient of the developing solvent should be added to cover the bottom to a depth of about 5 mm. This chamber should be covered and allowed to stand for at least 15 minutes to establish equilibrium between liquid and vapor phase throughout the vessel. Use a cork to stopper the Erlenmeyer flask and aluminum foil to cover the beaker.

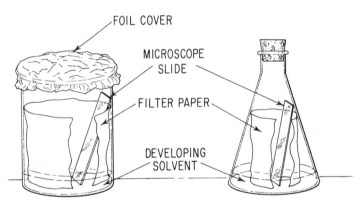

FIG. 3.   TLC developing chambers.

Preparation of tlc plates. Microscope slides, 25 × 75 mm, are thoroughly cleaned with soap and water, rinsed with water and then with methanol, and then thoroughly dried.

Prepare a slurry of 35 g of silica gel G and 100 ml of chloroform in a wide-mouthed bottle of size sufficient to completely immerse a microscope slide. Stopper and shake vigorously for 3 minutes. Pinch two clean microscope slides together with tongs, dip completely into the suspension with a brief stir, withdraw slowly, allow to drain, separate the plates, and permit to dry horizontally. [*Note:* This silica gel contains calcium sulfate as a binder (see below) which helps to adhere to the glass plate; this adherence is greatly increased by steaming. Remove the inner rings of a steam bath and place an inverted powder funnel over the opening. With tongs hold a coated microscope slide horizontally with the layer down and gently steam the layer only until wet.] To activate the adsorbent, bake in an oven at 105° for 30 minutes, or let stand at room temperature for at least 24 hours, or heat on a wire gauze placed on a hot plate for 5 minutes.

Note on tlc adsorbents. Silica gel (SiO_2) is the most commonly used tlc adsorbent, for which purpose it must have a mean particle diameter of 4–40 μ and may contain a binding agent to confer mechanical stability upon an otherwise fragile layer. When layers are to be sprayed with detection reagents, such stability is especially important. Silica gel G (E. Merck Co., Darmstadt, Germany) contains 13% of $CaSO_4 \cdot \frac{1}{2} H_2O$, a metastable hydrate which, when exposed to water and subsequently heated to dryness below 110°, precipitates as $CaSO_4 \cdot 2 H_2O$ in long intermeshed needles of high mechanical strength.

Round spots after elution indicate theoretically ideal conditions of tlc. Streaking of spots is often observed; usually "tailing" can be minimized by employing an adsorbent of smaller and more uniform particle size [e.g., Kiesel gel D-5 (Camag Co., Muttenz, Switzerland), which is also silica gel].

Other adsorbents available, each with distinctive chromatographic properties, are alumina, cellulose, and some ion exchange resins.

Tlc of plant pigments. Use the concentrated extracts prepared as directed under "Paper Chromatography." At one end, apply one extract to the left side of the plate and one to the right side. If a third extract is available, this may be applied to the middle of the plate. Do not attempt to apply more than three different solutions to a single microscope slide.

Application of the extract is made by dipping the capillary into the solution to be chromatographed, holding it vertically over the thin layer plate (laying on a flat surface), and touching it briefly and gently to the layer about 1 cm from the bottom of the plate. Avoid digging into the layer with the capillary. (If done properly with a fine capillary, one such "touch" delivers about 1 μl of solution.) Thoroughly dry the spot with a stream of nitrogen before applying additional solution. Since microscope slides are smaller than the standard 5 × 20 cm tlc plates, the smaller the application spot, the better. Use a clean, dry capillary for each different solution.

Develop the spinach extract chromatography plate with chloroform and the carrot and tomato extract plates with hexane:benzene, 4:1. The slide should be inserted into either chamber described only after the chamber has been allowed to equilibrate. Development is allowed to continue until solvent has risen approximately to within 1 cm of the top of the slide. Alternatively, a line may be drawn across the slide 1 cm from the top before development is started, then the slide is removed when the solvent front reaches this line. During this development, which will take about 20–30 minutes, the developing chamber must be tightly covered.

After the slide is removed, it is freed of solvent by placing it briefly on a steam bath or hot plate. A second developing solvent, 24:1 mixture of chloroform:methanol, is now used to resolve the pigments remaining at the origin in the carrot and tomato plates. The visible spots are due to the carotenes (orange to red), the chlorophylls (green to blue-green), and the xanthophylls (yellow).

A record of your chromatogram should be made. This can be done by pressing a piece of transparent tape on the layer. The tape and the portion of the layer which adheres to it are then removed and an additional piece of tape is placed on the back, covering the layer. The resulting "tape sandwich" is preserved, taped in your notebook, as a record of your chromatogram. Also, a diagram of your chromatogram may be drawn in your notebook.

Spinach extract contains the chlorophylls (a and b) as well as carotenes and xanthophylls. Since the carotenes are polyunsaturated hydrocarbons, they are the least polar of the pigments and, on polar adsorbents, have the greatest R_f's, that is, move closest to the solvent front. The chlorophylls are more polar and move more slowly. Xanthophylls are carotenes substituted with carbonyl, hydroxyl, and oxide functions. As a result, they display a variety of polarities and are found above and below the chlorophyll. Neither carrot (a root) nor tomato (a fruit) are photosynthetic units, hence they contain no chlorophyll. The chief pigment of carrot is β-carotene; that of tomato is lycopene.

Chlorophyll
a, $R = CH_3$ b, $R = CHO$

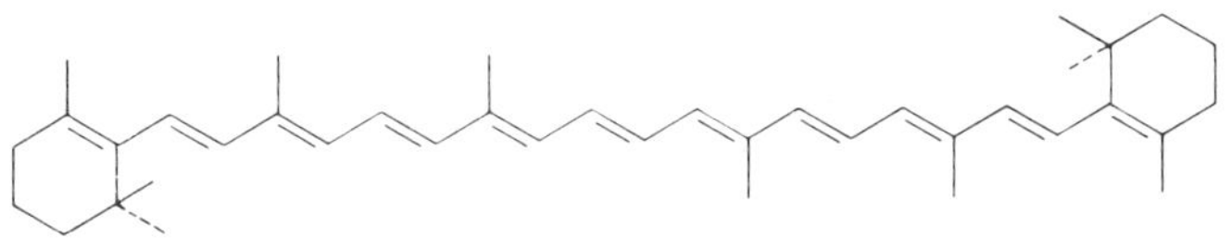

β-Carotene

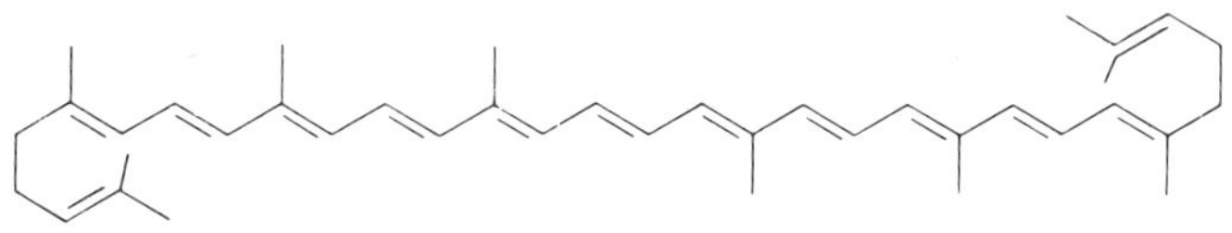

Lycopene

Tlc of amino acids. Tlc microscope slides are prepared as directed above. The developing solvent to be placed in the developing chamber is *n*-butanol:acetic acid:water, 4:1:1 by volume. Also, the same procedure as described above is used to develop the chromatogram.

Amino acids may be detected by ninhydrin which is a general reagent for visualizing all of the common amino acids. Certain amino acids may also be visualized by more selective methods such as Ehrlich's reagent or fluorescence on irradiation with UV light.

After the slide has been developed, place it on a hot plate to evaporate the residual eluent, examine the slide under UV light, record the R_f and appearance of any visible spot, then spray with ninhydrin until the plate is damp. Finally, heat on a hot plate at about 100°C. In a few minutes the colored spots will begin to appear. Record the colors and R_f's of the spots. You may also wish to run separate slides for detection with Ehrlich's reagent. Do this for each of the standard amino acids (*histidine, glycine, proline, tryptophan,* and *valine*) and also for a mixture of all five (up to three samples may be spotted on each plate).

Prepare a chromatogram of an unknown amino acid obtained from the storeroom or teaching assistant. From the R_f and detection characteristics (i.e., color with ninhydrin, UV fluorescence, reaction with Ehrlich's reagent) you should be able to make a preliminary identification of the unknown. To confirm the identification: spot the unknown and the standard solution of the suspected amino acid on the same plate, and also spot them both in the same place. After development and detection, if the preliminary identification was correct, all should have the same R_f and color characteristics, and the standard-unknown mixture should show only one spot. The structures of the five amino acids being considered here are:

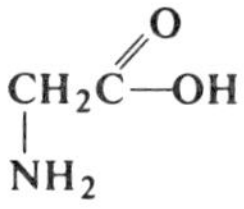

Glycine 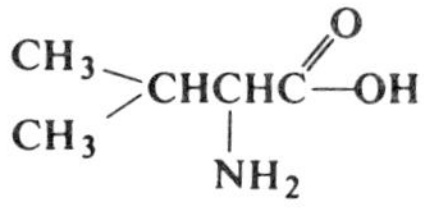   Valine 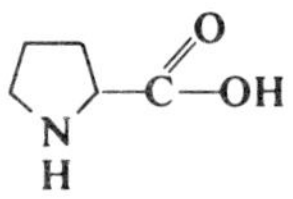   Proline

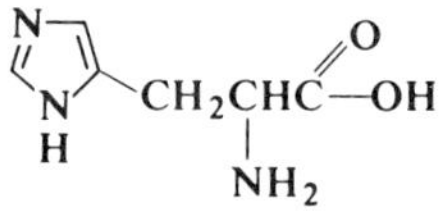

Histidine 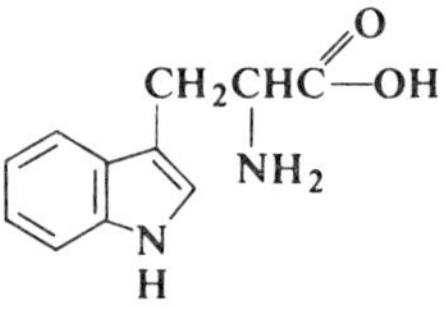   Tryptophan

All give colors with ninhydrin (triketohydrindene hydrate) due to the following reaction:

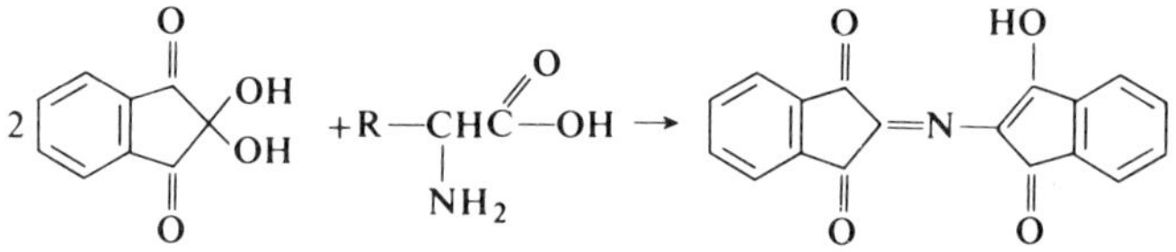

Ninhydrin

$$+ CO_2 + RCHO + 3H_2O$$

With proline, a different colored compound is formed, involving decarboxylation and condensation at both α-positions of the pyrrolidine ring. Only tryptophan gives a positive test with the Ehrlich reagent, which is used for the detection of indoles and pyrroles.

Alkyl Halides

8

Alkyl halides constitute the class of organic compounds most often encountered in a synthetic sequence. This results from the fact that halogen is among a very small number of leaving groups that are sufficiently reactive to be conveniently displaced in a simple displacement reaction (S_N2 reaction). Furthermore, the alkyl halides are far more easily synthesized and purified than compounds containing any of the other good leaving groups. In view of this importance of alkyl halides in synthesis, it is appropriate that they should constitute our initial study of preparative organic chemistry.

By far the most common synthesis of alkyl halides depends on replacement of the hydroxyl of an alcohol by halogen; however, hydroxyl is such a poor leaving group that it cannot be displaced *directly* by the halide ion. It is always necessary to convert hydroxyl to some better leaving group which can be displaced by halide. The oxonium salt of the alcohol is frequently satisfactory, and this intermediate is conveniently formed by treating the alcohol with halogen acid. Displacement by the halide ion follows, as in Eq. 1. This synthesis of alkyl halides is illustrated in the

$$\text{R—OH} + \text{HX} \rightleftarrows \text{R—}\overset{+}{\underset{H}{O}}\text{H} + \text{X}^- \rightleftarrows \text{R—X} + \text{HOH} \qquad (8\text{-}1)$$

present chapter by preparation of *n*-butyl bromide, and is involved in part in the preparation of ethyl iodide. In instances where the alkyl group, R, is tertiary there is so much hindrance to the backside displacement occurring in the second step in Eq. 1 that dissociation to a carbonium ion occurs. This latter type of reaction is illustrated by synthesis of *tert*-butyl bromide, and the reactivity of the tertiary halide in an S_N1 type of reaction (ionic intermediate) is illustrated by solvolysis in an aqueous solvent. Another type of good leaving group to which the hydroxyl may be converted is an inorganic ester. This process is illustrated in synthesis of ethyl iodide by use of phosphorus triiodide.

ALKYL IODIDES

Since this is the first preparative experiment, *ethyl iodide* will be considered in detail as regards both the form and content of the notebook write-up, as outlined in Chap. 1. This will serve as a model for all preparative experiments. The title of the experiment and sections I through III, omitting discussion, are entered on a *left-hand page* (cf. Chap. 1).

I. Main Reactions

$$P + 3I \rightarrow PI_3 \tag{8-2}$$

$$3CH_3CH_2-OH + PI_3 \rightleftarrows (CH_3CH_2O)_3P + 3HI \rightarrow 3CH_3CH_2I + H_3PO_3 \tag{8-3}$$

$$PI_3 + 3H_2O \rightarrow 3HI + H_3PO_3 \tag{8-4}$$

$$CH_3CH_2OH + HI \rightleftarrows CH_3CH_2I + H_2O \tag{8-5}$$

In this preparation, all four equations above comprise the main reactions. Equations 3 and 5 involve the oxonium salts of the oxygen functions as intermediates (cf. Eq. 1), and Eq. 3 obviously involves three steps; the iodide atoms must be displaced one at a time since it is statistically improbable for three ethyl alcohol molecules to encounter a phosphorus triiodide simultaneously. For present purposes, the equations are written in a form convenient for determining stoichiometry, so as to facilitate a study of the ratios of reagents used. Thus, Eq. 1 is written as involving atoms of phosphorus and iodine, although both elements actually exist as polyatomic molecules. For consideration of stoichiometry, the reaction is conveniently written as between atoms.

Equation 3 is included because the ethyl alcohol used is the common commercial grade of alcohol (190 proof), which is 95% alcohol by volume (92% by weight), with the remainder water. Thus, some water is introduced into the reaction mixture, and this water is regenerated in Eq. 5 as it is consumed in Eq. 4.

II. Side Reaction

$$CH_3CH_2I + HI \rightarrow CH_3CH_3 + I_2 \tag{8-6}$$

This side reaction is unimportant, for the reaction is slow below about 100°. Both ethyl iodide and ethyl alcohol have boiling points considerably lower than 100°. Some lowering of yield is caused by the reversibility of Eq. 5; however, the preparation of ethyl iodide is a high-yield synthesis. Side reactions give an unusually small amount of difficulty.

III. Other Methods of Preparation

The two methods used in combination above are the chief means of preparing ethyl iodide and most other alkyl iodides as well. However, in some cases where the alkyl chloride or bromide is readily available but the more reactive iodide is desired, the alkyl iodide may be prepared by the following displacement reaction where R represents an alkyl group:

$$RCl + NaI \rightleftarrows RI + NaCl \tag{8-7}$$

In order to get complete alkyl iodide formation, the reaction is carried out in a solvent such as anhydrous acetone, in which all the substances are readily soluble except sodium chloride, which is quite insoluble. Thus the precipitation of the sodium chloride, as the reaction proceeds, shifts the equilibrium to the right and results in an excellent conversion of alkyl chloride to iodide.

This completes the information entered on the left-hand page; the remaining sections, IV through VII, are entered on the opposite *right-hand page.*

IV. Table of Reactants and Products

After such a table is completed, a consideration of the theoretical molar ratio and of the molar ratio actually used allows one to determine the limit-

Compound	M. W.	Wt Used, g	Moles Used	Ratio		Other Data
				Theory	Used	
Phosphorus	31	2.5	0.081	1	1	
Iodine	127	30	0.236	3	2.92	
Ethyl alcohol	46	22.4	0.487	3	6.00	30 ml of 95% by vol, 92% by wt $d = 0.81$
Ethyl iodide	156			3		

Limiting reagent: iodine.

ing reagent. In the preparation above, it is seen that the iodine is the limiting reagent and that the ethyl alcohol is used in large excess. The chief factor influencing the choice of the limiting reagent is very frequently the relative cost of the compounds; in this case, the quantities are chosen so as to secure maximum utilization of the iodine, by far the most expensive of the reagents. Another factor frequently influencing the choice of the limiting reagent is the purification of the desired product. Excess of a reagent that can be separated from the product only with great difficulty is, of course, to be avoided. An example of this latter type is the preparation of butyryl chloride, Chap. 11.

V. Yield Data

$$\text{Theoretical yield} = (156)(0.236) = 36.7 \text{ g}$$
$$\text{Actual yield} =$$
$$\text{Percentage yield} =$$

When the notebook report is completed through the theoretical yield calculation, it is presented to the laboratory instructor for initialing; the approved notebook is then presented at the storeroom to obtain the starting material.

VI. Observed Properties of the Product

Here are entered the physical properties of the product actually observed, such as boiling range, melting range, gas chromatography behavior, spectral properties, and so on. It is very important to record these properties accurately.

VII. Short Experiments or Tests

In this preparation, there are no entries to be made in this section, but in some experiments there will be. Balanced equations should be given and observations recorded for all reactions carried out.

Section VII concludes the notebook report, and this, together with the bottled and properly labeled product, is turned in to the instructor on or before the date due.

Purification

A very important phase of synthetic organic chemistry is the purification of the desired product. Because of the many and varied reactions organic compounds undergo, frequently the most difficult step in the preparation of a compound is not its actual formation, but its separation in a pure form from the many side products and unreacted starting materials. In order to accomplish this, it is well to list all the possible compounds present from a consideration of the main and side reactions, and to devise a purification scheme, using the flow-sheet method, for eliminating all the undesired substances. For ethyl iodide, such a schematic purification plan takes the following form:

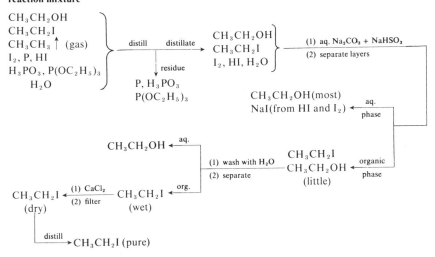

Compounds in reaction mixture

By examining a purification method in this manner, one can easily determine the purpose for each step and also detect any impurity that might pass through unremoved. In future experiments, such a detailed flow-sheet will not be given, but the student is strongly urged to construct one for himself. The extraction method for removing water-soluble impurities will be discussed below. Note should be taken of the drying of the ethyl iodide. All the water must be removed by the calcium chloride; otherwise, the distillate will be wet, since the water will steam-distill with the ethyl iodide.

Techniques

There are several techniques used by the student for the first time in this experiment; they shall be discussed here. The first is the method for heating under reflux, using the apparatus illustrated in Fig. 1, omitting the trap assembly attached to the top of the condenser. This is a device for conducting a reaction at the boiling point of the solution, since the vapors are condensed and drop back into the reaction mixture. In order to obtain the

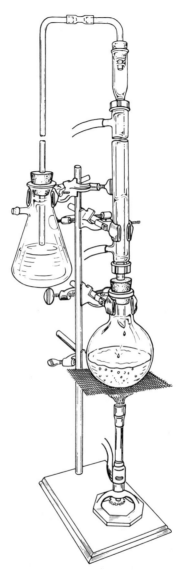

FIG. 1. Apparatus for heating under reflux with a gas trap attached. If large volumes of noxious or toxic gases are being evolved, more positive trapping of the gas is provided by the device shown in Fig. 5. Of course, in case no objectionable gases are evolved, the trap and tube attached to the top of the condenser are omitted. This apparatus is assembled most conveniently by use of a ground-jointed condenser and round-bottomed flask (cf. Appendix 1).

most efficient cooling, water is led in at the bottom of the condenser so that the jacket is completely filled.

If equipment with ground-glass joints is available, the apparatus should be assembled using a round-bottomed flask and condenser with ground joints. This makes possible the rapid assembly of a vapor-tight apparatus.

The method of *extraction* is an exceedingly useful process in the purification procedure. It consists of shaking an organic substance, insoluble in water, with water and then allowing the layers to separate. The various substances present will distribute themselves between the two layers according to their relative solubilities. Thus, inorganic salts will be found in the water phase and nonpolar organic compounds will be in the organic phase. For each substance and each pair of solvents at a given temperature, there is a definite constant relationship between the amounts found in each layer; this is known as the *distribution coefficient*, K. For any substance (X), it may be expressed by Eq. 8.

$$K = \frac{\text{Concentration of } X \text{ in the organic layer}}{\text{Concentration of } X \text{ in the water layer}} \tag{8-8}$$

For an inorganic salt, K, as expressed in Eq. 8, is essentially zero. In other words, the salt is all in the water. If X is ethyl alcohol and the organic layer is ethyl iodide, K is a small fraction. This means that some ethyl alcohol is in each layer but that the concentration in the water layer is much higher.

In the present experiment, use is made of the extraction principle to remove the excess ethyl alcohol as well as inorganic salt from the ethyl iodide. When the mixture is shaken with water, most of the ethyl alcohol, which is miscible with water, passes into the aqueous phase, while the water-insoluble ethyl iodide remains as a separate layer. The small amount of ethyl alcohol now remaining in the ethyl iodide layer is largely removed by washing the ethyl iodide once again with water, for the distribution coefficient of ethyl alcohol is quite favorable to water. It may be shown by rather simple mathematics that in a case of this kind removal of ethyl alcohol is accomplished much more effectively by two water washes than by one wash using the same total volume of water.

The apparatus used to carry out this extraction is shown in Fig. 2. Here is illustrated the separatory funnel containing the mixture in the process of being shaken. The shaking is done in this position so that any pressure developing in the funnel, either from a gas being liberated or the presence of a volatile organic solvent, may be frequently vented by turning the stopcock. The stopper is held securely and the funnel inverted, after which the stopcock is opened to release any pressure before starting to shake. At first, shaking should be moderate and only of short duration, followed by

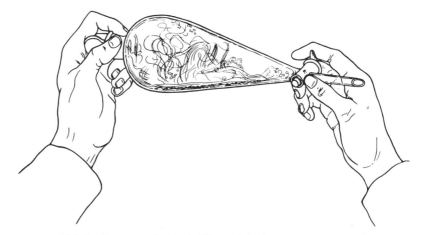

FIG. 2.   Proper method for holding and shaking a separatory funnel.

venting through the stopcock to prevent building up large pressures. When the rush of gas upon opening the stopcock is very slight, the funnel may be shaken more vigorously for a period of about one-half minute. During this time, the stopcock is held closed and securely in place with the right hand. Of course, the hand positions may be reversed if more convenient. The funnel is vented, and then placed upright (stopcock closed) in an iron ring protected by slit lengths of rubber tubing (Fig. 3), after which the stopper is removed and the layers allowed to separate.

After the layers have separated, the lower layer is drawn off through the stopcock until the phase boundary reaches the stopcock. Next the funnel is lifted and swirled gently so as to encourage the film of lower layer on the sides of the funnel to settle to the bottom. After the funnel has stood for an additional minute or two, the accumulated small lower layer is drawn off slowly and the stopcock is turned just as the phase boundary is passing through the stopcock bore. This technique, which is not time-consuming, gives very clean separation of the extracted material. The upper layer is left in the separatory funnel if there is an additional extraction of it; otherwise, it is allowed to run into an appropriate flask for the next operation.

A word of caution should be injected at this point regarding possible confusion as to which layer is water and which is organic. Of course the phase of higher density settles to the bottom, and the density of the organic layer may be learned by consulting a handbook of chemistry. This may not be straightforward, however, when the organic layer is a solution of products in a solvent, or when the water layer has salts or acids dissolved in it. It is rather simple to ascertain which layer is water by drawing off a small volume into a test tube and adding a few drops of water to it. As a back-up

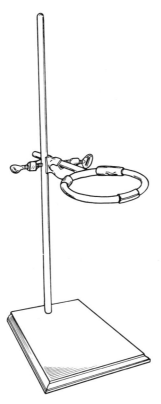

FIG. 3.   Padded ring for support of separatory funnel.

precaution, in case one forgets to identify the layers, it is *good practice to save all layers until the final product has been isolated.*

Figure 4 illustrates the apparatus to be used for distilling the ethyl iodide from the reaction mixture. The point to be noted is the method of collecting the distillate by having the adapter extend into water. The ethyl iodide, being heavier than water, sinks to the bottom, and the upper water layer prevents evaporation of the very volatile ethyl iodide. This volatility must also be kept in mind when drying with calcium chloride in the last stages of purification. If allowed to stand overnight, the flask should be tightly stoppered to prevent evaporation of the ethyl iodide.

ALKYL BROMIDES

Primary Alkyl Bromides

These are prepared most often by heating the alcohol with concentrated hydrobromic acid, according to Eq. 9; however, a satisfactory conversion

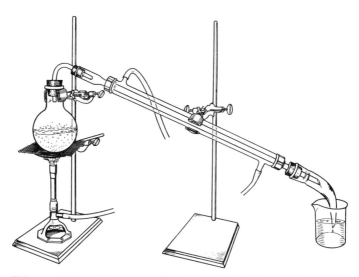

FIG. 4. Distillation of ethyl iodide from the reaction mixture. If ground-jointed equipment is used (Appendix 1), the bent tube (gooseneck) is replaced by the distillation head. Since the distillation temperature of this crude product is of no interest, the thermometer in the distillation head is not needed. The top of the head may be closed with a small cork (cf. Fig. 5-5).

can be realized only if some means is adopted to shift this equilibrium reaction forward. For primary alcohols, addition of concentrated sulfuric acid is quite effective, for it shifts the equilibria forward in two ways. It shifts the first equilibrium in Eq. 9 forward according to the law of mass action by increasing the concentration of protons on the left side of the equilibrium. In addition, it shifts the second equilibrium forward by com-

$$R-CH_2CH_2-OH + H^+Br^- \rightleftarrows R-CH_2CH_2-\overset{+}{\underset{H}{O}}H + Br^- \rightleftarrows R-CH_2CH_2-Br$$
$$+ HOH \qquad (8\text{-}9)$$

bining with and inactivating the water which is one product of the reaction. By addition of an appropriate amount of sulfuric acid, yields in this conversion can be raised to more than 90%.

For the lower molecular weight primary alcohols, this mixture of hydrobromic and sulfuric acids may be obtained in three ways. The simplest method is merely to mix appropriate amounts of constant-boiling (48%) aqueous hydrobromic acid and concentrated sulfuric acid. A second method is to generate the hydrobromic acid in the reaction mixture with the sulfuric acid already present by making use of the equilibrium reaction between sodium bromide and sulfuric acid (Eq. 10). Third, a suitable mix-

$$NaBr + H_2SO_4 \rightleftarrows HBr + NaHSO_4 \qquad (8\text{-}10)$$

ture of acids is realized by bubbling sulfur dioxide into a mixture of bromine and water (Eq. 11). While all three procedures give good yields with
the simpler alcohols, the high molecular weight primary bromides are

$$Br_2 + 2H_2O + SO_2 \rightleftarrows H_2SO_4 + 2HBr \qquad (8\text{-}11)$$

best prepared by the first method. The solubility of the requisite alcohol
is very seriously decreased by the presence of the salts in the sodium
bromide modification. In fact, with some of the higher alcohols, because of
their very limited solubility in any aqueous reaction mixture, the best
yields are obtained by bubbling in anhydrous hydrobromic acid.

Secondary Alkyl Bromides

In the case of secondary alcohols, displacement of water from the
oxonium salt by bromide ion becomes more subject to hindrance than is
the case with primary alcohols. Furthermore, dissociation of the oxonium
salt to give a carbonium ion is favored on account of the lower energy of
the secondary carbonium ion. If the carbonium ion is formed, it is prone to
lose a proton to give alkene (net reaction in Eq. 16), and even if the ion
picks up a bromide ion to give alkyl bromide, it will rearrange in part prior
to going to alkyl bromide. For these reasons, sulfuric acid must not be used
in making a secondary bromide, because this increases the concentration
of the oxonium salt. Also, heating must be avoided, for this favors dissociation of the oxonium salt. Thus, hydrobromic acid becomes a relatively
unattractive reagent for synthesis of secondary bromides. Preferred
methods for secondary bromides involve use of phosphorus tribromide
(Eq. 12) or thionyl bromide (Eq. 13). Even with these reagents, there is a

$$3ROH + PBr_3 \rightarrow 3RBr + H_3PO_3 \qquad (8\text{-}12)$$

$$ROH + SOBr_2 \rightarrow RBr + HBr + SO_2 \qquad (8\text{-}13)$$

small percentage of the molecules that react to give the carbonium ion,
which in turn rearranges before going to alkyl bromide. Special methods
must be used to avoid rearrangement entirely, in converting a secondary
alcohol to the corresponding bromide.

Tertiary Alkyl Bromides

In the case of tertiary alcohols, hindrance to backside displacement
becomes very severe, but dissociation of the oxonium salt to the carbonium

ion becomes highly favored for two reasons. The steric interference generated by four groups attached to a single carbon atom is greatly relieved by dissociation, for only three groups then remain attached to the single carbon atom. In addition, the tertiary carbonium ion is of lower energy than the secondary ion, in turn of lower energy than the primary ion. This combination of properties causes dissociation of tertiary structures to occur quite readily (see *tert*-butyl bromide preparation below), but there is no difficulty with rearrangement of the resultant tertiary carbonium ion, for the rearranged ion would be secondary, hence of much higher energy. Thus, tertiary bromides may be readily prepared with cold aqueous hydrobromic acid.

On account of hindrance to displacement, the tertiary bromides have very limited use; indeed, conversion to the Grignard reagent is the only significant application of tertiary halides in synthesis. Fortunately, the Grignard reagent has numerous applications in organic synthesis. Even in aqueous solvents at room temperature, the tertiary bromide dissociates to give the carbonium ion, which may give either alkene or tertiary alcohol, as shown in Eq. 14. In demonstration of the facility of the reactions shown in Eq. 14, *tert*-butyl bromide, which is prepared as one of the syntheses in this chapter, is solvolyzed and the rate of the reaction is followed quantitatively.

$$
\underset{\overset{|}{CH_3}}{\overset{\overset{CH_3}{|}}{CH_3-C-Br}} \xrightarrow[\text{room temp.}]{\text{aq. solvent}} \underset{\overset{|}{CH_3}}{\overset{\overset{CH_3}{|}}{CH_3-C^+}} + Br^- \xrightarrow{HOH} \underset{\overset{|}{CH_3}}{\overset{\overset{CH_3}{|}}{CH_3-C-OH}} + HBr \qquad (8\text{-}14)
$$

$$
\longrightarrow \underset{\overset{|}{CH_3}}{CH_3-C=CH_2} + HBr
$$

n-Butyl Bromide

The *main reaction* for the preparation of *n*-butyl bromide is shown in Eq. 15. As has been discussed, sulfuric acid plays an important role in

$$
C_2H_5CH_2CH_2OH + HBr \underset{\Delta}{\overset{H_2SO_4}{\rightleftarrows}} C_2H_5CH_2CH_2Br + H_2O \qquad (8\text{-}15)
$$

improving the yield in this conversion; however, it also leads to *side reactions*. The principal side reactions in the preparation (Eqs. 16–18) are

$$
C_2H_5CH_2CH_2OH + H_2SO_4 \rightleftarrows \underset{\overset{|}{H}}{C_2H_5CH_2CH_2\overset{+}{O}H} + {}^-OSO_2OH
$$

$$
\xrightarrow{\text{heat}} C_2H_5CH=CH_2 + H_2SO_4 + HOH \qquad (8\text{-}16)
$$

$$C_2H_5CH_2CH_2OH + C_2H_5CH_2CH_2\overset{+}{\underset{H}{OH}} \xrightarrow{\text{heat}} C_2H_5CH_2CH_2-O-CH_2CH_2C_2H_5$$

$$+ HOH + H^+ \quad (8\text{-}17)$$

$$C_2H_5CH_2CH_2OH + H_2SO_4 \rightleftarrows C_2H_5CH_2CH_2-OSO_2OH + HOH \quad (8\text{-}18)$$

encouraged by sulfuric acid; however, none of these side reactions are serious with primary alcohols. Both alkene formation (Eq. 16) and ether formation (Eq. 17) are slow at temperatures below about 125° for the primary structure. Butyl hydrogen sulfate is formed in a reversible reaction (Eq. 18) with a small equilibrium constant, and the impact of this reaction is reduced by use of excess hydrobromic acid to displace the equilibrium in Eq. 15 forward. In addition, and probably more importantly, the bisulfate anion is an excellent leaving group, so direct displacement by bromide can probably convert the butyl hydrogen sulfate directly to butyl bromide. Displacement by alcohol could also give dibutyl ether, a by-product, but this would be trivial because an alcohol is a poor nucleophile. A final side reaction is that between sulfuric and hydrobromic acids, on heating, to give a small amount of bromine and sulfur dioxide, the reverse of Eq. 11.

The first step in *purification* of *n*-butyl bromide is its direct steam distillation from the reaction mixture. Most of the butene escapes as a gas, but any di-*n*-butyl ether will also steam distill, for it is insoluble in water. Any bromine present and most of the hydrobromic acid are washed from the organic layer with aqueous sodium bisulfite, which converts bromine to bromide. The organic phase is finally washed with cold concentrated sulfuric acid, which dissolves nearly all organic compounds except hydrocarbons and their halogen derivatives. This latter procedure is a splendid method for purifying butyl bromide. There remains only an alkaline wash to remove acid, followed by a final water wash and drying. As usual, attention must be directed to complete drying prior to distillation, for water will cause loss of butyl bromide as a forerun, on account of steam distillation.

EXPERIMENTAL PROCEDURES

Ethyl Iodide

In a 250-ml round-bottomed flask are placed 2.5 g of red phosphorus and 30 ml of 95% ethyl alcohol. To the mixture 30 g of iodine is added in small portions, during about 15 minutes. The mixture should be swirled during the addition and cooled in a pan of cold water. After addition is complete, a water-cooled reflux condenser is attached (Fig. 1, omitting trap); the mixture is allowed to stand for about 5 minutes and is then warmed slowly on a water bath. Preparation should be made to remove the heating bath and apply cooling if there is a vigorous evolution of heat. When there is no further exothermic reaction, the mixture is heated under reflux on the water bath for about one-half hour.

The flask is then cooled, and the condenser is arranged for distillation, being connected to the flask by means of a bent 8-mm tube (Fig. 4) or a distilling head. A small flame is used for distillation, and the residue at the end of the distillation should not be overheated. The distillate is received in a small beaker containing 50 ml of water and 10 ml of 10% sodium carbonate solution. The adapter attached to the condenser should dip just below the surface of the water. After distillation is complete, the mixture is transferred to a separatory funnel, and, after the addition of a few drops of sodium hydroxide, the funnel is shaken briefly. If the iodine color is not removed, a few more drops of sodium hydroxide or a milliliter of dilute sodium bisulfite solution is added. The lower layer of ethyl iodide is separated and washed once with an equal volume of water. The carefully separated ethyl iodide is dried in a small Erlenmeyer flask over 3–4 g of anhydrous calcium chloride. Drying may be for 20–30 minutes with frequent swirling or overnight without swirling. If overnight, special care must be taken that the flask is tightly stoppered. The clear liquid is decanted into a small distilling flask, by filtering through a small gravity filter to remove any suspended drying agent, and is then redistilled. The product is collected over a range of about three degrees (recorded b.p. 72.3°). The average yield amounts to 24–28 g. It is turned in properly labeled, as described on page 3.

n-Butyl Bromide

30 gm or 3 7.4 ml

To a 500-ml round-bottomed flask containing 105 g (71 ml) of 48% hydrobromic acid cooled in an ice bath, is slowly added 31 g (17 ml) of concentrated sulfuric acid. Cooling is continued and 37 g of *n*-butyl alcohol is added, followed by an additional 25 g (13.5 ml) of concentrated sulfuric acid. The mixture is swirled gently, removed from the ice bath, and wiped dry. After one or two boiling chips have been added, the flask is attached to a reflux condenser fitted with a trap, as shown in Fig. 1. The rubber connection used should be short, and the exit tube must be above the surface of the water in the filter flask. If hydrogen bromide escapes during the reflux period, a few ml of 6N sodium hydroxide should be added to the trap. Another type of trap is shown in Fig. 5. Any irritating or noxious fumes are led from the top of the condenser into the trap, from where they are swept down the drain dissolved in a stream of water. This stream of water may be supplied by the emergent flow from the condenser. Water placed in the U-tube acts as a seal and pressure vent. Either the trap of Fig.

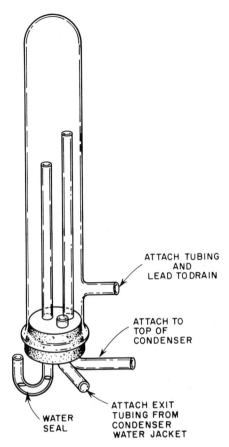

ATTACH TUBING
AND
LEAD TO DRAIN

ATTACH TO
TOP OF
CONDENSER

WATER
SEAL

ATTACH EXIT
TUBING FROM
CONDENSER
WATER JACKET

FIG. 5.   Improved trap for noxious or toxic gases. If gases are sparingly soluble in water or some aqueous solution, or if the gases are being evolved quite rapidly, this trap is much more effective than that shown in Fig. 1. In order to close the side exit with water, it may be necessary to tip the tube slightly so as to raise the tip of the side exit.

1 or the trap of Fig. 5 may be used. If large amounts of a noxious gas are formed in a reaction, the more efficient trap in Fig. 5 is recommended.[1]

The reaction mixture is heated gently under reflux for 2 hours, after which it is cooled slightly and fitted for distillation as illustrated in Fig. 4, except that an empty Erlenmeyer flask is used as a receiver. Distillation is continued until water-insoluble material no longer comes over. 69°

The total distillate is transferred to a separatory funnel, 50 ml of water

[1]This type of trap was first described by I. A. Kaye, L. Sattler, and R. Tweed, *J. Chem. Educ.*, **31**, 266 (1954).

containing a spatula-tip full of sodium bisulfite is added, and the mixture is shaken. The water layer (which?) is separated as thoroughly as possible, and the organic layer is then washed with an equal volume of cold, concentrated sulfuric acid. *Proper precautions must be taken in handling the sulfuric acid.* After the acid is removed as completely as possible (which layer?) the butyl bromide is washed with successive, equal-volume portions of water, 10% sodium carbonate solution, and water. Caution should be exercised when washing with carbonate because of the liberation of carbon dioxide, which requires frequent venting. The carbonate washing should be basic to litmus. The butyl bromide is now transferred to a dry Erlenmeyer flask and dried by swirling frequently with about 5 g of calcium chloride for 30 minutes. If allowed to stand overnight, the flask should be stoppered.

The dried liquid is decanted into a 125-ml distilling flask, by filtering through a small gravity filter, and distilled. The butyl bromide is collected over the range of 99–103°. The average yield is about 50 g.

tert-Butyl Bromide

In a 250-ml separatory funnel are placed 22 g of *tert*-butyl alcohol and 125 ml of concentrated hydrobromic acid. The mixture is shaken cautiously for a minute or less, then the funnel is vented by opening the stopcock. This prevents generation of excessive pressure, which may tend to develop on account of warming of the mixture from the heat of reaction. Gentle shaking, with periodic venting of the funnel, is continued for about 10 minutes, then the reaction is allowed to stand 10 minutes longer, with shaking and venting of the funnel three or four times during the period. This procedure allows adequate time for formation of the *tert*-butyl bromide.

The bromide is separated from the aqueous layer (which layer?), then washed with about an equal volume of ice-cold 5% aqueous solution of sodium carbonate. *Caution* should be exercised against generation of pressure in the separatory funnel, from evolution of carbon dioxide. The product is again separated (which layer?), washed with an equal volume of ice water, and finally dried over 3–4 g of anhydrous calcium chloride. After it is dry, the bromide is filtered through a small gravity filter into the 50-ml distilling flask. Distillate is collected over a range of about three degrees (reported b.p. of *tert*-butyl bromide is 73.3°). The yield amounts to 70% of the theory, or better.

Tertiary bromides eliminate hydrogen bromide so easily that they turn brown on standing. A discolored sample should be redistilled before use in the solvolysis experiment.

Solvolysis of *tert*-Butyl Bromide

A room-temperature bath is prepared by allowing a large beaker of water to stand on the workbench for at least a half hour. During the solvolysis run, the temperature of the bath is recorded at intervals. A solution of 80% alcohol, prepared by diluting 15 ml of water to 100 ml with 95% ethanol, is placed in an Erlenmeyer flask, then allowed to stand in the bath for 15 minutes. A 2.0-ml portion of *tert*-butyl bromide is added to the alcohol, then the mixture is shaken well and placed in the bath. Without delay, a 10-ml aliquot is removed and added to 20 ml of ice-cold 95% ethanol. This mixture is titrated immediately with 0.1N sodium hydroxide to a phenolphthalein end-point. Titrations should be carried out in an ice bath. At 15-minute intervals, additional 10-ml aliquots are taken, added to 20 ml of ice-cold ethanol, and titrated immediately. At least four such determinations should be made. An "infinity" point is determined after several hours, or during the next laboratory period.

The equation describing this first-order reaction is

$$2.303 \log (V_\infty - V_t) = kt$$

where V is the volume of 0.10N NaOH required to titrate an aliquot. The value of the rate constant k may be determined by plotting $\log (V_\infty - V_t)$ vs. time t. The slope of the resultant line, multiplied by 2.303, gives the rate constant in units of min^{-1}.

If the above procedure is applied to *n*-butyl bromide, no solvolysis is detected. This reflects failure of the primary bromide to ionize under these mild conditions.

Ethers

9

Ethers may be considered as arising by the elimination of one molecule of water from two molecules of an alcohol, as in Eq. 1. This direct dehydra-

$$2R—OH \rightarrow R—O—R + H_2O \qquad (9-1)$$

tion may be accomplished by using a powerful dehydrating agent such as sulfuric acid. The method is of general utility only for primary alcohols, because secondary alcohols usually give alkenes as principal products of the reaction (cf. Chap. 10). There is no effective method for preparing ethers from tertiary alcohols.

An alternative method for synthesis of ethers is by heating an alkoxide with an alkyl halide, as in Eq. 2. This method, which is known as the Williamson synthesis, may be used for preparation of *sec*-alkyl ethers, in contrast with the direct dehydration just described. In addition, the Williamson method is well adapted to synthesis of "mixed ethers" (unsymmetrical ethers), for there is no problem encountered in use of different alkyl groups, as indicated in Eq. 2. In direct dehydration (Eq. 1), synthesis of

$$R—O—Na + R'—X \rightarrow R—O—R' + NaX \qquad (9-2)$$

mixed ethers is unsatisfactory, for use of two alcohols in the process leads to a mixture of three ethers.

Because of their rather unreactive nature, ethers are seldom employed as reagents for synthesis; however, a methyl ether of a phenol is sometimes prepared in order to protect the hydroxyl against reaction with some reagent used for altering another functional group. At a later stage in the synthesis, the ether may be cleaved in order to regenerate the phenol.

Making methyl ethers for such purposes is a major use of the Williamson synthesis. The most general use of ethers is for solvent purposes, on account of their inertness to reaction and moderately good solvent properties. Since cheapness is normally a requisite for a solvent, the simple low molecular weight primary alkyl ethers are the ones used, and they are usually prepared by a direct dehydration. Diethyl ether is especially widely used, not only as a reaction medium but for extraction of organic material from water.

A *serious hazard* encountered in use of ethers as solvents is their facility at forming *peroxides* by reaction with air. These peroxides will detonate on overheating, so low-boiling ethers should always be distilled from a water bath or steam bath, and old samples should be tested for peroxides before use. Peroxides may be removed by washing with an acidified aqueous solution of ferrous sulfate. Certain ethers are notorious for readily

$$
\begin{array}{c}
CH_2 \!-\!\!-\!\!-\! CH_2 \\
| \qquad\quad | \\
CH_2 \qquad CH_2 \\
\diagdown \quad \diagup \\
O
\end{array}
$$

Tetrahydrofuran

forming peroxides that will detonate at relatively low temperatures, possibly below 100°. *Diisopropyl ether is so dangerous that it should not be used.* Tetrahydrofuran is dangerous, but has so many important uses as solvent that it is rather often employed. An experimenter should use tetrahydrofuran only after thorough briefing on the hazards involved and their avoidance.

The *main reactions*[1] involved in preparation of di-*n*-butyl ether are those in Eqs. 3 and 4. It should be noted that the products of these two

$$C_2H_5CH_2CH_2\text{—}OH + H_2SO_4 \rightleftarrows C_2H_5CH_2CH_2\overset{+}{\underset{H}{\text{—}OH}} + {}^-OSO_2OH \qquad (9\text{-}3)$$

$$C_2H_5CH_2CH_2\overset{+}{\underset{H}{\text{—}OH}} + C_2H_5CH_2CH_2\text{—}OH \overset{\Delta}{\rightleftarrows} C_2H_5CH_2CH_2\text{—}O\text{—}CH_2CH_2C_2H_5$$

$$+ H_2O + H^+ \qquad (9\text{-}4)$$

reactions include H^+ and ${}^-OSO_2OH$ (H_2SO_4); therefore, the sulfuric acid is not consumed, and need be used in only catalytic amount. Indeed, as discussed in connection with side reactions, use of more sulfuric acid would cause a lowering of yield, on account of formation of *n*-butyl hydro-

---

[1] Di-*n*-butyl ether may also be formed by reaction of *n*-butyl hydrogen sulfate with *n*-butyl alcohol (cf. Eq. 5), and this may be a significant route of formation of the desired ether; however, the products and over-all considerations are the same as those involved in the sequence dependent on Eqs. 3 and 4.

gen sulfate. The success of the preparation depends on removal of water, for at least two reasons. Accumulation of water will prevent the equilibrium in Eq. 4 from proceeding forward sufficiently to give a good yield. Moreover, water gives azeotropes boiling below 100° with butyl alcohol, as well as with butyl alcohol and butyl ether; therefore, even if the water does not form a second phase and cause steam distillation, azeotrope formation will prevent the pot temperature from becoming sufficiently high to give a reasonable rate of ether formation.

In order to accomplish the required removal of water, the reaction mixture is heated under a fractionating column so as to give reflux along with slow distillation. The more volatile components consist of azeotropes (cf. Note 3 in the "Experimental Procedure"), two of which contain water, so the slow fractional distillation results in removal of water formed in the reaction, along with some of the butyl alcohol and dibutyl ether. Periodically, the organic layer is separated from the distillate and returned to the reaction pot. As the reaction proceeds and the higher boiling butyl ether is formed, the pot temperature rises and the rate of reaction increases. Completion of the reaction is signalled by rise of the pot temperature above the boiling point of di-*n*-butyl ether. This removal of low-boiling azeotropes, first by fractionation into the upper parts of the fractionating column, then by slow removal of distillate, is essential to accelerating the rate of reaction by allowing an increase in pot temperature. Use of ordinary distillation, without a fractionating column, would give removal of much larger amounts of butyl alcohol in order to remove water as formed.

Side reactions occur on account of the several ways in which an alcohol may react with sulfuric acid. In this connection, the similar situation involved in preparation of *n*-butyl bromide (Chap. 8) should be reviewed. Although formation of the butyl hydrogen sulfate (eq. 5) is reversible, re-

$$C_2H_5CH_2CH_2-OH + H_2SO_4 \rightleftarrows C_2H_5CH_2CH_2-OSO_2OH + H_2O \quad (9\text{-}5)$$

moval of water in order to accomplish the main reaction also prevents reversal of the reaction in Eq. 5. Dibutyl sulfate is formed (Eq. 6) at a slow

$$C_2H_5CH_2CH_2-OSO_2OH + C_2H_5CH_2CH_2-OH \overset{\Delta}{\rightleftarrows}$$

$$C_2H_5CH_2CH_2-OSO_2O-CH_2CH_2C_2H_5 + H_2SO_4 \quad (9\text{-}6)$$

but significant rate at the temperatures required for formation of the ether. Alkene is also formed (eq. 7), but with a primary alcohol this remains a

$$C_2H_5CH_2CH_2-OSO_2OH \overset{\Delta}{\longrightarrow} C_2H_5-CH{=}CH_2 + H_2SO_4 \quad (9\text{-}7)$$

side reaction. With a secondary alcohol, ethers cannot be formed by the presently discussed process, for alkene formation becomes the most rapid reaction (cf. Chap. 10). At temperatures above 100°, concentrated sulfuric acid gives general decomposition (charring) of most organic compounds, sometimes expressed as in Eq. 8.

$$\text{Organic compound} + H_2SO_4 \rightarrow C + CO_2 + SO_2 + H_2O \qquad (9\text{-}8)$$

Purification

Although the di-*n*-butyl ether is fairly volatile, isolating it from the reaction mixture by direct distillation would lead to serious losses because of the action of the sulfuric acid (Eq. 8) on the ether at the high temperatures that would be needed. Therefore, the reaction mixture is washed with dilute sodium hydroxide to remove sulfuric acid and *n*-butyl hydrogen sulfate, then alkali is removed by a water wash. Any butyl alcohol that remained unconverted to ether is removed very slowly by water washing, since it is only slightly soluble in water; therefore it remains in part in the organic phase. Water is removed from the organic phase by drying with calcium chloride. The yield will be lowered by the presence of either water or butyl alcohol in the mixture distilled, for both these substances form azeotropes with di-*n*-butyl ether and result in lower-boiling fractions. The residue remaining after di-*n*-butyl ether has been distilled is chiefly di-*n*-butyl sulfate. Since ethers are known to form explosive peroxides, this residue should not be overheated, and the source of heat should be removed immediately if decomposition sets in.

EXPERIMENTAL PROCEDURE

Di-*n*-Butyl Ether

In the 250-ml flask with ground joint and side tubes (cf. Appendix I) is placed 100 g of *n*-butyl alcohol and, with continuous swirling, 14 ml of concentrated sulfuric acid is added slowly (Note 1). After the contents of the flask have been mixed thoroughly, the flask is fitted with a small separatory funnel in one side tube, a thermometer extending *into the liquid* in the other side tube, and the packed fractionating column (Fig. 5–4) in the ground-jointed center neck. Distillate is collected in a graduated cylinder as the flask is heated (Note 2) with a sufficiently small flame so that very slow distillation occurs, and the temperature in the head of the column does not rise above about 93°. Intermittent distillation and drop of head temperature to about 80° is no disadvantage. The pot temperature is recorded at 15-minute intervals (Note 3). When the total volume of distillate reaches about 20 ml (containing 5 to 5.5 ml of water), it is transferred to a separatory funnel, the water is separated, and the organic phase is added to the separatory funnel in the side neck of the reaction flask. This organic phase is allowed to run back into the reaction mixture. Distillation is continued until the temperature in the reaction pot has risen to about 145°. A total of about 15 ml of water is usually collected, but this varies with the amount of water in the sulfuric acid which was used (Note 4). About three 20-ml portions of distillate will have been collected over this period, the first during about one hour and the others progressively faster (Note 3). Total time to this point is about 2.5 hours. After the pot temperature reaches 145°, the final return of organic liquid is made and heating is continued for 15 minutes or until the pot temperature reaches 146°. The heat input should be so adjusted that no distillation occurs during this final heating period. The reaction mixture should remain light brown and clear to the end of the heating period; if charring should set in before the pot temperature reaches 146°, heating should be discontinued at once and the reaction worked up.

After the fittings have been removed from the reaction flask, the contents are cooled in an ice bath for a few minutes, then transferred to a separatory funnel and washed *cautiously* (heat evolution!) with 180 ml of 3N sodium hydroxide (washing alkaline to litmus), followed by 60 ml of water. The organic phase is dried over 8–10 g of calcium chloride, then filtered through a small gravity funnel into the 100-ml round-bottomed ground-jointed flask, which is fitted with the fractionating column attached to a condenser. The mixture is distilled slowly until any low-boiling azeotrope has been removed and the head temperature has reached about 135°. Heat is removed from the flask, the flame is extinguished, and the column is allowed to drain into the flask for 2–3 minutes. The column is replaced by the simple distillation head equipped with ground joint (no flames as the transfer is made), and the di-*n*-butyl ether is distilled. The product is collected over a range of about five degrees (reported b.p. 142°). There is a small residue of di-*n*-butyl sulfate, which *must not be overheated* in an effort to distill a few more drops of the ether. A yield of 40–45 g may be expected (Note 5).

NOTES

1. The ground-jointed flask with side tubes is especially convenient for this reaction. If this equipment is not available, the wide-necked flask known as an extraction flask may be used for attachment of the fractionating column and thermometer through a cork. It is usually difficult to also insert the separatory funnel in the cork. It may prove necessary to interrupt the heating for return of organic distillate by running it down the column after removal of the thermometer.
2. In order that charring of the contents of the pot by overheating the walls

of the flask may be positively avoided, there is placed between the flask and the supporting wire gauze a square of asbestos paper the size of the wire gauze and with a one-inch hole in the center.

3. The compounds in this reaction mixture form a remarkable number of azeotropes, two binary and one tertiary:

      n-butyl alcohol and water (42.5%), b.p. 93°
      n-butyl alcohol and di-*n*-butyl ether (12%), b.p. 117°
      n-butyl alcohol, di-*n*-butyl ether (28%) and water (29%), b.p. 91°

These low-boiling azeotropes keep the reaction pot temperature near 120° until about half of the butyl alcohol has reacted, then the temperature begins to rise and so the reaction is accelerated. Increase in rate of distillation during the early part of the heating period (causing the head temperature to rise above 93°) does not remove water faster but merely removes the organic distillate faster.

4. Since concentrated sulfuric acid absorbs water extremely rapidly, each time that the shelf reagent is used its water content is increased as a result of the exposure to air. Thus, the water distilled during ether formation will vary proportionately. The pot temperature is the most reliable criterion for completion of ether formation.

5. Since azeotropes are not applicable in gas chromatography, any butyl alcohol in the ether may be detected. The product should be gas chromatographed, and the tracing included in the notebook report. Silicone fluid is usually the best partitioning agent for alcohols; even on silicone, they tend to give a peak with a trailing edge.

Alkenes

Nuclear Magnetic Resonance Spectroscopy

10

One method for preparing alkenes is the direct elimination of a molecule of water from an alcohol, as shown in Eq. 1 wherein the cyclic alcohol,

$$\text{(cyclohexanol with OH)} \rightarrow \text{(cyclohexene)} + H_2O \qquad (10\text{-}1)$$

cyclohexanol,[1] is used as the prototype. This elimination of water can be accomplished by use of powerful dehydrating agents such as concentrated sulfuric acid and syrupy phosphoric acid. Alternative methods of alkene synthesis include elimination of hydrogen halide (Eq. 2) and cracking of an ester (Eq. 3). These two methods actually represent indirect methods for dehydrating an alcohol, since the alkyl halide and ester are normally synthesized from the corresponding alcohol. The processes

$$\text{(cyclohexyl-Br)} + KOH \rightarrow \text{(cyclohexene)} + KBr + H_2O \qquad (10\text{-}2)$$

$$\text{(cyclohexyl–O–C(=O)–CH}_3) \xrightarrow[\text{tube}]{\text{hot}} \text{(cyclohexene)} + CH_3\text{—}CO_2H \qquad (10\text{-}3)$$

[1] Throughout this book, structures of cyclic compounds will be depicted as simple line formulas in which all hydrogens are omitted, but other substituents are shown. Double bonds are written in the usual manner. Thus, cyclohexane and benzene, respectively, are indicated as follows:

outlined in Eqs. 2 and 3 have the advantage that the carbonium ion is not an intermediate, so rearrangement does not occur. In the direct dehydration with acid, where the carbonium ion is normally expected[2] as a reaction intermediate, rearrangement to isomeric carbonium ions occurs rapidly in instances where isomeric ions are structurally possible. In the case of cyclohexene synthesis, rearrangement of the carbonium ion can lead only to the same structure, so a single alkene is conveniently obtained by this simple method of dehydration. As an illustration of a synthesis in which isomeric alkenes may be formed, dehydration of 2-methycyclohexanol will be considered after cyclohexanol has been discussed.

The *main reactions*[3] for preparation of *cyclohexene* are those in Eqs. 4 and 5. Since sulfuric acid is regenerated, only a small amount is needed to accomplish the reaction. Indeed, a larger amount of acid decreases the yield by formation of more alkyl hydrogen sulfate (Eq. 6).

$$\text{(cyclohexanol with OH)} + H_2SO_4 \rightleftharpoons \text{(cyclohexane with }\overset{+}{O}H\text{, }H\text{)} + {}^-OSO_2OH \qquad (10\text{-}4)$$

$$\text{(cyclohexane with }\overset{+}{O}H\text{, }H\text{)} \xrightarrow{\text{heat}} \text{(cyclohexene)} + H_2O + H^+ \qquad (10\text{-}5)$$

Side reactions in this preparation include acid-catalyzed polymerization of the alkene, oxidation by hot sulfuric acid (cf. Eq. 9–8), formation of dicyclohexyl ether (as in Eq. 9–4), and equilibration with cyclohexyl hydrogen sulfate (Eq. 6). As discussed in Chap. 9, ether formation is quite slow below 125°, so this is a minor side reaction in formation of the alkene from a secondary alcohol. The reaction shown in Eq. 5 proceeds rapidly at 100° or slightly above; however, if water is left in the reaction mixture, steam distillation (cf. Chap. 6) keeps the temperature considerably below 100°. Moreover, removal of water is desirable in order to displace the equilibrium in Eq. 5 forward (although the equilibrium in Eq. 6 is also displaced forward). Finally, removal of cyclohexene from the reaction mixture as rapidly as formed is desirable for two reasons: the equilibrium

---

[2]Even if the carbonium ion is not actually a reaction intermediate, acid can add a proton to the alkene and thus give the same carbonium ion. If this should be the actual route of carbonium ion formation (and subsequent rearrangement), it follows that rapid removal of alkene from the acid reaction mixture is of prime importance if avoidance of rearrangement is desirable.

[3]The alkyl hydrogen sulfate may function as an alternate intermediate in this process. This reaction route has previously been discussed in Chaps. 8 and 9. As before, the over-all stoichiometry is the same by the two routes.

$$\text{(cyclohexanol)} + H_2SO_4 \rightleftharpoons \text{(cyclohexyl hydrogen sulfate)} + H_2O \qquad (10\text{-}6)$$

is shifted forward, and the acid-catalyzed polymerization of the alkene is minimized.

Removal of both cyclohexene and water from the reaction mixture is accomplished by carrying out the reaction under a fractionating column and adjusting the heat so that there is slow fractional steam distillation. This delivers the more volatile cyclohexene as the principal component of the organic phase in the distillate and returns essentially all the much higher boiling cyclohexanol to the pot for further reaction with the hot acid. Removal of the volatile constituents by steam distillation also allows a high enough temperature in the pot to give a rapid rate of dehydration. Thus, running the reaction under the fractionating column allows ideal reaction conditions.

Purification

Fractional steam distillation from the reaction mixture separates the cyclohexene from all impurities except water and sulfur dioxide. Thus, the organic phase in the steam distillate is washed with sodium carbonate solution, then dried and distilled. The product so obtained is essentially pure; however, in common with most alkenes, it will darken on standing. This darkening involves poorly defined reactions including air oxidation and polymerization.

Dehydration of 2-Methylcyclohexanol

This process is subject to the same principles which have been considered in detail as applied to cyclohexanol; however, there are additional considerations in the case of 2-methylcyclohexanol. First of all, dehydration may give two alkenes (Eq. 7), even if there is no rearrangement of an intermediate carbonium ion. The intermediate carbonium ion can give either the 1-methyl or 3-methylcyclohexene, depending on which proton is lost.

$$\text{(2-methylcyclohexanol)} \xrightarrow[H_2SO_4]{heat} \text{(1-methylcyclohexene)} \text{ and } \text{(3-methylcyclohexene)} + H_2O \qquad (10\text{-}7)$$

If there is an intermediate carbonium ion in the acid-catalyzed dehydration of 2-methylcyclohexanol, its very rapid rearrangement to the tertiary ion would be expected (Eq. 8), for the tertiary ion is of much lower energy than the secondary ion, and there is hardly any activation en-

$$\text{(10-8)}$$

ergy involved in rearrangement of a carbonium ion. If the tertiary carbonium ion is formed, then either 1-methylcyclohexene or methylenecyclohexane may be formed, as shown in Eq. 8. If the initially formed secondary carbonium ion should rearrange to another secondary carbonium ion, 4-methylcyclohexene could be formed; however, the much lower energy of the tertiary carbonium ion would limit formation of the 4-methylcyclohexene to very small amounts. In view of these considerations, it is of interest to know the composition of the alkene mixture which actually is formed. In gas chromatography on either silicone fluid or Carbowax, separation of the methylenecyclohexane from the methylcyclohexenes failed. The 1-methyl- and 3-methylcyclohexenes were easily separated from each other on silicone,[4] even at rather short retention times; however, methylenecyclohexane proved to have a retention time identical with that of 3-methylcyclohexene. One solution to such difficulties as this is search for another partitioning agent which will separate the isomers; however, in the present instance the problem proves much more easily resolved by examination of the *nuclear magnetic resonance (NMR) spectra* of the alkenes involved.

The two hydrogens in the methylene group in methylenecyclohexane are in identical environments; therefore, they would appear in the same resonance line in the NMR spectrum. In addition, there are no hydrogens on the adjacent carbon to the methylene group, so there would be no splitting of this band from spin-spin coupling. Thus, the band in the NMR spectrum of methylenecyclohexane, which is due to the vinyl hydrogens, will be a "spike," a narrow unsplit band. In Fig. 1, Tracing *B*, is shown the vinyl proton region in the NMR spectrum taken on a commercial sample of methylenecyclohexane. The expected type of narrow resonance line is observed at about δ 4.6.

Since 1-methylcyclohexene is separable by gas chromatography from the isomeric alkenes obtained in this dehydration, a sample collected from chromatography was used for the spectrum shown in Fig. 1, Tracing *A*. The single vinyl hydrogen in this molecule is flanked by two hydrogens which are non-equivalent on account of being in a ring structure. In this structure, the coupling constants for the splitting, which determine the separation between the resultant peaks, are so small that the splitting is poorly resolved under the conditions of the spectrum recorded in Fig. 1.

[4] At the A settings on the Carle instrument, retention time for the 3-methylcyclohexene was 1 minute, 56 seconds, while that of the 1-methyl isomer was 2 minutes, 18 seconds. For injection of a small sample (0.5 μl), the tracing almost returned to baseline between the peaks.

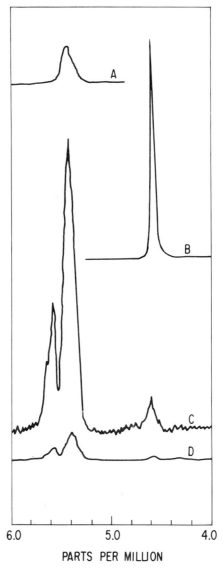

PARTS PER MILLION

FIG. 1. Nuclear magnetic resonance spectra of alkenes, taken neat (without solvent) on Varian T-60 NMR spectrometer, with reference to tetramethylsilane (TMS) as internal standard at δ 0.0. Only the region in which vinyl hydrogens are located is shown. Tracing *A*: 1-methylcyclohexene, collected from gas chromatography of product from dehydration of 2-methylcyclohexanol. Tracing *B*: methylenecyclohexane (Aldrich Chemical Co.). Tracings *C* and *D*: alkenes obtained by dehydration of 2-methylcyclohexanol. Tracing *C* was recorded at ten times the amplitude of Tracing *D*.

The width of the resonance line, however, compared to Tracing *B*, demonstrates the occurrence of splitting in the spectrum of the vinyl hydrogen in 1-methylcyclohexene. For present considerations, the type of splitting is of minor interest; the important observation is that the resonance line for the vinyl hydrogen in 1-methylcyclohexene is entirely clear of that due to methylenecyclohexane. If the resonance line from vinyl hydrogens in 3-methylcyclohexene is also clear of the region at δ 4.6, it follows that the presence of even small amounts of methylenecyclohexane in the mixture may be determined quantitatively by use of NMR spectroscopy. Quantitative determination is possible because *area under a peak in the recording of an NMR spectrum is proportional to the concentration of the specific hydrogens giving the signal responsible for that peak.*

In Fig. 1, Tracings *C* and *D*, are recorded spectra at two different amplitudes from a sample of the dehydration product. It will be noted that the resonance line from the third component (3-methylcyclohexene) appears slightly further downfield (to larger δ values) than is the 1-methyl isomer, so the δ 4.6 region is clear and subject to detailed examination for presence of methylenecyclohexane. Further, there is only small overlap in the peaks from the 1-methyl- and 3-methylcyclohexenes. The rather vague shape of the peak from the 3-methyl isomer is expected since splitting in this isomer should be complex. One vinyl hydrogen in this isomer has three non-equivalent hydrogens on adjacent carbons, and the other is flanked by two non-equivalent hydrogens.

Even in Tracing *D*, of lower amplitude, the presence of methylene-cyclohexane is clearly detectable at δ 4.6. At the higher amplitude (Tracing *C*), a moderately accurate quantitative analysis of the alkene mixture is possible. The relative areas under the three peaks, in arbitrary units, prove to be in the ratio 28:79:10. Since the 1-methylcyclohexene has only one vinyl hydrogen, and each of the other two isomers has two vinyl hydrogens, area for the 1-methyl isomer must be multiplied by two in order to give numbers proportional to the concentrations of the respective molecules. This gives the composition of this sample of alkene mixture as 14% 3-methylcyclohexene, 81% 1-methylcyclohexene and 5% methylenecyclohexane. This ratio of products is consistent with the well-established principle that, unless steric interference becomes large, a more substituted alkene is of lower energy. Methylenecyclohexane and 3-methylcyclohexene are disubstituted (two other carbon atoms attached to the doubly-bonded carbon atoms), whereas 1-methylcyclohexene is trisubstituted. The low percentage of the methylenecyclohexane is also consistent with the fact that an *exo* double bond (external to the ring) is of higher energy than an *endo* double bond (inside the ring). Thus, the results of this dehydration are consistent with, indeed illustrate, widely applicable principles of alkene stability.

Tests

The tests to be performed with cyclohexene, or the mixture of methyl-cyclohexenes, are general reactions illustrative of the properties of olefins. With bromine in carbon tetrachloride solution, the double bond is saturated by the addition of a molecule of bromine (Eq. 9). The observation that makes this reaction of diagnostic value is the rapid disappearance of the bromine color to give a colorless solution. When the same reaction is applied to cyclohexane, the bromine color persists and the bromine is consumed only very slowly, if exposed to light. In the latter case, a substitution reaction is involved and hydrogen bromide is liberated (as evidenced by the cloud produced by breathing across the mouth of the tube).

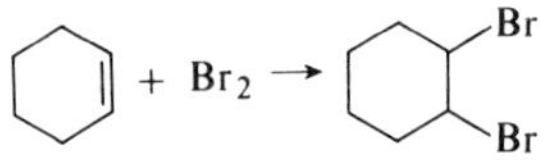

$$\text{(cyclohexene)} + Br_2 \rightarrow \text{(dibromocyclohexane)} \qquad (10\text{-}9)$$

The second test illustrates the facile oxidation of an olefin by permanganate. The first stage of the oxidation,[5] Eq. 10, produces the 1,2-

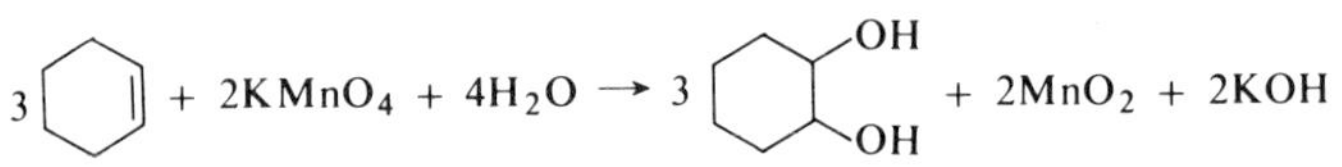

$$3\,\text{(cyclohexene)} + 2KMnO_4 + 4H_2O \rightarrow 3\,\text{(diol)} + 2MnO_2 + 2KOH \qquad (10\text{-}10)$$

dihydroxy compound, which is itself easily further oxidized on slight warming. In this test, carried out at room temperature, the appearance of the brown manganese dioxide precipitate and the disappearance of the original purple permanganate color indicate that the test compound contained an easily oxidized group. When applied to cyclohexane, the saturated compound, no reaction takes place. It is this reactivity of alkenes that makes them useful in synthetic and structural work.

EXPERIMENTAL PROCEDURES

Cyclohexene

In a 200-ml round-bottomed flask with ground-glass joint is placed 40 g of cyclohexanol, then 3 ml of concentrated sulfuric acid is added slowly with swirling. Finally, the contents of the flask are mixed thoroughly. The flask is fitted with a fractionating column (Fig. 5–4) which is attached to a condenser fitted with an adapter that passes well into a 125-ml Erlen-

---

[5]See Chaps. 14, 15, 20 for a system for balancing oxidation-reduction equations through utilization of half reactions.

Almost Best

meyer flask surrounded by an ice and water bath. The flask is heated gently over a wire gauze with a small flame, so that the cyclohexene and water distill through the column (Note 1). The temperature observed at the top of the column is below the boiling point of cyclohexene (why?), unless distillation is excessively fast. Distillation is continued until no more cyclohexene distills and a dark residue is left in the flask. This usually requires 15–20 minutes.

The distillate is transferred to a separatory funnel, about 5 ml of 10% sodium carbonate solution is added to neutralize traces of acid, then the mixture is shaken carefully (*CAUTION! Pressure from generation of carbon dioxide*). After the layers have separated, the lower water layer is separated carefully, then the hydrocarbon layer is run into a small, dry Erlenmeyer flask. After 3–4 g of anhydrous calcium chloride has been added, the flask is corked tightly to prevent loss of the volatile product, then the mixture is allowed to stand for about an hour, with occasional swirling. Standing overnight is recommended (Note 2). The dried product is decanted through a gravity funnel containing a small filter paper into a small distillation flask, then distilled. The product is collected over a range of about five degrees (reported b.p. 83°). The yield of clear, colorless cyclohexene is in the range 20–25 g.

$B - 80.°C$

NOTES

1. If there are drafts around the fractionating column, a larger flame is needed in order to give reasonably steady distillation. The yield is adversely affected if the flame is so low that the mixture is being heated under reflux, with little or no distillation. This allows the alkene to run back into the reaction flask, where it will be exposed to the hot sulfuric acid and suffer polymerization or other side reactions. On the other hand, excessively rapid distillation may result in loss of unreacted alcohol.

2. Cyclohexene forms an azeotrope with water, which contains 10% water and boils at 71°. Since the boiling point of this azeotrope is not far below that of cyclohexene, the product must be dried thoroughly before distillation in order to avoid loss in a forerun.

Tests

1. Two drops of the product are dissolved in 1 ml of carbon tetrachloride, and a solution of bromine in carbon tetrachloride is added dropwise until the bromine color persists. Note the number of drops required.

2. Two drops of the product are dissolved in 1 ml of acetone and 1 ml of methanol, and two drops of a 0.1M potassium permanganate solution are added. Note the results. Repeat the addition until the color of perman-

ganate remains, and record the number of drops added. Run a concurrent blank on the acetone-methanol solvent.

3. Repeat the above two tests, using *cyclohexane.*

Dehydration of 2-Methylcyclohexanol

This dehydration is carried out in the same manner described for cyclohexanol except that there are used 20 g of 2-methylcyclohexanol and 1.5 ml of concentrated sulfuric acid. On account of the smaller amount of starting material (dictated by the expense of 2-methylcyclohexanol), drafts on the fractionating column are more likely to interfere with distillation. Wrapping the jacket of the column with asbestos paper or tape is helpful.

Reported boiling points are 103° for 3-methylcyclohexene and 110° for the 1-methyl isomer, so the product should be collected over a relatively broad range, usually 100-110°. The composition of the product is determined by gas chromatography on silicone, which gives a better separation than does Carbowax. On the Carle instrument, A settings give satisfactory results, although a lower temperature (oven heat off) gives improved separation. Since the compounds are isomers, results are reasonably precise if the same response factor is assumed for the two products, so composition is calculated directly from ratio of areas. In instances where the tracing does not go to baseline between the peaks, it will be noted that a rather accurate extrapolation of each peak can be made.

The label on this product should carry, in addition to usual data, the isomeric composition of the alkenes, and the gc tracing should be attached to a notebook page. Of course the composition determined by gc gives per cent of 1-methylcyclohexene and per cent of the other two isomers combined. If an NMR spectrometer is available, the composition in terms of all three alkenes should be determined.

Acid Chlorides

11

The carboxylic acid derivative in which hydroxyl has been replaced by chlorine is the acid chloride or acyl chloride, whose general formula may be represented as $R-C{\overset{\displaystyle O}{\underset{\displaystyle Cl}{}}}$. Other acyl halides (bromides and iodides) are known, but are more expensive than the acid chlorides, and offer no advantage, hence are rarely used. The acid chlorides are very important, indeed, for synthesis of other acid derivatives, for the bond between the carbonyl carbon and chlorine is a very low-energy bond. Thus, the acid chlorides are high-energy compounds which will react rapidly and exothermally with many reagents to give other acid derivatives.

In order to prepare the high-energy acid chloride from a carboxylic acid, reagents must be used which are able to prevent a reverse reaction in some way. The reagents commonly used give, in addition to the acid chloride, another product (or products) which is a very poor nucleophile, insoluble in the reaction medium, or a low-energy species (or a combination of these factors). The most useful reagents are acid chlorides of inorganic acids, notably phosphorus trichloride, phosphorus pentachloride, and thionyl chloride. Any of these three reagents are satisfactory in many instances, whereas for some compounds one reagent is superior to the others. Some pertinent considerations in choice of reagent will be included in the subsequent discussion.

The *main reaction* for our preparation of *butyryl chloride*, utilizing phosphorus trichloride, is presented in Eq. 1. This conversion involves

$$3CH_3CH_2CH_2-C\overset{\displaystyle O}{\underset{\displaystyle OH}{\diagup}} + PCl_3 \rightarrow 3CH_3CH_2CH_2-C\overset{\displaystyle O}{\underset{\displaystyle Cl}{\diagup}} + H_3PO_3 \quad (11\text{-}1)$$

reaction of the carboxylic acid with the acid chloride of phosphorous acid to yield the acid chloride of the carboxylic acid and inorganic acid. With a small excess of phosphorus trichloride, the reaction proceeds smoothly with evolution of heat, to give a good yield of the butyryl chloride.

Side Reactions

A major potential side reaction is that of butyryl chloride with water to form the starting material, butyric acid (Eq. 2). The phosphorus trichloride is also hydrolyzed in the same manner; for this reason, it is important that the reaction be run in dry apparatus and with exclusion of atmospheric moisture. Even with these precautions, water is not completely eliminated, for the butyric acid is a technical grade and contains a small amount of water. The over-all effect of any water present is the consumption of phosphorus trichloride, since the butyric acid formed in Eq. 2 is im-

$$CH_3CH_2CH_2-C\overset{\displaystyle O}{\underset{\displaystyle Cl}{\diagup}} + H_2O \rightarrow CH_3CH_2CH_2-C\overset{\displaystyle O}{\underset{\displaystyle OH}{\diagup}} + HCl \quad (11\text{-}2)$$

mediately reconverted to acid chloride if sufficient phosphorus trichloride is present. Thus, the use of a slightly larger excess of phosphorus trichloride will compensate for small amounts of water present, and will be more expedient than drying the butyric acid. However, this facile reaction with water must be kept in mind, and the acid chloride, once isolated, must be protected from moist air.

This ease of hydrolysis of acid chlorides is a characteristic reaction and should be contrasted with the action of alkyl halides (for example, *n*-butyl bromide), which in most cases are stable to boiling water. Even the tertiary halides (cf. Chap. 8) react far less rapidly with water than do acid chlorides. The lower molecular weight acid chlorides react quite rapidly with water at room temperature. The more sluggish reaction of the higher molecular weight acid chlorides is caused by the low solubility of water in the acid chloride. When an appropriate solvent is used, even high molecular weight acid chlorides react vigorously with water, as well as other hydroxylic reagents.

Another side reaction is the interaction of butyryl chloride with some unconverted butyric acid to give butyric anhydride (Eq. 3).

$$CH_3CH_2CH_2-C{\overset{O}{\underset{Cl}{\Big\langle}}} + CH_3CH_2CH_2-C{\overset{O}{\underset{OH}{\Big\langle}}} \rightleftarrows \quad \begin{matrix} CH_3CH_2CH_2-C{\overset{O}{\Big\langle}} \\ \quad O \\ CH_3CH_2CH_2-C{\underset{O}{\Big\langle}} \end{matrix} + HCl$$

$$(11\text{-}3)$$

Since this side reaction is reversible and the main reaction is not, the equilibrium is shifted to the left as butyric acid is converted to butyryl chloride. The only losses resulting from this side reaction are caused by the escape of hydrogen chloride. For each molecule of hydrogen chloride that escapes, one molecule of butyric anhydride is left in the reaction mixture.

Another side reaction, which is not encountered in the preparation of butyryl chloride because it is low-boiling, is the thermal decomposition of acid chlorides. In general, prolonged heating above 160° should be avoided; above 190° decomposition is usually relatively rapid. With aliphatic acid chlorides this decomposition occurs with the loss of hydrogen chloride to give ketenes which then polymerize. With aromatic acid chlorides, pyrolysis results in the loss of carbon monoxide, and a variety of products (mostly polymeric) results.

Purification

To purify the butyryl chloride, the reaction mixture is decanted from the syrupy phosphonic acid and then distilled. The various compounds that may be in the decanted portion, from a consideration of the main and side reactions, are butyric acid (b.p. 164°), phosphorus trichloride (b.p. 76°), butyryl chloride (b.p. 102°), and butyric anhydride (b.p. 198°). An inspection of their respective boiling points shows us that butyryl chloride may be easily separated in a pure condition by fractional distillation. The only substance that might be difficult to eliminate by this process is phosphorus trichloride, if it were present in large amounts. Since only a slight excess of phosphorus trichloride was used, the small quantity that remains unreacted is easily removed as a forerun with very little loss of butyryl chloride.

Other Methods of Preparation

Other commonly used processes involve either phosphorus pentachloride or thionyl chloride. Let us consider first the case in which phosphorus pentachloride is used to prepare butyryl chloride, Eq. 4. Since only one of the five chlorine atoms is converted into acid chloride, this process is much less efficient, based on chlorine consumption, than the one involving phosphorus trichloride. It is often stated that the use of the sodium salt in place of the free acid will overcome this objection, since the sodium salt can then react with the phosphorus oxychloride to form more acid chloride (Eq. 5). Although this modification does result in an increased economy with respect to chlorine, anhydride formation, which was only a minor side reaction with the free acid (Eq. 3), becomes very serious when the sodium salt is used. In fact, Eq. 6 represents a good method for actually preparing anhydrides. Also, it should be borne in mind that old samples of phosphorus pentachloride that have been exposed to moisture contain phosphoric acid. Distillation of high molecular weight acid chlorides from this substance may lead to decomposition.

$$CH_3CH_2CH_2-C\overset{\displaystyle O}{\underset{\displaystyle OH}{\big<}} + PCl_5 \rightarrow CH_3CH_2CH_2-C\overset{\displaystyle O}{\underset{\displaystyle Cl}{\big<}} + POCl_3 + HCl \quad (11\text{-}4)$$

$$2CH_3CH_2CH_2-CO_2Na + POCl_3 \rightarrow 2CH_3CH_2CH_2-C\overset{\displaystyle O}{\underset{\displaystyle Cl}{\big<}} + NaCl + NaPO_3$$

$$(11\text{-}5)$$

$$CH_3CH_2CH_2-CO_2Na + CH_3CH_2CH_2-C\overset{\displaystyle O}{\underset{\displaystyle Cl}{\big<}} \rightarrow \begin{matrix} CH_3CH_2CH_2-C\overset{\displaystyle O}{\big<} \\ O \\ CH_3CH_2CH_2-C\underset{\displaystyle O}{\big<} \end{matrix} + NaCl$$

$$(11\text{-}6)$$

In addition to the points mentioned above, a much more serious criticism of the use of phosphorus pentachloride in this specific instance is the fact that the butyryl chloride (b.p. 102°) is essentially impossible to separate from the phosphorus oxychloride (b.p. 105°), due to the very close proximity of their boiling points.

With thionyl chloride and butyric acid, the reaction is shown in Eq. 7.

$$CH_3CH_2CH_2CO_2H + SOCl_2 \rightarrow CH_3CH_2CH_2C\overset{\displaystyle O}{\underset{\displaystyle Cl}{\big<}} + SO_2 + HCl \quad (11\text{-}7)$$

A great advantage in using this reagent is that both the reactants and products are volatile, and one merely distills the reaction mixture to obtain the acid chloride. If at least a 100 mole per cent excess of thionyl chloride is used, anhydride formation (Eq. 3) is negligible, and nearly quantitative yields of acid chloride may be obtained. Since anhydride formation, as shown in Eq. 3, is reversible, excess thionyl chloride displaces this equilibrium to the left, not only by removing carboxylic acid as in Eq. 7, but also by thus keeping up a good supply of hydrogen chloride. Use of more than two moles of thionyl chloride per mole of acid is little, if any, advantage, but reducing this quantity to 1.2 moles usually lowers the yield by 10-20%. With butyryl chloride, this excess becomes troublesome in the purification because the separation of a large amount of thionyl chloride (b.p.77°) from butyryl chloride (b.p. 102°) involves a long and careful fractionation. Thus we can see that for the preparation of butyryl chloride, phosphorus trichloride is the preferred reagent.

In general, in selecting a reagent for acid chloride formation, one should keep in mind the various factors discussed above. Of primary importance are the relative boiling points of reagents and products. In deciding between phosphorus trichloride (b.p. 76°) and thionyl chloride (b.p. 77°), the point that a much larger excess of thionyl chloride is required and might complicate the purification should be considered. Furthermore, thionyl chloride is more expensive. With higher molecular weight and more expensive acids, the fact that all the products are volatile makes thionyl chloride the preferred reagent. Also, certain types of acid chlorides are obtained in better yields when thionyl chloride or phosphorus pentachloride is used.

It should be mentioned that special care must be taken in preparing acid chlorides of expensive, unsaturated acids and other acids sensitive to mineral acid (such as pyrrolecarboxylic acids). Usually, the reagent of choice in such instances is phosphorus trichloride since little hydrogen chloride is evolved in its reaction with an acid. However, in a number of instances the relatively expensive oxalyl chloride has been used to good advantage. Reaction takes place between the thoroughly dried sodium salt of the acid, suspended in benzene, and oxalyl chloride. On slight warming,

$$R-CO_2Na + Cl-\overset{\overset{\displaystyle O}{\|}}{C}-\overset{\overset{\displaystyle O}{\|}}{C}-Cl \rightarrow R-\overset{\overset{\displaystyle O}{\|}}{C}-O-\overset{\overset{\displaystyle O}{\|}}{C}-\overset{\overset{\displaystyle O}{\|}}{C}-Cl + NaCl \qquad (11\text{-}8)$$

$$\underset{\Delta}{\Big\downarrow}$$

$$R-C\overset{\displaystyle \nearrow O}{\underset{\searrow Cl}{}} + CO + CO_2$$

the initial product decomposes to form acid chloride according to Eq. 8 in the complete absence of any mineral acid.

Tests

The extreme reactivity of acid chlorides is illustrated by treating butyryl chloride with ethyl alcohol. Merely on mixing, an exothermic reaction takes place to form the ester, ethyl butyrate (Eq. 9). These lower molecular

$$CH_3CH_2CH_2C\underset{Cl}{\overset{O}{\diagup}} + CH_3CH_2OH \rightarrow CH_3CH_2CH_2C\underset{OC_2H_5}{\overset{O}{\diagup}} + HCl \quad (11\text{-}9)$$

weight esters have pleasant, fruity odors that are easily recognized, and are in marked constrast to the odors of the acids!

EXPERIMENTAL PROCEDURE

n-Butyryl Chloride

In a carefully dried 250-ml Erlenmeyer flask are placed 40 g (25.5 ml) of phosphorus trichloride (Note 1), followed by 60 g (62.5 ml) of *n*-butyric acid (Note 2). These additions are made in the hood, and the contents are mixed by swirling during the second addition. A reflux condenser protected by a calcium chloride tube is immediately attached, the apparatus is taken to your bench, and the drying tube is attached to a gas trap such as that used for the butyl bromide preparation (Fig. 8-1 or 8-5). The mixture is allowed to stand about one-half hour at room temperature, and is then heated on a water bath at 50–60° for about one-half hour. With the condenser and calcium chloride tube still attached, the flask is cooled, without shaking, for about 15 minutes in an ice bath. The acid chloride is carefully decanted from the syrupy phosphonic acid into a dry 250-ml round-bottomed flask. (At this point, the mixture may be allowed to stand until the next laboratory period if the flask is very tightly corked.)

The flask is attached to a packed column arranged for distillation (Fig. 5-4), and a 50-ml distilling flask protected by a calcium chloride tube is used as a receiver. By careful distillation, a forerun is collected up to 99° (make any correction to your thermometer reading that was indicated by the distillation of benzene in an earlier experiment). Receivers are then changed and, in a similarly fitted 125-ml distilling flask, *n*-butyryl chloride (b.p. 99–102°) is collected. The product is placed in a dry bottle with a well-fitting glass stopper. The yield is about 55 g.

What are the principal products separated from *n*-butyryl chloride by the fractional distillation through the column? How would you modify this process for making propionyl chloride?

NOTES

1. Phosphorus trichloride, in common with most acid chlorides, is highly corrosive and should be handled with care in a fume hood. It also reacts violently

with water, so some of the reagent is destroyed each time the bottle is opened and thus exposed to moist air. It should be measured volumetrically, in the interest of minimum exposure to air, and the reagent bottle should be kept closed at all times except when material is being removed.

2. Butyric acid has an obnoxious and persistent odor, so care should be exercised not to spill it. It is especially difficult to remove from cloth or the skin.

Test Reaction

One ml of ethyl alcohol is placed in a test tube and, as the tube is cooled in water, an equal volume of butyryl chloride is added dropwise with shaking. About 2 ml of water is then added, and the odor of the ethyl butyrate which separates is noted—the contrast with butyric acid is apparent! The ethyl butyrate may be separated from the water by use of a small separatory funnel, or by removing the lower layer of water with a small bulb pipette (Fig. 30–1). After the ethyl butyrate (b.p. 122°) has been clarified by drying with a few granules of calcium chloride, its purity may be checked by glpc on a silicone column. Any butyric acid present will appear in a distorted band (long trailing edge) of longer retention time than the ethyl butyrate. Other partitioning agents are of no value for detecting carboxylic acids by glpc. Gas chromatography of carboxylic acids and esters, as well as differences in their infrared spectra, are discussed in Chap. 12.

Esters

12

A widely applicable method for preparing the ester of a carboxylic acid is that illustrated in Eq. 1. Since this method is most commonly used with

$$R—CO_2H + R'OH \overset{H^+}{\rightleftarrows} R—CO_2R' + HOH \qquad (12\text{-}1)$$

cheap, low-boiling alcohols, it is common practice to heat the reaction mixture under reflux for one or two hours (in absence of steric hindrance). Without the acid catalyst, the rate of the reaction is too slow to be practical.

As is shown by the equation, this is a reversible reaction and, in order to obtain maximum yields of ester, the *equilibrium* must be shifted to the right, either by removing products or by increasing the concentration of reactants. Since the alcohol, $R'OH$, is frequently one of the lower, inexpensive ones such as methyl or ethyl, this driving of the reaction to the right is most easily accomplished by using a large excess of alcohol. This procedure is wasteful of alcohol but results in very high conversions based on acid, which, in these cases, is the more expensive reagent. An alternative method is to remove the water (and sometimes the ester) from the reaction mixture as it is formed, but this usually requires a fairly complicated distillation procedure and provision for returning the alcohol, which is also partly removed.

From the discussion above, it is seen that in the direct esterification process some of the original acid must remain unconverted to ester. By using a heating period of sufficient duration and a large excess of alcohol, most acids can be esterified in yields greater than 90%, and the remaining acid may be easily recovered as described below in the purification procedure. In instances where the acid is especially expensive or rare, difficult to esterify directly, or itself sensitive to the action of hot mineral acid, an alternative procedure has been used to obtain complete conversion to the ester. It consists of heating the silver salt of the acid with excess alkyl iodide, Eq. 2.

$$R-CO_2Ag + R'I \rightarrow R-CO_2R' + AgI \qquad (12-2)$$

The cases considered to this point have been based on the premise that the acid is the more valuable reagent and that all steps should be taken to maximize the yield on this basis. Frequently the reverse is true and it is necessary to carry out an esterification in which the alcohol has been used most efficiently. Usually, this is accomplished by using a reactive acid derivative, such as an acid chloride or anhydride (cf. Chap. 11), in order to esterify the alcohol almost quantitatively (Eqs. 3 and 4). Except for acetic anhydride,

$$R-C\overset{\displaystyle O}{\underset{\displaystyle Cl}{\big\backslash}} + R'OH \rightarrow R-CO_2R' + HCl \qquad (12-3)$$

$$\begin{array}{c} R-C\overset{\displaystyle O}{\big\backslash} \\ O + R'OH \rightarrow R-CO_2R' + R-CO_2H \\ R-C\diagdown_O \end{array} \qquad (12-4)$$

which is cheaply available commercially, the acid chloride is much cheaper than the anhydride, as well as more reactive; therefore, the process in Eq. 4 is applied largely with acetic anhydride. The acid chloride is also used in instances of severe hindrance. In case R in Eq. 3 is *tert*-alkyl, direct esterification (Eq. 1) or use of the silver salt (Eq. 2) becomes so slow as to be impractical, whereas the acid chloride reacts rapidly and exothermally in spite of the steric hindrance.

The *main reaction* for the preparation of *methyl benzoate* is the direct esterification of benzoic acid with methyl alcohol in the presence of sulfuric acid, Eq. 5. The sulfuric acid acts as a catalyst and speeds up attainment of

$$\underset{\displaystyle}{\bigcirc}\!\!-\!CO_2H + CH_3OH \underset{}{\overset{H_2SO_4}{\rightleftharpoons}} \underset{\displaystyle}{\bigcirc}\!\!-\!CO_2CH_3 + H_2O \qquad (12-5)$$

equilibrium. It also functions as a dehydrating agent to help displace the equilibrium to the right. The maximizing of the yield of ester by shifting the equilibrium to the right is chiefly accomplished, however, by employing a large excess of methanol. By heating this mixture under reflux for about 1 hour, an excellent yield of methyl benzoate is obtained. There are no significant *side reactions*, and the only reason the yield is not quantitative is that a small amount of benzoic acid remains unesterified, for the equilibrium is still not shifted completely to the right.

Purification

All five substances—benzoic acid, methanol, methyl benzoate, water, and sulfuric acid—are present when the reaction is concluded, and the first step of the purification consists in distributing these compounds between benzene and water. Distillation of most of the methanol from the reaction mixture prior to this step, as has occasionally been suggested, would of course decrease the yield of ester because of shifting the equilibrium in reaction 5. In fact, equilibrium is maintained as methanol is distilled, and the result is the same as if less methanol had been used originally. When the reaction mixture is treated with water and benzene, the highly polar methanol and sulfuric acid dissolve in the aqueous phase, whereas the methyl benzoate and benzoic acid are much more soluble in the benzene. The benzene layer could then be separated into its components by fractional distillation, since the benzene boils much lower than the ester and the benzoic acid boils somewhat higher. This would be a laborious process, however; therefore, advantage is taken of the fact that benzoic acid forms a salt with alkali and that this salt, being ionic, is now soluble in water and insoluble in benzene. Thus the benzene solution is shaken with aqueous sodium carbonate, and the benzoic acid, in the form of sodium benzoate, is extracted into the water. By subsequent acidification, the benzoic acid may be recovered. Use of sodium hydroxide instead of carbonate for this extraction might cause some loss of ester, since it is hydrolyzed by strong alkali (see below) to benzoic acid and methanol.

The benzene layer, after the alkaline extraction, contains only the methyl benzoate and a small amount of dissolved water (provided the phase separation was made carefully). By distillation, the water is removed with some of the benzene as an azeotrope (constant-boiling mixture); then, after the residual benzene has been distilled, the methyl benzoate is easily obtained pure, for it boils about 120° higher than benzene.

The principle, used in the above purification, of separating an acidic from a neutral substance by converting the former to a salt and extracting the salt into water, while the neutral substance remains in the organic phase, is very commonly employed in purification schemes. The same method may be used in effecting the separation of a basic from a neutral substance, by forming the salt of the basic compound with acid and extracting it into water.

The *main reaction* for the preparation of *methyl salicylate* (Eq. 6) is the same as that for methyl benzoate, except that salicylic acid is used. The striking difference between the two acids is the markedly slower rate at

$$\underset{\text{OH}}{\overset{\text{CO}_2\text{H}}{\bigcirc}} + \text{CH}_3\text{OH} \underset{\text{H}_2\text{SO}_4}{\rightleftharpoons} \underset{\text{OH}}{\overset{\text{CO}_2\text{CH}_3}{\bigcirc}} + \text{H}_2\text{O} \qquad (12\text{-}6)$$

which direct esterification proceeds with salicylic acid. This is due primarily to two factors. One is the steric hindrance afforded by the ortho-hydroxyl group, and the other is the interaction between the hydroxyl and carboxyl groups (similar to that between hydroxyl and nitro groups, Chap. 18). Both factors result in decreased reactivity of the carboxyl group. By extending the period of reflux from one hour to three hours and increasing the amount of sulfuric acid, 60 to 70% of the salicylic acid is converted to methyl ester. However, equilibrium is still not attained, and the significant amount of salicylic acid remaining requires a modification in the isolation procedure.

Since salicylic acid is not very soluble in water or benzene, to pour the reaction mixture into water and to extract with benzene would leave an insoluble phase of salicylic acid. This difficulty is overcome by adding the esterification mixture to a sodium carbonate solution; this results in solution of the salicylic acid as sodium salicylate. Benzene extraction then removes the methyl salicylate, easily recognized by its characteristic pungent odor (oil of wintergreen). Acidification of the carbonate solution precipitates the unesterified salicylic acid which is recrystallized from water for removal of adhering sodium chloride and sodium sulfate.

Hydrolysis

When an ester is heated with sodium hydroxide, the esterification reaction (Eqs. 5, 6) is reversed, and the salt of the acid results in quantitative yield. The driving force for this hydrolysis is the irreversible removal of the acid from the equilibrium as its salt (Eq. 7). This reaction may be carried out with aqueous alkali, in which case the insoluble ester phase slowly

$$\overset{\text{CO}_2\text{CH}_3}{\bigcirc} + \text{}^-\text{OH} \longrightarrow \overset{\text{CO}_2^-}{\bigcirc} + \text{CH}_3\text{OH} \qquad (12\text{-}7)$$

disappears and the solution becomes homogeneous when hydrolysis is complete. Since many esters are quite insoluble in water, the reaction is frequently carried out by using alcoholic alkali.

The quantitative aspect of this reaction makes it very useful for the characterization of esters because the amount of alkali consumed in the hydrolysis will be a function of the ester's molecular weight. Also, the acid and alcohol fragments of the ester may be obtained and identified. Commonly, this hydrolytic process is called *saponification*, a name derived from the fact that soaps are made by alkaline hydrolysis of naturally occurring esters.

Glpc of Carboxylic Acids

In gas liquid partition chromatography, the compound is distributed between the gas phase and solution in a liquid phase (cf. Chap. 4). As this
distribution is more favorable to the gas phase, the substance passes
through the column more rapidly; however, the basis for the process is
equilibration between the liquid and gas phases. In the case of a carboxylic
acid, the molecules are paired off as dimers in the liquid phase, on account
of hydrogen bonding, as in the following formulation:

$$R—C{\overset{\displaystyle \diagup O\text{-}\text{-}\text{-}H\text{--}O}{\diagdown O\text{--}H\text{-}\text{-}\text{-}O}}C—R$$

As depicted in this structure, hydrogen-bonded atoms (dotted lines) are
further apart than those held together by normal covalences; however, the
polar attraction known as hydrogen bonding does maintain oriented positions for the molecules. Frequent dissociation and re-bonding occurs.
Thus, when a carboxylic acid passes from liquid to gas phase, there must
be a dissociation of the dimer in addition to the change of state, for most
acids are monomeric in the gas phase. This results in a considerable slowing of the equilibration process, so that a carboxylic acid does not travel
through the gas chromatography column in a rather sharply defined zone,
but is *spread out* over a larger distance. For most partitioning agents, this
spreading of the zone for a carboxylic acid is so pronounced that the recording in gas chromatography shows a very broad flat band, frequently difficult
to detect at all. Certain special partitioning agents, usually a mixture of several things, have been developed for reasonably satisfactory glpc of carboxylic acids; however, such partitioning agents are usually unsatisfactory
for other types of compounds. Silicone fluid is moderately satisfactory
for carboxylic acids (cf. Fig. 1), however, and is nearly always used in in-

---

FIG. 1. Gas chromatography of methyl benzoate containing 10% of
benzoic acid as impurity. A 5-ft silicone column was used with the Carle
instrument; attenuation was 1 throughout the left-hand tracing and was
changed as indicated in the right-hand tracing. Although the weight of
benzoic acid is one-tenth that of methyl benzoate, the area under the benzoic
acid peak is quite small compared to that under the methyl benzoate peak.
Furthermore, the width of the benzoic acid band is about 1.5 minutes on
account of the tailing which is especially apparent in the left-hand tracing.
In the right-hand tracing, it may be noted that the column is badly over-
loaded with benzoic acid, in spite of the fact that the injection of benzoic
acid was only about 0.2 mg. In contrast, no overloading of methyl benzoate
is indicated in the left-hand tracing, although the injection was about 0.45
mg of the ester.

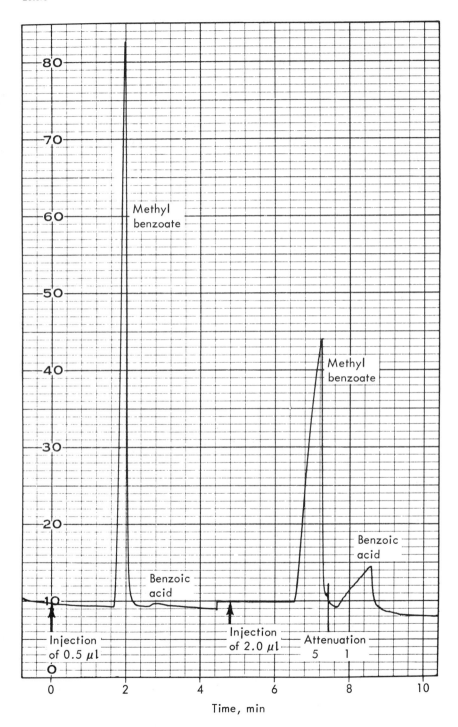

Time, min

stances where mixtures of carboxylic acids and other types of compounds are chromatographed.

Infrared Spectra

The absorption of radiation in the infrared region by organic molecules is very useful in several respects. For example, as discussed in many textbooks, the infrared spectrum of a compound is a valuable physical constant, especially useful as an identifying characteristic for the compound. Perhaps the greatest utility of infrared absorption is the detection of *polar functional groups* in a compound. Such groups include carboxyl, the various carboxylic acid derivatives, the carbonyl group (cf. Chap. 15), and the hydroxyl group. Although there is a hydroxyl group in carboxylic acids, it is strongly hydrogen-bonded in solution, as discussed in the preceding section, so its absorption is not below 3 μ (microns), as is the case for alcohols. The hydroxyl absorption in carboxylic acids is shifted to a longer wavelength so that it merges into the lower edge of the C—H absorption in the region above 3 μ (Fig. 2). Even when alcohols are hydrogen-bonded in solution the absorption is rarely above 3 μ. The other characteristic absorption of carboxylic acids is caused by the carbonyl group; this occurs in

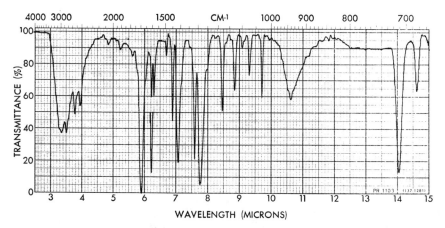

FIG. 2. Infrared absorption spectrum of benzoic acid, determined in 4% (weight/volume) solution in carbon tetrachloride, with 0.1-mm path length. The aromatic ring causes a spectrum of considerably more complexity than is the case for aliphatic carboxylic acids. The region between about 12.5 and 13.5 μ is "blacked out" by the absorption of the solvent in that region. The separate tracing for the single sharp peak at 6.22 μ in this tracing is absorption recorded for polystyrene, and the true location of this peak is 6.24 μ. This peak is included in spectra for calibration purposes and shows the present recording to be located almost exactly at the true wavelengths.

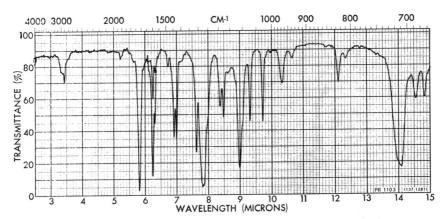

FIG. 3. Infrared absorption spectrum of methyl benzoate, determined on a thin film of the liquid. As in the acid spectrum (Fig. 2), the complexity of the aromatic system is noted, but the absorption of the hydrogen-bonded hydroxyl is absent. The carbonyl absorption for the ester is also at shorter wavelength than is the case for the acid, although presence of the adjacent aromatic ring shifts the carbonyl absorption slightly to longer wavelength. Esters wherein the carbonyl is attached to a saturated group absorb near 5.75 μ.

The location of the 6.24 μ peak on this spectrum shows the recording to be at the true wavelengths.

the region between 5.8 and 5.9 μ. In the case of an ester (Fig. 3), the carbonyl absorption is at a slightly shorter wavelength, and there is no hydroxyl absorption to "smear out" the lower edge of the C—H band.

Other acid derivatives absorb at slightly different wavelengths. For example, the acid chloride absorbs near 5.6 μ, while the amide (Chap. 13) is at longer wavelength, near 6.1 μ. The nitrile, with the triple bond (Chap. 13), absorbs at a considerably shorter wavelength, about 4.5 μ. Thus, determination of the infrared absorption is a rapid and reliable method for discovering functional groups present in a compound. In many instances, this method is not only faster but much more reliable than testing by chemical reactions (cf. Chap. 30).

EXPERIMENTAL PROCEDURES

Methyl Benzoate

In a 250-ml round-bottomed flask are placed 24.4 g of benzoic acid and 50 ml of methyl alcohol (specific gravity 0.79). Since the benzoic acid is rather fluffy, it is convenient to place portions of it on a piece of clean paper and allow it to slide into the flask from the tilted paper. The flask is swirled until the benzoic acid is well dispersed (not necessarily dissolved), then 4 ml of concentrated sulfuric acid is added cautiously, with continued swirling. After a reflux condenser has been attached with a well-fitted cork or a ground joint, a boiling chip is added and the mixture is heated under reflux for 1 hour. A small flame is used to give gentle reflux.

At the end of the heating period, the flame is extinguished and the warm mixture is poured into 250 ml of water contained in a 500-ml separatory funnel. The ester forms a separate phase. To the mixture is added 50 ml of benzene, part of which is used first to rinse the reaction flask. After the mixture has been shaken for 1–2 minutes, the phases are allowed to separate and the water layer is drawn off, as care is taken to get good separation from the organic phase. The benzene solution is next extracted with 50 ml of approximately one molar (10%) sodium carbonate. *CAUTION* must be exercised against development of pressure in the separatory funnel on account of carbon dioxide evolution. This is precluded by gentle shaking (and only for very short periods) and frequent venting of the pressure until effervescence has ceased, after which the funnel may be shaken vigorously. The carbonate extract is separated and reserved. The benzene solution is washed once with 25 ml of water, and the wash is added to the carbonate extract. This combined aqueous solution, in a 500-ml beaker, is cautiously acidified with concentrated hydrochloric acid *(FROTHING)*, and any benzoic acid which separates is collected by suction filtration, dried, and weighed. The melting point of the dried product is determined. The percentage of the benzoic acid that is thus recovered is calculated, and this gives the position of equilibrium in the esterification reaction.

The washed benzene solution which has been very carefully separated from the aqueous phase is allowed to run into a 125-ml distilling flask. The solution is usually cloudy with water, but, if no aqueous phase is present, the solution may be dried by simple distillation because of the water being removed as a minimum-boiling azeotrope with benzene. The flask is arranged for distillation, and the benzene is distilled with a small flame. *CAUTION: Benzene is highly inflammable, and care must be taken that no vapor passes the condenser.* The boiling point remains at or near that of benzene until most of the benzene has been removed. When the temperature begins to rise, distillation is continued carefully and slowly in order to keep to a minimum the loss of methyl benzoate in the intermediate fraction. If a relatively large intermediate fraction boiling above 100° is obtained, this fraction should be redistilled. The methyl benzoate (recorded b.p. 199°) is collected over a range of about five degrees, usually in the range 193–198°. For such high-boiling material, it is important that the thermometer not be placed too high. The average yield is about 20 g.

The methyl benzoate should be analyzed by glpc in order to determine if the benzoic acid was separated by extraction with alkali and the benzene solvent by distillation. For this purpose, a 2.5-μl sample should be injected, using a silicone column and D settings on the Carle Basic Gas Chromatograph. Under these conditions, the retention time of benzene is only about 22 seconds, but as little as 0.05% of benzene can be detected, using the Heath 10-mv span recorder, and as little as 0.2% content of benzene can be determined with reasonable accuracy. It will be necessary to record the benzene at an attenuation of 1, then shift to attenuation of 5 to keep the methyl benzoate on scale, finally back to attenuation 1 for the region where benzoic acid appears (cf. Fig. 1). From the tracing in Fig. 1 it is apparent that benzoic acid can be detected only if more than 1% is present.

Methyl Salicylate

Proceeding in the manner described for methyl benzoate, 27.6 g of salicylic acid, 50 ml of methyl alcohol, and 6 ml of concentrated sulfuric acid are heated under reflux for 3 hours (note longer reaction time).

At the end of the heating period, the flame is extinguished and the warm mixture is poured *cautiously* into 250 ml of 10% aqueous sodium carbonate contained in a 500-ml separatory funnel. The ester forms a separate phase. To the mixture is added 50 ml of benzene, part of which is used first to rinse the reaction flask. *CAUTION* must be exercised against development of pressure in the separatory funnel on account of carbon dioxide evolution. This is precluded by gentle shaking (and only for very short periods) and frequent venting of the pressure until effervescence has ceased, after which the funnel may be shaken somewhat more vigorously (Note 1). The carbonate extract is separated and reserved. The benzene solution is washed once with 25 ml of water (Note 2), and the wash is added to the carbonate extract. This combined aqueous solution, in a one-liter beaker, is cautiously acidified with concentrated hydrochloric acid *(FROTHING)*, and any salicylic acid which separates is collected by suction filtration. It is recrystallized by solution in a small amount of boiling water followed by slow cooling, finally in an ice bath. The salicylic acid thus recovered is collected by suction filtration, dried, and weighed; then its melting point is determined. This acid is turned in as one product.

The washed benzene solution, which has been very carefully separated from the aqueous phase, is allowed to run into a 125-ml distilling flask. The solution is usually cloudy with water, but, if no aqueous phase is present, the solution may be dried by simple distillation because of the water being removed as a minimum-boiling azeotrope with benzene. The flask is arranged for distillation, and the benzene is distilled with a small flame. *CAUTION: Benzene is highly inflammable, and care must be taken that no vapor passes the condenser.* The boiling point remains at or near that of benzene until most of the benzene has been removed. When the temperature begins to rise, distillation is continued carefully and slowly in order to keep to a minimum the loss of methyl salicylate in the intermediate fraction. If a relatively large intermediate fraction boiling above 100° is obtained, it should be redistilled. The methyl salicylate (recorded b.p. 223°) is collected over a range of about five degrees, usually in the range 217–222°. For such high-boiling material, it is important that the thermometer not be placed too high. The average yield is about 15 g.

The methyl salicylate is analyzed by glpc in the same way as was described for methyl benzoate. Since the boiling point of methyl salicylate is higher, benzene is more readily separated.

NOTES

1. The separatory funnel should never be shaken violently, for this tends to promote formation of an emulsion by beating the mixture into tiny droplets. If any sodium salicylate remains insoluble, this also promotes formation of an emulsion. If necessary, more water should be added to dissolve all the salt. If an emulsion persists, it is sometimes broken by allowing 1–2 ml of methanol to run slowly down the wall of the funnel as the funnel is moved so as to cause the liquid to rotate gently. If this fails to clear the emulsion, and if any solid appears still present, it is advisable to filter the two-phase solution by gentle suction, then return it to the separatory funnel for separation. If the emulsion partly separates, the lower water layer should be drawn off until the emulsion approaches the stopcock; then the mixture is allowed to stand for further separation. If a small emulsified layer remains, it is left with the benzene for the subsequent wash with water.

2. In some instances, trouble with emulsions is greater during the water wash, on account of the lower concentration of ions, so excessively vigorous shaking remains inadvisable. Any emulsion encountered is attacked as described in Note 1, except that addition of a few milliliters of saturated sodium chloride solution may be helpful in breaking an emulsion formed at this stage. Any persistent small emulsified layer is rejected, rather than included with the benzene layer for eventual distillation.

Saponification

This procedure may be applied to either methyl benzoate or methyl salicylate. A 2.0-g sample of the ester is weighed into a 125-ml Erlenmeyer flask, 20 ml of 2N sodium hydroxide solution is added, and the flask is fitted with a reflux condenser. A boiling chip is added, and the solution is heated under reflux until it becomes homogeneous (usually about one-half hour). After the solution has been cooled somewhat, it is acidified with concentrated hydrochloric acid and heated to boiling, then just enough water is added so that the acid dissolves in the boiling solution. The solution is cooled without agitation, in water, and finally allowed to stand for about 20 minutes at room temperature. The crystals are collected by suction filtration and washed with a little cold water. After the product has been dried, the yield and the melting point are determined, and it is turned in properly labeled.

Acid Amides

13

Amides are acid derivatives in which the—OH of the carboxyl group has been replaced by—NH_2 (NHR or NR_2 in substituted amides). In most cases, amides are prepared from the acid or an acid chloride by reaction with ammonia or an appropriate amine.[1] Direct amide formation from the free acid is represented in Eq. 1. These reactions are reversible, and tem-

$$R-CO_2H + NH_3 \rightleftarrows R-C{\overset{\displaystyle O}{\diagdown NH_2}} + HOH \qquad (13\text{-}1)$$

$$R-C{\overset{\displaystyle O}{\diagdown ONH_4}}$$

peratures of 100° or higher are required to attain a reasonable rate of reaction in amide formation. Obviously, there is difficulty with loss of ammonia on heating, so the reactions are normally carried out industrially in a closed vessel under pressure. For amides of cheap, low molecular weight acids, there may be used a large excess of the acid to drive the

[1]The synthesis of substituted amides has been subjected to rather intensive study on account of the basic importance of the amide linkage in proteins, the high molecular weight compounds on which the life processes of plants and animals depend. The very effective methods which have been developed for synthesis of complex substituted amides are beyond the intended scope of the present discussion; however, an excellent review of these methods has been published by M. Goodman and G. W. Kenner in *Advances in Protein Chemistry,* **12,** 465 (1957). A description of "Automated Synthesis of Peptides" has been published by R. B. Merrifield in *Science,* **150,** 178 (1965). This article includes references to other papers concerned with various technological advances in application of methods of amide synthesis to construction of high molecular weight polypeptides.

equilibrium mostly in favor of the ammonium salt and thus avoid rapid loss of ammonia on heating under reflux; however, the method is rarely used for laboratory preparation of amides.

Amides may be prepared from esters (Eq. 2); however, the equilib-

$$R-CO_2CH_3 + NH_3 \rightleftarrows R-C\overset{\displaystyle O}{\underset{\displaystyle NH_2}{\big\langle}} + CH_3OH \qquad (13\text{-}2)$$

rium is not especially favorable to the amide, and the only cheap solvent which will dissolve the ester and a large excess of ammonia is a low molecular weight alcohol. Since the alcohol is a product in the equilibrium reaction, it is obviously intolerable unless the amide is insoluble in the alcohol. Use of a second alcohol only worsens the situation, for this would give equilibration with a second ester.

Amides of acetic acid are frequently made from the cheap acetic anhydride (cf. Chap. 21), but the method nearly always used for laboratory preparation of other amides involves the acid chloride (Eq. 3). The reaction

$$R-C\overset{\displaystyle O}{\underset{\displaystyle Cl}{\big\langle}} + 2NH_3 \rightleftarrows R-C\overset{\displaystyle O}{\underset{\displaystyle NH_2}{\big\langle}} + NH_4Cl \qquad (13\text{-}3)$$

is rapid and suffers from no significant side reactions; indeed, the reaction is quite successful with aqueous ammonia. Ammonia is much more soluble in an organic solvent than is water, so highly preferential reaction occurs with the ammonia in aqueous ammonium hydroxide. In addition, an amine may be substituted for ammonia so that mono- or disubstituted amides may be secured in high yield. In case an expensive amine is used, a cheap base is added to neutralize hydrogen chloride and thus avoid consumption of a second mole of amine.

Amides may be made by hydrolysis of a nitrile, using either an acid or base as catalyst (Eq. 4); however, this is rarely a satisfactory method of preparation. In most instances, further hydrolysis of the amide, as shown in Eq. 4, proceeds at about the same rate as does the first step; therefore, a

$$R-C{\equiv}N + H_2O \xrightarrow[\text{heat}]{^-OH \text{ or } H^+} R-C\overset{\displaystyle O}{\underset{\displaystyle NH_2}{\big\langle}} \xrightarrow{H_2O} R-C\overset{\displaystyle O}{\underset{\displaystyle ONH_4}{\big\langle}} \qquad (13\text{-}4)$$

satisfactory yield of amide does not accumulate in the reaction. This difficulty can be circumvented in certain ways, one of which involves addition of sulfuric acid to the nitrile and hydrolysis of this intermediate in ice water (Eq. 5). This method is successful because sulfuric acid adds to the

$$R-C{\equiv}N + H_2SO_4 \xrightarrow[\text{(conc.)}]{\text{warm}} R-C\overset{\displaystyle NH}{\underset{\displaystyle OSO_2OH}{\big\langle}} \xrightarrow[\text{water}]{\text{cold}} R-C\overset{\displaystyle O}{\underset{\displaystyle NH_2}{\big\langle}} + H_2SO_4 \,(13\text{-}5)$$

nitrile only once, and the adduct is hydrolyzed rapidly at low temperature. This method can be used only if the nitrile contains no groups sensitive to concentrated sulfuric acid.

The *main reactions* for the preparation of *capramide (decanamide)* are, first, the preparation of capryl chloride, and second, its treatment with concentrated aqueous ammonia (Eq. 6).

$$3CH_3-(CH_2)_8-CO_2H + PCl_3 \rightarrow 3CH_3-(CH_2)_8-C\overset{O}{\underset{Cl}{\diagup}} + H_3PO_3 \qquad (13\text{-}6)$$

$$\xrightarrow{6NH_3} 3CH_3-(CH_2)_8-C\overset{O}{\underset{NH_2}{\diagup}} + 3NH_4Cl$$

The *side reactions* that occur during formation of the acid chloride are the same as those discussed for butyryl chloride (Chap. 11), and they result in the formation of small amounts of acid and acid anhydride. When the reaction mixture is treated with ammonia, however, the anhydride will form amide; therefore, the only organic impurity is capric acid (decanoic acid), which will be present as its water-soluble ammonium salt. The acid chloride is also susceptible to hydrolysis by the water in the ammonium hydroxide solution; however, this side reaction is minor as discussed above. If water is allowed to enter the reaction during formation of the acid chloride, either phosphorus trichloride or the acid chloride will be hydrolyzed, so this will increase the amount of ammonium caprate in the final reaction product.

Purification

It follows from the main and side reactions that ammonium chloride, phosphonic acid, and ammonium caprate are the side products which must be separated from capramide. Since all of these are soluble in water, filtration and washing of the precipitated amide might be expected to remove nearly all the impurities; however, this is likely to prove not so straightforward. Since the ammonium chloride is formed simultaneously with the amide (Eq. 6), the precipitating amide is likely to occlude considerable amounts of the salt, and the ammonium chloride proves difficult to wash out of the mass of finely divided, water-insoluble amide. Furthermore, ammonium caprate is a soap which is only moderately soluble in water. The most convenient method for reliable removal of water-soluble impurities is stirring of the amide with water that is heated sufficiently to melt the crude amide. This ensures extraction of both ammonium chloride and ammonium caprate from the melted amide. Final purification, which is by crystallization as described in Chap. 3, eliminates small amounts of homologous amides which result from homologous acids present in the technical starting material.

In aqueous solvents, amides are neutral compounds; however, on acid or alkaline hydrolysis, the acid (and amine from a substituted amide) is regenerated and may be recovered. This property is useful in the purification of some compounds, especially since most amides are crystalline solids, useful for identification purposes (cf. Chap. 30). In syntheses, simple amides may be degraded to amines with sodium hypobromite, or may be dehydrated to nitriles. Nitriles are synthesized most often by displacement of halogen with cyanide (cf. Chap. 35); however, this displacement fails with tertiary halides. In such instances, or where the required bromide is less accessible than the amide, the nitrile is likely to be prepared by dehydration of the amide. In illustration of this process *caprinitrile may be prepared* by dehydration of capramide with phosphorus oxychloride (Eq. 7). This synthesis is described as a reaction of capramide. There are

$$3CH_3-(CH_2)_8-C\overset{O}{\underset{NH_2}{\diagdown}} + POCl_3 \rightarrow 3CH_3-(CH_2)_8-CN + H_3PO_4 + 3HCl \quad (13\text{-}7)$$

no significant side reactions in this process, provided that the amide is thoroughly dried and a good grade of phosphorus oxychloride is used. The nitrile is easily isolated because other products of the reaction are water-soluble.

EXPERIMENTAL PROCEDURES

Capramide

In a thoroughly dried 250-ml Erlenmeyer flask are placed 75 ml of hexane (or similar petroleum ether fraction), 6.7 g (4.25 ml) of phosphorus trichloride (Note 1), and 20 g of technical capric acid. A dry condenser, surmounted by a calcium chloride drying tube, is attached to the flask immediately. The mixture is swirled until homogeneous, then allowed to stand about 30 minutes at room temperature, finally heated on a water bath or steam bath to reflux for about 30 minutes. *CAU-TION! Hexane is highly inflammable and so volatile that it is easily boiled vigorously enough to pass through the condenser.* The reaction mixture is cooled in water with the condenser and calcium chloride tube still attached, and without agitation, so that the viscous phosphonic acid will adhere to the walls of the flask. The cooled hexane solution is poured, during

2–3 minutes, with care, into 140 ml of ice-cold concentrated ammonium hydroxide solution contained in a 500-ml Erlenmeyer flask. Cooling with ice is continued during the addition, and the contents of the flask are swirled continuously. After addition has been completed, swirling and cooling are continued for about 5 minutes longer, as the lumpy precipitate is broken up with a stirring rod or spatula (Note 2).

The capramide is collected by suction filtration on a Büchner funnel of the two-phase solution, and the product is pressed and drained well on the funnel (Note 2). Since thorough washing is important (Notes 2 and 3), the well-drained amide is transferred to a 400-ml beaker and heated with about 100 ml of water (Note 4). After the amide melts, the hot mixture is stirred for 2–3 minutes, then cooled with stirring until the amide has completely solidified. After the mixture has been cooled in water to room temperature, the amide is again colllected by suction filtration and washed with water. This filtration should be rapid, and thorough drainage of water should be easy (Note 5).

The crude moist amide is transferred to a 250-ml Erlenmeyer flask for crystallization. After about 50 ml of methanol (Notes 3 and 5) and a boiling chip have been added to the flask, the product is dissolved by heating under reflux (Note 6). If necessary for solution of the amide, an additional small portion of methanol may be added, but no more than 5–10 ml should be required. Any material not dissolving is probably ammonium chloride, and if the solution is not clear it should be filtered hot by gravity, with all flames extinguished (Note 6). Filtration and subsequent concentration are handled in the usual fashion (cf. Chap. 3). Crystallization is induced by cooling, with final chilling in an ice bath for about 20 minutes. The solution becomes filled with iridescent blades of capramide, which are collected by suction filtration, pressed down well on the funnel, and finally washed with about 15 ml of cold methanol in two portions. The total filtrate is concentrated (Note 6) to about 20 ml, and a second crop of crystals is collected. After each crop has been dried, the melting point and weight are determined. If the second crop melts more than about two degrees lower than the first crop, it should be recrystallized from a minimum amount of methanol or acetone. If the technique used in carrying out the reaction has been good, the total yield of pure capramide is in the range 13–15 g.

In the chemical literature, the melting point of supposedly pure capramide has been reported at various temperatures in the range from 98° to 108°. What value is indicated by your work to be the correct one? One author reported that he heated his melting-point bath at the uniform rate of five degrees per minute. At which end of the range mentioned above would you expect this author's melting point to be located?

NOTES

1. Phosphorus trichloride reacts even more violently with water than does capryl chloride; so it is imperative that all apparatus used in this reaction be thoroughly dried, and that the reaction mixture be protected by a calcium chloride drying tube. The latter is especially important if the acid chloride solution is allowed to stand before it is added to ammonia. It is also of obvious importance that the bottle of phosphorus trichloride be kept tightly closed except when reagent is being removed. Of course old reagent which contains so much phosphonic acid as to be viscous should be discarded. The required small amount of phosphorus trichloride is best measured in a 10-ml graduated pipette actuated with a rubber bulb. Pouring into a graduate causes excessive exposure to air. Since the reagent is highly corrosive (fumes in moist air on account of the hydrogen chloride formed), it should be stored and handled in a hood, and should *never be sucked into a pipette with the mouth.*

2. If the precipitated capramide is not granular, but is rather foamy and forms something of a *soufflé*, presence of larger-than-normal amounts of the soapy ammonium caprate is indicated. This results from use of phosphorus trichloride which contains much phosphonic acid, or from allowing water to enter the reaction forming the acid chloride. Such runs of amide may give reasonable yields (dependent on the extent of the defection) if properly worked up. The most important features of such work-ups are: (1) allowing plenty of time for the soapy material to drain on the funnel so that it may finally be pressed to a reasonably granular mass; (2) after this drainage, heating with 200 ml of water instead of 100 ml. If the amide is to be used for preparation of caprinitrile, removal of ammonium caprate becomes quite important.

3. Acetone is actually a somewhat better solvent than methanol for crystallization of capramide, in that acetone is nontoxic, and the amide has a lower solubility in cold acetone than in methanol. If acetone is used as the solvent for crystallization, however, it is imperative that all ammonia be removed from the crude amide by careful washing with water. Any retained ammonia will react with acetone to give an unstable imine which usually decomposes to colored material which is very difficult to remove from the capramide. A volume of 50–75 ml of acetone is required for the crystallization.

4. Unless hexane has been well drained from the crude amide by suction filtration, it will volatilize and cause a fire if heating over water is by means of a flame. The safest procedure is to heat the water to boiling, extinguish the flame, then add the amide to the boiling water. Since the amide usually melts only when the water is near its boiling point, heating on a steam bath is unsatisfactory unless the water has been preheated to boiling.

5. It is unnecessary to dry the crude product before crystallization, for water is miscible with the solvent used for crystallization; however, it is important that the amide be drained well on the suction funnel. If an excessive amount of water is left on the amide, it will dilute the methanol (or acetone, cf. Note 3) and render it less suitable as a solvent for crystallization. In particular, the aqueous solvent may

dissolve some ammonium chloride which will crystallize in part on cooling, and thus contaminate the product. If the crude amide is dried before crystallization, somewhat less solvent will be required for crystallization.

6. Since methanol is moderately toxic, it should not be boiled in an open flask in the laboratory, even if fire hazard is avoided by use of steam heating. It may be heated in an open flask on a steam bath in a forced-draft hood. Filtration of the hot methanol solution may be carried out in the laboratory unless the ventilation is rather poor. Of course, the hot solution in the funnel should be covered with a watch glass as usual, and boiling of the filtrate *(on a steam bath or hot water bath, no flames)* should be sufficiently gentle that nearly all the vapor is condensed by the funnel placed on top of the flask. If steam is not available for heating, a hot water bath may be used provided that the flame used for heating is extinguished before filtration is started. The flask receiving the filtrate is clamped in a suitable position in the hot water bath.

Caprinitrile

A carefully dried (Note 1) 100-ml round-bottomed flask (preferably with ground-glass joint) is fitted with a dry reflux condenser, which is connected via a calcium chloride tube to a gas trap, as described for butyryl chloride (Chap. 11). In the flask are placed 10 g of dry capramide and 16 ml (27 g) of phosphorus oxychloride (Note 1), and this mixture is heated under reflux for 2 hours. After the reaction mixture has been cooled thoroughly in an ice bath, it is poured in a thin stream, with stirring, into about 70 g of ice contained in a 400-ml beaker. The resultant mixture is stirred until the ice has melted, then transferred to a separatory funnel. The beaker is rinsed with about 30 ml of benzene, which is also added to the separatory funnel, then the mixture is shaken gently (Note 2). After the phases have been allowed to separate, the water layer is drawn off, and the benzene layer is washed with 20 ml of water, 20 ml of 10% sodium carbonate solution (Note 2) (washing alkaline to litmus), and finally 20 ml of water. The last separation is made very carefully. If there is evidence of presence of soap (Note 2), after the last wash, additional washing is recommended; otherwise, frothing will render distillation difficult (Note 3).

If the benzene solution is relatively clear it may be distilled directly, with dependence on azeotropic drying; however, if there is enough suspended water to render the solution rather opaque, it should be dried over anhydrous magnesium sulfate for at least 30 minutes, with occasional shaking. The benzene solution (filtered from magnesium sulfate, if it is used) is distilled from a 125-ml distilling flask, in a usual setup with a condenser, taking *precautions* against escape of highly flammable benzene vapors. Distillation is continued until most of the benzene has been removed, as evidenced by a slowing in rate of distillation and a rise in boiling point measured by the thermometer in the vapor. At this point, the flame used for heating is extinguished, the distillation flask is disconnected from the apparatus *(CAUTION! Escape of benzene vapors probable!)*, the distillation residue is cooled somewhat, then the residual caprinitrile is transferred with a small bulb pipette (Fig. 30-1) to the 25-ml distilling flask. Nearly quantitative transfer is effected by use of a 2-ml portion of benzene for rinsing. The small distilling flask is equipped with a thermometer, and the side arm is fitted with a bored cork for attachment to a side-arm test tube so that the tip of the side-arm to the distilling flask extends about half-way to the bottom of the side-arm test tube. This apparatus is arranged in position for distillation (boiling chip added), and the side-arm test tube is immersed, about to the tip of the flask side-arm, in water contained in a pan or beaker. The small amount of benzene is distilled carefully until nearly all of it has been distilled, then the flame is turned up until the boiling ring of caprinitrile reaches the thermometer bulb. Before caprinitrile passes into the distillate, the flame is removed temporarily, the side-arm test tube containing benzene is removed, and the side-arm test tube is replaced with an ordinary tared test tube which is *not attached to the cork* (which would give a closed system) but is clamped with the side arm of the distilling flask extending into it. For this amount of such high-boiling material, no cooling of the test tube receiver is ordinarily required. In case vapors threaten to escape from the test tube, a wet cloth may be applied briefly. Since caprinitrile is rather high-boiling for distillation at atmospheric pressure (reported b.p. 244°), a larger flame than usual is needed for distillation, and the product should be collected over a relatively wide range, such as 235–245°. After proper labeling, the test tube may be corked and used as a container for turning in the caprinitrile. The yield in a well-executed experiment, in which pure and dry capramide was utilized, is 4–6 g (Note 4).

NOTES

1. Since phosphorus oxychloride reacts readily with water, dry apparatus must be used, and the phosphorus oxychloride should be measured and transferred to the reaction flask with a 10-ml bulb pipette (two charges necessary, of course). The molecular weight of water is so low that a small weight of it destroys considerable phosphorus oxychloride. Of course the bottle of the oxychloride should be kept tightly closed except when reagent is being withdrawn, and old samples which have become viscous from their phosphoric acid content should be discarded.

2. If a small amount of insoluble solid separates during the washing procedure, it is likely to promote formation of an emulsion, so vigorous shaking should be

avoided. If the capramide contained ammonium caprate, precipitation of a soapy solid (sodium caprate) and formation of an emulsion during the carbonate wash are very likely. In order to break this emulsion, it is usually necessary to filter the two-phase solution by *gentle* suction, using a Buchner funnel. For a discussion of methods for coping with emulsions, cf. the methyl salicylate preparation, Chap. 12.

3. If serious frothing occurs during distillation of benzene, it may be controlled, so that foaming-over is avoided, by cautious heating of the *top of the bulb and neck* of the distillation flask with a *small* flame. This heat is applied very carefully with a burner held in the hand, only as needed to keep down the foam.

4. Gas chromatography of the caprinitrile may be accomplished on a silicone column, using D settings for the Carle instrument. For such a high-boiling substance, if distillation has been properly executed, no benzene should be detected in the glpc.

Carboxylic Acids

14

The carboxylic acids are one of the most important groups of organic compounds. This importance stems not only from their direct use as such, but also from the versatility of the carboxyl group for further synthesis. Although the chief sources of the aliphatic acids are natural products, a large number of general syntheses have been developed for the nonoccurring or difficultly accessible acids. In subsequent chapters are discussed three methods for synthesizing carboxylic acids: hydrolysis of nitriles (Chap. 35), alkylation and hydrolysis of malonic ester (Chap. 36), and carbonation of the Grignard reagent (Chap. 38). In the present chapter, we shall be concerned with the synthesis of an acid from a natural product. Many of the acids are available in nature as the free acid or as an ester that is readily saponified to the free acid. An additional source of acids is the oxidation of a readily available natural product. This latter path is the method used to prepare azelaic acid.

The *main reactions* for the preparation of *azelaic acid* consist of two steps: the saponification of castor oil to give glycerol and ricinoleic acid (Eq. 1), and the oxidation of ricinoleic acid to azelaic acid (Eq. 2).

Since castor oil consists largely of the triglyceride of ricinoleic acid, the saponification of this ester is illustrated in Eq. 1; however, this oil also contains about 5% each of oleic (9-octadecenoic) acid and linoleic (9,12-octadecanedienoic) acid. The presence of these acids does not interfere with the preparation of azelaic acid, however, for each contains a double bond in the 9-position; therefore, oxidation of each of them yields azelaic acid. Since these two acids also have molecular weights differing only slightly from that of ricinoleic acid, it is appropriate to calculate the theoretical yield on the same basis as if ricinoleic acid were the only component acid in castor oil.

$$CH_2O-\overset{\overset{\displaystyle O}{\|}}{C}-(CH_2)_7-CH=CH-CH_2-\underset{\underset{\displaystyle OH}{|}}{CH}-(CH_2)_5-CH_3$$

$$CHO-\overset{\overset{\displaystyle O}{\|}}{C}-(CH_2)_7-CH=CH-CH_2-\underset{\underset{\displaystyle OH}{|}}{CH}-(CH_2)_5-CH_3 + 3KOH \rightarrow$$

$$CH_2O-\overset{\overset{\displaystyle O}{\|}}{C}-(CH_2)_7-CH=CH-CH_2-\underset{\underset{\displaystyle OH}{|}}{CH}-(CH_2)_5-CH_3$$

$$\begin{array}{l} CH_2OH \\ | \\ CHOH + 3CH_3-(CH_2)_5-\underset{\underset{\displaystyle OH}{|}}{CH}-CH_2-CH=CH-(CH_2)_7-CO_2K \quad (14\text{-}1) \\ | \\ CH_2OH \end{array}$$

$$CH_3(CH_2)_5-\underset{\underset{\displaystyle OH}{|}}{CH}-CH_2-CH=CH-(CH_2)_7-CO_2K + 5[O] + 2KOH \rightarrow$$

$$KO_2C-(CH_2)_7-CO_2K + CH_3-(CH_2)_5-\overset{\overset{\displaystyle O}{\|}}{C}-CH_2-CO_2K + 3H_2O \quad (14\text{-}2)$$

$$\downarrow H^+ \qquad\qquad\qquad\qquad\qquad\qquad \downarrow H^+$$

$$HO_2C-(CH_2)_7-CO_2H \qquad\qquad CH_3-(CH_2)_5-\overset{\overset{\displaystyle O}{\|}}{C}-CH_3$$
$$\text{Azelaic acid}$$

The second product of the oxidation shown in Eq. 2 is the salt of a β-keto acid, a structure which decarboxylates readily in acidic medium; therefore, the substance actually obtained after acidification is the product of decarboxylation, methyl hexyl ketone. This neutral product is separated from azelaic acid by taking advantage of the solubility of the latter in hot water.

Potassium permanganate is used for the oxidation shown in Eq. 2, and in the presence of a reducing agent it breaks down according to the half reaction shown in Eq. 3. As in most organic oxidation and reduction reac-

$$2KMnO_4 + H_2O \rightarrow 2MnO_2 + 2KOH + 3[O] \qquad (14\text{-}3)$$

tions, the equation-balancing is much simplified by using the half reactions as in Eqs. 2 and 3. A net reaction may be obtained by adding the two half reactions; however, addition of the two equations is not necessary in order to determine the theoretical ratio of oxidizing agent. By inspection, it may be noted that Eq. 2 requires 15[O] for oxidation of 3 moles of ricinoleic acid, while Eq. 3 shows that 15[O] will be supplied by 10 moles of permanganate. It may also be noted that oxidation of 3 moles of acid results in consumption of 6 moles of alkali, but from the required 10 moles of permanganate there are generated 10 moles of alkali.

The oxidation is carried out in alkaline solution, and additional alkali is generated during the reaction, so the desired product, azelaic acid, is in solution as its potassium salt, as shown in Eq. 2. Addition of a strong acid to the solution liberates the weak acid from its salt, and it crystallizes from the cooled water solution.

Side Reactions

If the theoretical requirement of potassium permanganate is determined as outlined above, and this is compared to the amount specified in the experimental procedure, it will be noted that a large excess of the oxidizing agent is used. Much oxidizing agent is consumed in further oxidation of the β-keto acid (present as its salt) to lower molecular weight acids; however, another side reaction that is significant is the further degradation of azelaic acid to lower dibasic acids (Eq. 4, where $n < 7$). In order to prevent

$$HO_2C-(CH_2)_7-CO_2H + 3[O] \xrightarrow[KMnO_4]{\Delta} HO_2C-(CH_2)_n-CO_2H + H_2O + CO_2$$

$$(14\text{-}4)$$

an excessive amount of this further degradation, neither too much oxidant nor too vigorous heating should be used. This necessity for moderation in the oxidation means that there is likely to be left at the end of the reaction some of the trihydroxy acid (Eq. 5), which is the first intermediate formed

$$CH_3-(CH_2)_5-\underset{\underset{OH}{|}}{CH}-CH_2-CH=CH-(CH_2)_7-CO_2H + H_2O + [O] \xrightarrow[KMnO_4]{\text{mild conditions}}$$

$$CH_3-(CH_2)_5-\underset{\underset{OH}{|}}{CH}-CH_2-\underset{\underset{OH}{|}}{CH}-\underset{\underset{OH}{|}}{CH}-(CH_2)_7-CO_2H \quad (14\text{-}5)$$

when ricinoleic acid is oxidized with permanganate. Further oxidation of the trihydroxy acid cleaves the chain to give the final products shown in Eq. 2. If enough permanganate to oxidize the last of the trihydroxy acid is used, an excessive amount of azelaic acid will be destroyed; therefore, a balance must be struck between these two side reactions.

Purification

The ricinoleic acid (containing the small amounts of oleic and linoleic acids) is easily obtained by diluting the saponification mixture with water and acidifying with sulfuric acid to Congo red paper. This precipitates the organic acid as an oil which is used without purification for the oxidation. Since ricinoleic acid polymerizes on standing, the oxidation should be carried out without excessive delay, and any storage of the acid should be in basic solution.

After the oxidation has been carried out at 35–60°, the reaction mixture is heated on a steam bath overnight. Since the permanganate has been consumed before this final heating period, the purpose of the heating is not to complete the oxidation, but rather to help coagulate the large amount of manganese dioxide that is formed. Even after the heating period, filtration of the manganese dioxide is rather slow, and complete clogging of the filter paper must be prevented by use of a diatomaceous earth as a filter aid.

The next step in the purification involves removal of the water-insoluble oily material (methyl hexyl ketone and a part of the by-product acids) from a hot water solution of the azelaic acid. This is accomplished by the device of filtering through a paper previously wetted with water. Since such a filter paper is rather impervious to the oil, it is filtered out much as a solid would be. A similar technique is sometimes successful in removing small volumes of water from a solution in an organic solvent; in this case, the paper is previously wetted with the organic solvent. Although the amount of oil removed by this filtration is small in comparison to the volume of water used, a very appreciable amount of azelaic acid remains dissolved in this oil on account of the fact that the distribution coefficient of azelaic acid is very much in favor of the oil. Most of the azelaic acid is recovered by extracting the oil a second time with hot water. The product is finally crystallized by cooling the combined water extracts to room temperature. It is important to cool only to room temperature since by-product acids, which remain in the filtrate, will also crystallize at lower temperatures.

Other Methods of Preparation

Since filtration of manganese dioxide in this preparation proves to be a rather troublesome operation, it might be presumed that some other more convenient method of oxidation could be found. A major virtue of alkaline permanganate as an oxidizing agent lies in the fact that it does not cause rearrangement prior to oxidation of a double bond or triple bond, and does not attack the carbon adjacent to the multiple bond. This property is shared by only a limited number of oxidizing agents, and the other agents not giving rearrangement usually require two or more steps. For example, ozonolysis (oxidation with ozone) yields the dangerously explosive ozonide which gives aldehydes on hydrolysis; and one of the best methods of oxidizing aldehydes to acids is with permanganate. Acidic oxidizing agents are especially likely to give rearrangement or attack at the position adjacent to the multiple bond. For example, oxidation of ricinoleic acid with nitric acid gives, in addition to azelaic acid, the eight-carbon dibasic acid, suberic acid.

Azelaic acid may be synthesized from heptamethylene dibromide by conversion of this to the dinitrile, followed by hydrolysis. This is a practical route for synthesis of some dibasic acids (cf. Chap. 35), but not for azelaic acid, on account of the relative inaccessibility of heptamethylene dibromide.

EXPERIMENTAL PROCEDURE

Azelaic Acid

To a solution of 3 g of potassium hydroxide in 30 ml of 95% ethanol in a 125-ml round-bottomed flask is added 15 g of castor oil. After this solution has been heated under reflux for $1\frac{1}{2}$ hours, it is cooled and poured into a 250-ml separatory funnel. The flask is rinsed with about 90 ml of water which is added to the separatory funnel. After the solution in the funnel has been mixed by swirling, it is acidified to Congo red paper (Note 1) by addition of a cooled solution of 3 ml of concentrated sulfuric acid in 10 ml of water. The water layer is separated from the precipitated oil, and the latter is washed in the separatory funnel with two 15-ml portions of warm water. All the mixing in the separatory funnel is accomplished by moderate swirling, since more vigorous shaking may cause an emulsion. The crude ricinoleic acid thus obtained is washed, without delay, into a 250-ml Erlenmeyer flask with a solution of 4 g of potassium hydroxide dissolved in 80 ml of water. (This solution of sodium ricinoleate may be stoppered and allowed to stand one or two days before proceeding with the oxidation. It is advisable to make the interval as short as possible.)

In a one-liter Erlenmeyer flask are placed 38 g of potassium permanganate and 450 ml of water; the mixture is heated until all the permanganate has dissolved, after which the solution is cooled to 35°. The solution of ricinoleic acid prepared above is then added in one portion, and the flask is immediately stoppered with a cork stopper fitted with an air condenser (ordinary condenser, at least one foot long) and shaken vigorously during the next 15 min. The flask is then heated on the steam bath overnight (or longer). The hot mixture is filtered with suction into a one-liter filter flask, by use of a 15-cm Büchner funnel which has been covered previously with a thin layer of filter aid (Note 2). The mat of filter aid should be about 5 mm thick and is best placed on the filter paper by filtering with suction a slurry of filter aid and water (Note 3). In pouring the reaction mixture onto the funnel, care should be exercised to avoid pouring so vigorously as to stir up the mat of filter aid and expose the paper to the colloidal manganese dioxide. Furthermore, relatively light suction should be applied so as to avoid boiling the hot solution (Note 4).

After the solution has been filtered, the manganese dioxide is pressed on the funnel so as to close cracks which develop in the "mud" and allow drainage of the filtrate; however, it is not pressed so hard as to make a dense cake which cannot be washed at all. After moderate drainage, the filter cake is washed with two 50-ml portions of hot water (Note 4), and finally pressed well and drained thoroughly.

The total filtrate and washings from which manganese dioxide has been removed (Note 5) are acidified with a cooled solution of 7 ml of concentrated sulfuric acid in 40 ml of water. The acidified solution is filtered hot (Note 5) by gravity through a large, previously wetted, semi-fluted filter paper, and the filtrate is received in a one-liter Erlenmeyer flask which has been marked at the level of a 200-ml volume. After the filter has drained, the paper and the contained oily material are returned to the flask from which the solution was filtered and boiled with about 100 ml of water. This solution is filtered hot through a fresh semifluted paper, and the filtrate is collected with the first filtrate. The total filtrate is concentrated by boiling to a final volume of 200 ml. If any oily material is visible in the concentrated solution, 3–5 g of filter aid is added and the hot solution is again filtered by gravity through a previously wetted semifluted filter paper. The filtrate, which should be filtered again if not clear, is allowed to cool at room temperature overnight.

The product which crystallizes in the cooled solution is collected by suction filtration and washed with two 10-ml portions of cold water, then recrystallized from a minimum amount of water. The yield from the second crystallization is 2–3 g, and the melting point should be in the range 103–105°. Impure samples may melt below 100° or in some cases above 105°.

NOTES

1. When a carboxylic acid is precipitated from an aqueous solution of its sodium salt by addition of a strong mineral acid, it is necessary that the pH of the solution be lowered to about 4; otherwise, some of the organic acid may not be freed from its salt. For this reason, Congo red, which changes color at about pH 4, is a suitable indicator, whereas phenolphthalein (color change at about pH 9.5) and litmus (color change near pH 7) are unsatisfactory.

2. A filter aid is a finely divided material which will adsorb colloidal material and prevent it from passing through a filter paper or clogging its pores. It follows that the filter aid must not be too finely divided, else it will also tend to clog the filter paper. Filter aids are usually finely divided silica, frequently diatomaceous earth, which is a mineral deposit consisting of the skeletons of diatoms. A suitable, inexpensive filter aid is Super Cel, sold by the Johns-Manville Corporation.

3. The filter aid is filtered from a slurry with a separate portion of the solvent which is being used in the solution to be filtered. Of course the solvent filtered from the filter aid is rejected before the desired filtrate is collected. When the filter aid is used as a mat, the filtration must be carried out before the mat dries; otherwise, the dry filter paper is likely to curl up sufficiently to allow filter aid and colloidal material to pass under it into the filtrate. In the case of volatile organic solvents, this drying is quite rapid if air is being drawn through the suction funnel. It is also undesirable to release the suction after the mat of filter aid has been applied, for this is also likely to allow the paper to become dislodged.

4. It will be noted that the present procedure is an exception to the general policy of not filtering hot solutions by suction (cf. Chap. 3). The large heat of vaporization of water is very helpful in preventing evaporation at the reduced pressure in the filter flask; however, the principal reason that hot filtration may be accomplished here is that the solution is not saturated at the high temperature with a solute. The azelaic acid, and the acidic by-products of oxidation, are in solution as sodium salts. The filtration is carried out at a somewhat elevated temperature, not so much to keep material in solution, but because the mobility of the solution is increased and filtration is improved. Aqueous solutions of sodium salts of fatty acids tend to give semicolloidal solutions, whose viscosity is greatly decreased at higher temperatures. Salts of acids with fourteen or more carbons have the well-known properties of soaps.

5. If the filtered alkaline solution contains traces of colloidal manganese dioxide, which give it a dirty appearance, this is no disadvantage since this material will be removed in subsequent filtrations of the acidified solution. If such material is present, however, it is well to add 3–5 g of filter aid before the first filtration of the acidified solution; otherwise, the colloidal material may cause a slow filtration.

Aldehydes and Ketones

15

Aldehydes and ketones constitute a very important class of organic compounds because of their high order of reactivity. This reactivity resides in the carbonyl group, common to both aldehydes and ketones, and in the hydrogen atoms attached to the carbon next to the carbonyl group, the α-hydrogens. Condensations involving these α-hydrogens are quite useful in synthetic processes. For an example of this type of reaction, see Chap. 34. The present discussion shall be concerned with the preparation and carbonyl-group reactions of aldehydes and ketones.

One of the common methods for preparing aldehydes is by oxidation of a primary alcohol (Eq. 1). The aldehyde, which still contains a hydrogen

$$R—CH_2OH + [O] \rightarrow R—\overset{H}{C}{=}O + H_2O \qquad (15\text{-}1)$$

on the carbon bearing the oxygen atom, is further oxidized to form the acid (Eq. 2). In fact, oxidation of the aldehyde (Eq. 2) is generally more

$$R—\overset{H}{C}{=}O + [O] \rightarrow R—CO_2H \qquad (15\text{-}2)$$

easily accomplished than oxidation of the alcohol. In order to obtain appreciable yields of aldehyde, the oxidation must be very carefully controlled and the aldehyde removed from the site of oxidation as rapidly as it is formed. These considerations make the laboratory preparation of aldehydes by oxidation of very little use. One finds aldehydes more commonly prepared by reduction of acid derivatives; for example, by the Rosenmund reduction of acid chlorides, by the Stephen reduction of nitriles, and by the controlled reduction of amides and other acid derivatives with metallic hydrides.

For 'the preparation of ketones, these objections to the oxidative method no longer obtain, since the ketone, containing no hydrogens on the carbonyl carbon, is much more resistant to oxidation than is the starting secondary alcohol (Eq. 3). In order that oxidation continue, a carbon-

$$\underset{R}{\overset{R}{>}}CHOH + [O] \rightarrow \underset{R}{\overset{R}{>}}C{=}O + H_2O \qquad (15\text{-}3)$$

carbon bond must be broken, and this requires more vigorous conditions than the initial oxidation. Thus, the production of ketones by the oxidation of secondary alcohols becomes a feasible laboratory method of preparation. Industrially, good methods have been developed for the production of both aldehydes and ketones from the corresponding alcohols by catalytically removing the necessary hydrogens with metals such as copper and platinum.

The *main reaction* for the preparation of *cyclohexanone* consists of the oxidation of cyclohexanol (Eq. 4). Although an acid solution of potassium

$$\text{(cyclohexanol)} + [O] \rightarrow \text{(cyclohexanone)} + H_2O \qquad (15\text{-}4)$$

dichromate is used as the oxidizing agent, it is much more convenient to first write the reaction as if we had a source of "atomic" oxygen. After balancing the organic half of the reaction, one turns to the inorganic source of this available oxygen (Eq. 5). Addition of the equations for these two

$$Cr_2O_7^= + 8H^+ \rightarrow 2Cr^{+++} + 3[O] + 4H_2O \qquad (15\text{-}5)$$

half reactions will result in the over-all oxidation reaction (Eq. 6).[1]

$$3\,\text{(cyclohexanol)} + Cr_2O_7^= + 8H^+ \rightarrow 3\,\text{(cyclohexanone)} + 2Cr^{+++} + 7H_2O \qquad (15\text{-}6)$$

By controlling the reaction temperature at 55–60°, the oxidation of the cyclohexanol proceeds at a rapid but controllable rate, while the further oxidation of the cyclohexanone to adipic acid proceeds at a sufficiently slow rate that it amounts to no more than a minor *side reaction* (Eq. 7). Purification of the cyclohexanone and separation from adipic acid are easily effected by the extraction of the aqueous solution with benzene. Adipic

---

[1]The intermediate in this oxidation has been shown to be a chromate ester of the alcohol. Abstraction of the proton from the oxygen-bearing carbon is followed by decomposition of the ester to ketone and trivalent chromium.

$$\text{(cyclohexanone)} + 3[O] \xrightarrow{>60°} \begin{array}{c} CH_2 \\ CH_2 \qquad CO_2H \\ \\ CH_2 \qquad CO_2H \\ CH_2 \end{array} \qquad (15\text{-}7)$$

acid is more soluble in water than in benzene, whereas cyclohexanone is readily extracted into the benzene. Distillation of the benzene extracts affords cyclohexanone as the high-boiling fraction.

An alternative method for the preparation of cyclohexanone is pyrolysis of the seven-carbon dibasic acid, pimelic acid. This conversion is represented in Eq. 8. Although this method is general for preparation of

$$\begin{array}{c} CH_2{-}CH_2 \\ \qquad\qquad CO_2H \\ CH_2 \\ \qquad\qquad CO_2H \\ CH_2{-}CH_2 \end{array} \xrightarrow{\text{heat}} \text{(cyclohexanone)} + CO_2 + H_2O \qquad (15\text{-}8)$$

ketones having five or six atoms in the ring, and it gives a satisfactory yield of cyclohexanone, it is not a good method for preparing this particular ketone. The obstacle is that pimelic acid is far more expensive than is cyclohexanone.

Reactions of Aldehydes and Ketones

The first two reactions to be discussed, the formation of oximes and bisulfite addition products, are concerned with the preparation of solid derivatives from liquid aldehydes and ketones. Solid derivatives are of importance for both the characterization and purification of substances, for crystallization often provides an effective method for elimination of impurities in the final stages of purification. It will be recalled from the discussion in Chaps. 3 and 5 that two substances with the same boiling point cannot be separated by distillation, whereas if their melting points are the same they may still be separated by crystallization. Furthermore, the melting point and mixed melting-point determinations afford useful evidence as to identity. Even with solid aldehydes and ketones, the preparation of a solid derivative is a useful adjunct in purification or identification (cf. Chap. 30).

Oxime formation takes place when the carbonyl compound is warmed with hydroxylamine. Since hydroxylamine itself is an unstable liquid, it is used in the form of its solid hydrochloride. In addition to its greater stability, the hydrochloride is more convenient to use because small quantities of it can be more easily weighed. The free hydroxylamine, which reacts in oxime formation, is then liberated in the presence of the carbonyl compound by the addition of sodium acetate (Eq. 9) or pyridine.

$$\text{(cyclohexanone)} + HCl \cdot H_2NOH + CH_3CO_2Na \longrightarrow \text{(cyclohexanone oxime, NOH)} + NaCl + H_2O \quad (15\text{-}9)$$
$$+ CH_3CO_2H$$

If desired, the oxime may be hydrolyzed and the carbonyl compound regenerated by warming the oxime with mineral acid. Oximes (and similar carbonyl derivatives) also readily undergo exchange with pyruvic or levulinic acids, to form the oximes of these acids and liberate the free carbonyl compound.

Formation of a *sodium bisulfite addition compound* is not so general a reaction for carbonyl compounds as is oxime formation. In order for it to take place, the carbonyl group must be quite reactive and unhindered spatially. Thus, we find that bisulfite addition products are formed by nearly all aldehydes, but in the ketone series only by the methyl ketones (and there are some exceptions) and some of the cyclic ketones. The reaction (Eq. 10) is reversible, and, in order to get high yields, a large ex-

$$\underset{CH_3}{\overset{CH_3}{>}}C{=}O + NaHSO_3 \rightleftarrows \underset{CH_3}{\overset{CH_3}{>}}C\underset{SO_3Na}{\overset{OH}{<}} \quad (15\text{-}10)$$

$$H_2O + NaCl + SO_2 \overset{HCl}{\underset{Na_2CO_3}{\longleftarrow}} Na_2SO_3 + NaHCO_3$$

cess of saturated sodium bisulfite is used to drive the reaction to the right. This excess also helps precipitate the addition product, which is ionic, by a common ion effect. Another method for completing precipitation is the addition of alcohol, in which the saltlike product is much less soluble. The fact that the carbonyl compound may then be regenerated from the bisulfite addition product under extremely mild conditions makes this reaction very useful for purification. In order to recover the carbonyl compound, the addition product is dissolved in water, and the equilibrium shown in Eq. 10 is displaced completely to the left by adding sodium carbonate or dilute acid to destroy the sodium bisulfite.

The remaining reactions of aldehydes and ketones are diagnostic tests for the detection of certain structures by the formation of colors and/or precipitates. The first is *Schiff's test*, which is used to detect the presence of an aldehyde group. It depends upon the fact that fuchsin, a pink dye, is converted by sulfur dioxide to the colorless form and that this in turn is changed back to a pink-colored form by an aldehyde. The test is very sensitive and specific for aldehydes, provided that the test substance does not remove the sulfur dioxide.

Fehling's test is used to detect the presence of an easily oxidizable group. The reagent consists of an alkaline solution of copper sulfate in the presence of tartrate ion, which forms a complex with the cupric ion and thus keeps it from precipitating in the alkaline solution. The cupric ion, which oxidizes the aldehyde, is itself reduced to the cuprous state, and, since the latter does not form a complex with tartrate, it precipitates from the alkaline solution as cuprous oxide (Eq. 11). Positive tests are given by

$$\underset{}{R} \overset{H}{\underset{}{-}} C \overset{}{=} O + 2Cu^{++} \text{(tartrate complex)} + 4OH^- \rightarrow R-CO_2H + \underline{Cu_2O} + 2H_2O$$

$$(15-11)$$

aldehydes and α-hydroxyketones (oxidized to α,β-diketones), and the precipitate of cuprous oxide may vary in color from blue-green to red-brown, depending on its particle size.

Tollens' test is similar to Fehling's except that an alkaline solution of silver (kept in solution as the ammonia complex) is used as the oxidizing agent. The silver ion is reduced by the aldehyde or α-hydroxyketone to free silver, which precipitates as a gray-black solid or silvery mirror on the walls of the test tube, depending on the cleanliness of the tube and the rapidity of the precipitation.

The *iodoform reaction* is used as a test for a compound having a methyl group adjacent to the carbonyl. The reagent is a solution of iodine in alkali, which acts first to replace the hydrogens of the methyl group with iodines, and then cleaves the iodinated compound to iodoform and an acid (Eq. 12).

$$CH_3 \underset{\underset{O}{\|}}{-C-} CH_3 + 3NaOI \rightarrow CH_3 \underset{\underset{O}{\|}}{-C-} CI_3 + 3NaOH$$

$$\xrightarrow{\text{NaOH}} CH_3CO_2Na + CHI_3 \quad (15\text{-}12)$$

A positive reaction is recognizable by the characteristic odor and the yellow precipitate of iodoform, whose melting point (119°) may also be determined. This test is given not only by compounds that already contain the $CH_3 \underset{\underset{O}{\|}}{-C-}$

grouping, such as acetaldehyde and methyl ketones, but also by compounds that may be converted to this form by hypohalite, which is an oxidizing agent. For example, ethyl alcohol and secondary butyl alcohol will give positive tests, for the former is oxidized to acetaldehyde and the latter to methyl ethyl ketone by the reagent. The reagent then is useful as a test for the methyl carbonyl group either initially present or formed by mild oxidation.

Benzyl Alcohol

The *main reaction* for the preparation of benzyl alcohol is an example of the Cannizzaro reaction, a reaction given by aldehydes having no alpha hydrogens. Since the condensing agent is strong alkali, aldehydes with α-hydrogens react to give polymeric aldol-condensation products at a much more rapid rate than they undergo the Cannizzaro reaction. With benzaldehyde, the reaction takes the course shown in Eq. 13. It may be

$$2\ \text{C}_6\text{H}_5\text{CHO} + \text{KOH} \rightarrow \text{C}_6\text{H}_5\text{CH}_2\text{OH} + \text{C}_6\text{H}_5\text{CO}_2\text{K} \tag{15-13}$$

considered as an intermolecular dismutation reaction in which one mole of aldehyde is oxidized to acid and the other is reduced to alcohol. When used for synthetic purposes, the Cannizzaro reaction as formulated above is quite inefficient, for one mole of aldehyde is wasted for every mole converted to alcohol. However, by using a mixture of benzaldehyde and formaldehyde, much higher conversions can be realized (Eq. 14). Since

$$\text{C}_6\text{H}_5\text{CHO} + \text{HCHO} + \text{KOH} \rightarrow \text{C}_6\text{H}_5\text{CH}_2\text{OH} + \text{HCO}_2\text{K} \tag{15-14}$$

formaldehyde is much more easily oxidized than is benzaldehyde, the course of the reaction is to form potassium formate and benzyl alcohol. Under these conditions, the reaction is known as the "crossed Cannizzaro." The three other paths the reaction might take are: (1) two moles of benzaldehyde reacting as in Eq. 13, (2) one mole of benzaldehyde reacting with one mole of formaldehyde to give benzoic acid and methanol, and (3) two moles of formaldehyde reacting to form formic acid and methanol. Since formaldehyde is present in excess and is much more easily oxidized than benzaldehyde, very little of possibilities (1) and (2) will occur. Reaction (3) will take place to an appreciable extent but will have no deleterious effect on the yield, since formaldehyde, the cheapest reagent, is used in excess and the products of reaction (3) do not interfere in the purification.

The benzyl alcohol is obtained from the reaction mixture by adding water and extracting with benzene. Any benzoic acid, a small amount of which undoubtedly was present as impurity in the original benzaldehyde and some of which was formed in side reactions (1) and (2) above, is in the form of its potassium salt and is therefore soluble in the aqueous layer, as is potassium formate. The only compound to go into the benzene layer is the benzyl alcohol. Complete consumption of the benzaldehyde is expected on account of the large excess of formaldehyde. Any residual formaldehyde will remain in the aqueous phase, in which it is highly soluble. Distillation of the organic phase gives first the benzene-water azeotrope, then benzene, and finally benzyl alcohol as the high-boiling fraction.

Infrared Spectra

The carbonyl group, whether in aldehydes, ketones, esters, or acids, absorbs in the infrared between 5.6 and 5.9 μ. Only in rare and unusual structures does the absorption fall outside these limits. For open-chain (acyclic) aldehydes and ketones, the absorption normally lies in the region 5.8–5.9 μ, as illustrated in Fig. 1. This is also the region of absorption of

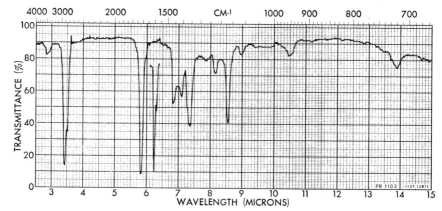

FIG. 1.   Infrared absorption spectrum of 2-octanone, determined on a thin film; 6.24 μ calibration line from the polystyrene spectrum.   The minor absorption below 3 μ suggests an alcohol as impurity in this commercial sample of ketone. This same type of absorption is also noted in Fig. 2. It is of interest that both these ketones are synthesized by oxidation of the corresponding alcohols.

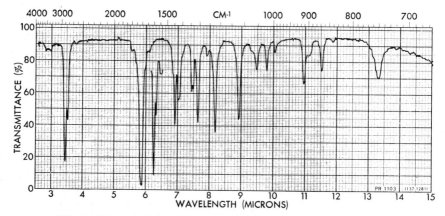

FIG. 2.   Infrared absorption spectrum of cyclohexanone, determined on a thin film; 6.24 μ calibration line from the polystyrene spectrum. It may be noted this this spectrum is considerably more complicated than that of acyclic ketones (Fig. 1).

carboxylic acids (cf. Chap. 12); however, the acids are readily differentiated by the hydroxyl absorption that merges into the C—H absorption band (cf. Fig. 12–2). For cyclic ketones, the location of the absorption band is affected by ring size, and this is frequently of analytical utility. For a six-membered ring as in cyclohexanone (Fig. 2), the absorption falls in the same region as in open-chain ketones, whereas cyclopentanones absorb at somewhat shorter wavelength, near 5.75 μ. It will be recalled (Chap. 12) that esters also absorb near 5.75 μ; however, a simple chemical test distinguishes between esters and cyclopentanones. Esters are saponified to yield an acid (Chap. 12), whereas ketones are not.

EXPERIMENTAL PROCEDURES

Cyclohexanone

In a 400-ml beaker are placed 24 g of sodium dichromate dihydrate and 100 ml of water. With stirring, there is added *carefully* 33 g (18 ml) of concentrated (18M) sulfuric acid, then the deep orange-red solution is cooled to about 30° and poured into a 250-ml separatory funnel. In a 500-ml Erlenmeyer flask are placed 20 g (21 ml) of cyclohexanol and 50 ml of water. This mixture is swirled as there is added, during about 5 minutes, the oxidizing mixture in the separatory funnel, which is supported at a convenient height in a padded ring (Fig. 8-3). The temperature of the reaction mixture is followed by placing a thermometer in the flask, and gentle cooling is applied if necessary to keep the temperature from rising above 60°. Cooling should not be sufficient to lower the temperature below 55°. After completion of the addition, the flask is allowed to stand with occasional swirling (occasional cooling may be necessary) until the temperature begins to drop spontaneously. At this point, the flask is allowed to stand an additional 15 minutes without cooling.

The reaction mixture is cooled to about 25°, then extracted with three 20-ml portions of benzene (Note 1). The initial reaction mixture may be sufficiently dark-colored to create some difficulty in seeing the phase boundary. It is helpful to mark the separatory funnel at the 25-ml level (Note 2) before extraction is started, so that the approximate location of the phase boundary is known. The first two benzene extracts are combined and washed with a 20-ml portion of water. The same portion of water is used to wash the final benzene extract. The water wash is separated very carefully from each benzene extract. Since the extracts are usually cloudy with suspended water, and may contain some flocculent solid, it is best to dry them for at least 30 minutes with occasional swirling, over anhydrous magnesium sulfate. The dried extract is filtered into a round-bottomed flask of 100–200-ml capacity, which is fitted (with ground joint, if available) for attachment to the fractionating column. The solution is heated with a small flame (*CAUTION! Benzene is inflammable.*) so that benzene is distilled through the column rather rapidly, for the fractionation of things boiling about 75° apart is sufficiently easy that slow distillation is unnecessary. A cloudy distillate (benzene-water azeotrope and benzene) distilling below 80° will be collected first, then benzene will distill near 80° after the last of the azeotrope has been distilled. Finally, the heat is increased sufficiently to boil cyclohexanone into the top part of the column. As soon as the vapor temperature begins to rise rapidly above 100° to about 145°, distillation is interrupted, the column is allowed to drain for 3–5 minutes, then the residue in the flask is transferred with the bulb pipette to the 50-ml distilling flask, which is arranged for distillation. Pouring of the liquid increases the mechanical loss in transferring to the smaller flask. There would also be a somewhat larger loss if a distilling head should be attached to the larger flask for distillation. If stripping of benzene was properly carried out in the column, there should be no forerun as the cyclohexanone is collected at about 150–155°. The actual boiling range should be recorded. The yield is in the range 13–16 g.

Gas chromatography of the product will reveal the presence of any starting material or benzene solvent in the cyclohexanone. Silicone is recommended as partitioning agent. The alcohol will appear (in a somewhat distorted band) at longer retention time than the ketone. The infrared spectrum will not reveal such small amounts of alcohol as will glpc, for the hydroxyl absorption below 3μ is a relatively weak band.

NOTES

1. Benzene has a very low order of toxicity; however, its toxic action is cumulative because it attacks the liver, which the body cannot repair. For this reason, gross exposure to benzene should be avoided. In the case of multiple extractions, as in the present experiment, the extractions should be performed in a forced-draft hood unless the laboratory is well ventilated.

2. Since location of the phase boundary is necessary after most of the lower layer has been drained from the separatory funnel, it is the volume of the upper layer that is important. The majority of the cyclohexanone will be in the first extraction, so its volume will be greater than 25 ml, while the volume of the last extract will be less than 25 ml.

Reactions of Aldehydes and Ketones

Cyclohexanone oxime.   In 20 ml of water in a 50-ml Erlenmeyer flask are dissolved 5 g of hydroxylamine hydrochloride and 7.5 g of sodium acetate crystals. After the solution has been warmed to about 40° and 5 g (5.3 ml) of cyclohexanone added, the flask is stoppered securely with a softened cork stopper and shaken vigorously for a few minutes. The oxime separates as a crystalline solid. The flask is cooled in an ice bath, and the crystals are filtered with suction, washed with a little ice-cold water, pressed as dry as possible on the funnel, and spread on a piece of filter paper to dry in the air, after which the melting point is taken. The recorded melting point of the oxime is 89–90°. The yield is 4.5–5.0 g. The product is turned in properly labeled.[2]

Acetone-sodium bisulfite addition compound. To 10 ml of a saturated solution of sodium bisulfite contained in a 50-ml Erlenmeyer flask immersed in an ice bath is added 4 g (5 ml) of acetone, drop by drop. The solution is shaken thoroughly and the product allowed to crystallize. After a few minutes, about 25 ml of ethanol is added to promote the precipitation and the crystals are filtered with suction, washed with alcohol and then ether, and allowed to dry. No attempt is made to determine the melting point. A small amount of the sodium bisulfite addition compound is treated with 5–10 ml of sodium carbonate solution (10%) and warmed, and any odor is noted. The experiment is repeated with 5–10 ml of dilute hydrochloric acid in place of the sodium carbonate solution. In this case, the odor is noted *cautiously*.

Schiff's fuchsin-aldehyde test. Two drops of acetaldehyde solution are added to about 2 ml of water, and to the solution is added about 1 ml of Schiff's fuchsin-aldehyde reagent.[3] The color is noted. This test is repeated as above with acetone and an alcoholic solution of benzoin. A blank test should be performed on the alcohol. Ketones do not give this test when they are perfectly pure, but the color reaction is very sensitive and will appear if a mere trace of an aldehyde is present.

Fehling's test. In a test tube is placed about 10 ml of freshly prepared Fehling's solution (made by mixing equal volumes of Fehling's solution No. 1 of copper sulfate and solution No. 2 of alkaline tartrate[4]). After a few drops of acetaldehyde are added, the solution is warmed in a

---

[2]Occasionally this oxime has a pink color, and spectrographic analysis has revealed this to be due to traces of aluminum or nickel with which the oxime has formed a complex. It follows that this material should not be handled with a nickel spatula.

[3]A filtered solution of 0.1 g of pure *p*-rosaniline hydrochloride in 100 ml of water, mixed thoroughly with an equal volume of water saturated with sulfur dioxide and the mixture allowed to stand overnight before use.

[4]Solution 1: 34.6 g of copper sulfate pentahydrate dissolved in water and diluted to 500 ml.

Solution 2: 173 g of sodium potassium tartrate (Rochelle salt) and 70 g of sodium hydroxide dissolved in water and diluted to 500 ml.

boiling-water bath for a few minutes, and the results observed. This test is repeated with acetone and an alcoholic solution of benzoin.

Tollens' test. In a clean test tube a solution of Tollens' reagent[5] is prepared by adding to 2 ml of Tollens' reagent No. 1 (silver nitrate), solution No. 2 until the brown silver oxide formed first just dissolves. A few drops of acetaldehyde are added and the solution allowed to stand at room temperature for a few minutes, then the results are noted. This test is repeated with acetone and an alcoholic solution of benzoin.

The final reagent should always be prepared just before use and *should not be stored,* since the solution decomposes on standing and deposits a highly explosive precipitate. The test solution should be washed down the drain immediately and the test tubes washed out with dilute nitric acid.

Iodoform reaction. This test is performed on samples of acetone and ethyl alcohol. To three drops of the test substance in 3 ml of water in a test tube is added 0.5 ml of a solution of iodine in potassium iodide,[6] followed by 10% sodium hydroxide added dropwise, and with shaking, until the iodine color is dispelled and the solution is slightly yellow. If the solution becomes colorless, more iodine is added to just restore the yellow color. After 2 minutes, the odor and appearance of the solution are noted. If no precipitate has formed, the tube is heated to 60° for several minutes and the observations repeated.

From the above results, state how you would differentiate an aldehyde, an α-hydroxyketone, and a ketone.

Benzyl Alcohol

A 250-ml Erlenmeyer flask is fitted with an air condenser, and a thermometer is suspended by a wire or string through the condenser tube so that the bulb of the thermometer is just above the bottom of the flask. In the flask are placed 15.9 g (15 ml) of benzaldehyde (Note 1), 15 ml of formalin (37% aqueous formaldehyde solution), and 50 ml of methanol. To this mixture is added 25 g of solid potassium hydroxide, the air condenser with thermometer is attached, and the mixture is swirled. The temperature rises rapidly (Note 2), principally from heat of solution of the alkali, and when it reaches about 50° the flask is cooled in a pan of water sufficiently to keep the temperature at 55–65°. Swirling is continued until all the potassium hydroxide has dissolved (about 5 minutes). The heat of reaction

[5]Solution 1: 0.1N silver nitrate solution.

Solution 2: 120 ml of 6N ammonium hydroxide plus 33 ml of 6N sodium hydroxide, mixed and diluted to two liters.

[6]Prepared by dissolving 25 g of iodine in a solution of 50 g of potassium iodide in 200 ml of water.

keeps the temperature above 60° for about 5 minutes, then the mixture is heated in a pan of water at 65° ± 5° for 1–1.5 hours (Note 3).

At the end of the heating period, the light yellow or deep red (Note 3) solution is poured into a separatory funnel containing 75 ml of water, and the flask is rinsed with 40 ml of benzene which is added to the separatory funnel and used to extract the aqueous phase. The aqueous phase is separated (Note 4) and extracted with two additional 20-ml portions of benzene. The second and third extracts are combined but kept separate from the first extract. The first extract is washed with 20 ml of water, and after the phases separate the water is run into a second separatory funnel containing the combined second and third extracts, which are also washed with this same portion of water. In the same manner, a second 20-ml portion of water is used to wash the extracts. Water is separated carefully from both benzene extracts, then the extracts (cloudiness from water is no disadvantage) are combined and distilled from a 250-ml distilling flask (conveniently assembled as in Fig. 5-5). After most of the benzene has been distilled, the flame is turned up gradually as the last of the benzene is distilled slowly in order to avoid loss of benzyl alcohol. When the boiling ring of benzyl alcohol reaches the thermometer, but before it begins to pass into the side arm, the flame is removed. The distillation flask is disconnected from the assembly and cooled below about 100°, then the residual benzyl alcohol is transferred to the 25-ml distilling flask by use of the small bulb pipette (Fig. 30-1). This technique for transfer keeps losses so low that rinsing with solvent is unnecessary. The small distilling flask is equipped with a thermometer and arranged for distillation. A tared test tube is clamped in position as receiver, with the side arm of the distilling flask extending about half-way to the bottom. The colorless benzyl alcohol is collected in the range 200–205° (reported b.p. 205°), as the test tube is cooled briefly with a wet cloth if necessary. Most of the product distills over a range of about 1°, and there is essentially no distillation residue. The yield is 10–12 g, depending on the quality of the benzaldehyde (Note 1).

Gas chromatography on a silicone column may be utilized to determine whether the product contains any benzaldehyde not converted in the reaction. The infrared spectrum will also reveal rather small amounts (1–2%) of benzaldehyde, for the carbonyl group has an intense absorption band.

NOTES

1. Benzoic acid, formed in benzaldehyde by air oxidation on standing, does no damage in this preparation except for lowering the yield. In runs made with benzaldehyde which had stood on the shelf in a capped bottle for one year, yields were 10–11.5 g.

2. The heat of solution of potassium hydroxide in methanol is quite high and care should be taken that this solution does not boil out of the flask. For larger-scale runs, the solution of potassium hydroxide in methanol should be prepared first, and to this cooled solution should then be added the benzaldehyde and formalin.

3. The exact time depends on the temperature range actually used; for example, at 60–65°, 1.5 hours is recommended. If the reaction is carried out as described, the darkening which may occur near the end of the reaction does no damage. The dark color remains entirely in the aqueous phase when the mixture is extracted. If the initial heating is above about 70°, darkening occurs soon after heating is started, benzaldehyde becomes involved in polymerization, and the yield is lowered to 0–6 g, depending on the initial temperature reached. Color remains in the benzene extract, and there is a large nonvolatile distillation residue.

4. Extraction of alkaline solutions with benzene frequently leads to emulsion formation which may be particularly troublesome with the water washes when the alkali is quite dilute. Shaking should be done carefully, and if an emulsion forms it is best broken by addition of a few milliters of a saturated sodium chloride solution. Tactics used for breaking emulsions are discussed in some detail in the notes to the methyl salicylate preparation.

Concerning the toxicity of benzene, reference should be made to Note 1 of the cyclohexanone preparation.

Sugars

16

A very important, as well as widely occurring, class of organic compounds is that known as *carbohydrates*. This name was derived from the fact that the composition of these compounds could be represented as hydrates of carbon, such as $C_n(H_2O)_n$ or $C_n(H_2O)_{n-1}$ and so forth. At a much later date, when the complex structures of these substances were elucidated, they proved to be far removed from hydrates of carbon; however, the name has persisted. Within this very large class of compounds, further groupings into subdivisions can be made; the term *sugar* is usually used for a carbohydrate of one or two saccharide units. These monosaccharides and disaccharides are distinguished from the polysaccharides, such as cellulose and starch, by the fact that the former are more or less sweet and of sufficiently low molecular weight to follow the usual rules for solution and reactivity.

All the sugars of any importance are isolated from natural sources. Although some have been synthesized, the starting material is invariably some other relatively abundant sugar. The synthesis and purification of a sugar are very difficult and tedious tasks, and a large part of this difficulty arises because sugars are polyhydroxy aldehydes or ketones. As such they are very soluble in water and practically insoluble in organic solvents. This makes their crystallization quite difficult, especially since their tendency to crystallize is greatly affected by traces of impurities. Also, most synthetic methods result in mixtures of stereoisomers with similar properties, and this naturally complicates the purification problem. For these reasons, the present chapter will be concerned with the isolation of a sugar from a natural source and the examination of a few reactions of sugars that bring out their polyhydroxy aldehyde (or ketone) character.

Isolation of Lactose

The sugar occurring in milk (milk sugar) is known as lactose and may be easily isolated by first removing the fat and protein present in the milk. Commercial skimmed (defatted) milk contains about 3% casein, 0.7% albumin, 4.5–5% lactose, and 1% minerals; the remainder is water. This material serves as an excellent source of lactose. First, the casein is precipitated by warming with dilute acetic acid. It is important that the heating not be excessive or the acid too strong, since these conditions will also hydrolyze the lactose into its components, glucose and galactose. After the casein has been removed, the acid is neutralized and the solution heated to a boil to precipitate the albumin. Concentration of the clear filtrate, followed by the addition of ethanol and cooling, results in crystalline lactose. As mentioned above, the crystallization of sugars is quite sensitive to the presence of traces of impurities and the final filtrate must be clear in order to obtain crystalline lactose. To help in the complete removal of all suspended material, the final filtration is carried out by using a filter covered with a silica filter aid; and the solution being filtered is treated with decolorizing carbon, which acts as an adsorbent for colloidal material.

Mucic Acid

Lactose, when heated with nitric acid, is hydrolyzed to glucose and galactose; these in turn, are oxidized to the respective dibasic acids, saccharic and mucic. The reaction is shown in Eq. 1, with monosaccharides in

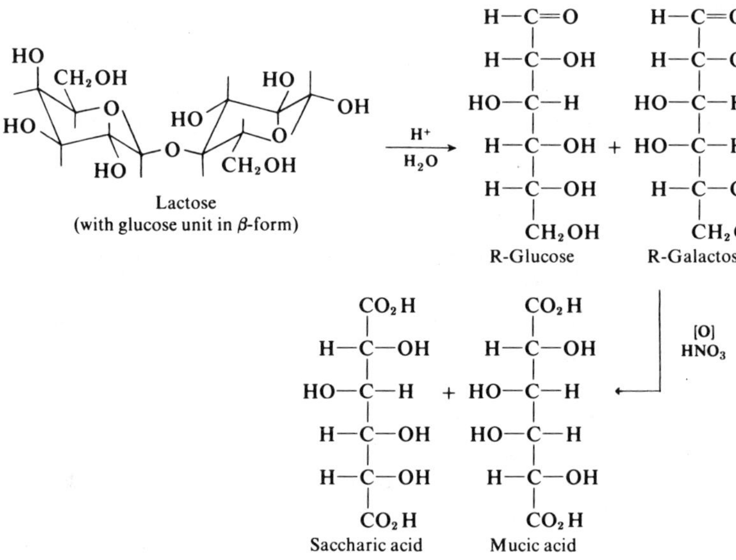

R-Glucose

R-Galactose

Saccharic acid

Mucic acid

Lactose
(with glucose unit in β-form)

(16-1)

the open-chain (aldehyde) forms[1] and the acids in the open-chain forms rather than as lactones. The sugars actually exist in solution largely as the cyclic hemi-acetals, as depicted for the glucose unit in lactose. Glucose in solution establishes the equilibrium shown in Eq. 2, where the open-chain

$$
\begin{array}{ccc}
\underset{\substack{\alpha\text{-R-Glucose}\\ [\alpha]_D \ = \ +109.6°}}{\text{HO}\overset{\text{CH}_2\text{OH}}{\underset{\text{HO}}{\bigwedge}}\hspace{-0.5em}\underset{\text{OH}}{\overset{\text{O}}{\diagup}}}
&
\rightleftarrows
&
\begin{array}{c}
\text{CHO} \\
\text{H} \!-\!\!-\! \text{OH} \\
\text{HO} \!-\!\!-\! \text{H} \\
\text{H} \!-\!\!-\! \text{OH} \\
\text{H} \!-\!\!-\! \text{OH} \\
\text{CH}_2\text{OH}
\end{array}
&
\rightleftarrows
&
\underset{\substack{\beta\text{-R-Glucose}\\ [\alpha]_D \ = \ +20.5°}}{\text{HO}\overset{\text{CH}_2\text{OH}}{\underset{\text{HO}}{\bigwedge}}\hspace{-0.5em}\underset{\text{HO}}{\overset{\text{O}}{\diagup}}\text{OH}}
\end{array}
\qquad (16\text{-}2)
$$

form is present in only trace amount (0.024% of the total). Since the axial hydroxyl in the hemi-acetal position of α-R-glucose results in a higher energy than when the hemi-acetal hydroxyl is equatorial as in β-R-glucose, the concentration of the β-isomer is higher at equilibrium (α:β = 37:63).

In addition to furnishing protons for acid-catalyzed hydrolysis of the lactose, nitric acid also acts as the oxidizing agent (Eq. 1). The half reaction for the reduction of nitric acid is shown in Eq. 3. Although the two di-

$$2HNO_3 \rightarrow 2NO + 3[O] + H_2O \qquad (16\text{-}3)$$

basic acids formed appear similar, they differ tremendously in solubility; the saccharic acid is soluble and the mucic acid is quite insoluble. Undoubtedly, the symmetry of the mucic acid, which has a plane of symmetry passing between carbons three and four and hence is optically inactive, contributes to this insolubility.

The only side reaction might result from the use of excessive temperatures or of nitric acid which is too concentrated. These more vigorous conditions would cause the further oxidation and breakdown of the organic material. Under the specified conditions, very little of this takes place; purification is obtained by filtering the mucic acid from all the other substances that are soluble. The oxidation of galactose or galactose-containing material is a general method for preparing mucic acid, and may even serve as a quantitative test under controlled conditions.

Pentaacetyl-β-R-Glucose

The presence of five hydroxyl groups in glucose may be easily demonstrated by the preparation of pentaesters; however, these five hydroxyl

[1]In accordance with Sequence Rule designation, the lower carbon in glucose and that in galactose (as written in Eq. 1) is of R-configuration, hence the designation R-glucose and R-galactose. In classical designation of sugar configurations, these sugars are termed D-glucose and D-galactose.

groups are not those shown in the aldehyde form (Eq. 1). There are four alcohol hydroxyls and one hemi-acetal hydroxyl, for in solution the principal species are the cyclic structures (Eq. 2). Since the hemi-acetal hydroxyls react more rapidly than the alcohol hydroxyls, the pentaacetates of the cyclic structures are formed. Under some conditions a mixture of the two isomers will be formed, but if the equilibrium mixture is acetylated with acetic anhydride in presence of sodium acetate as catalyst, a nearly pure sample of the beta derivative is obtained (Eq. 4). The nearly exclusive

$$\text{R—Glucose} + 5\text{Ac}_2\text{O} \xrightarrow{\text{NaOAc}} \text{Pentaacetyl-}\beta\text{-R-glucose} + 5\text{HOAc} \qquad (16\text{-}4)$$

(equilibrium mixture as in Eq. 2)

Pentaacetyl-β-R-glucose

formation of the beta derivative is attributable to the fact that when the hemi-acetal hydroxyl is in the less hindered equatorial position it reacts considerably more rapidly than does the axial hydroxyl. As the beta isomer is consumed, re-equilibration occurs (Eq. 2) to supply more beta isomer until finally nearly all the sugar is converted to pentaacetyl-β-R-glucose. Since acetic anhydride reacts with any water present in the reaction mixture and thus keeps it quite dry, no equilibration of the esters can occur by way of acid-catalyzed hydrolysis, followed by re-esterification.

Purification of the pentaacetate is easily effected by pouring the solution into water, which precipitates the ester and dissolves all the other substances. The pentaacetyl-β-R-glucose is then recrystallized from ethanol. It is this favorable solubility and ease of purification that make pentaacetates (and pentabenzoates) useful as sugar derivatives. In addition, they usually exhibit a distinct and sharp melting point.

Osazone Formation

The aldehyde or α-hydroxyketone character of sugars can be shown by applying the usual tests for these groups (see Chap. 15). Those tests that depend on the presence of easily oxidizable groups (Fehling's, Tollens') are positive with all the sugars except the nonreducing disaccharides. In the latter compounds the reducing groupings have been blocked by glycoside formation. Sucrose is an example of such a disaccharide. Only very small amounts of the sugars are present in the open-chain aldehyde form; however, if a reagent that effectively removes this form is used, the equilibrium can be shifted and the usual aldehyde or ketone derivatives of a sugar are obtained.

If glucose is treated with phenylhydrazine, a phenylhydrazone is formed; however, in the presence of excess reagent, the phenylhydrazone reacts further to form a phenylosazone. The over-all reaction is shown in Eq. 5. The alcohol group on carbon two is oxidized to a ketone, and aniline

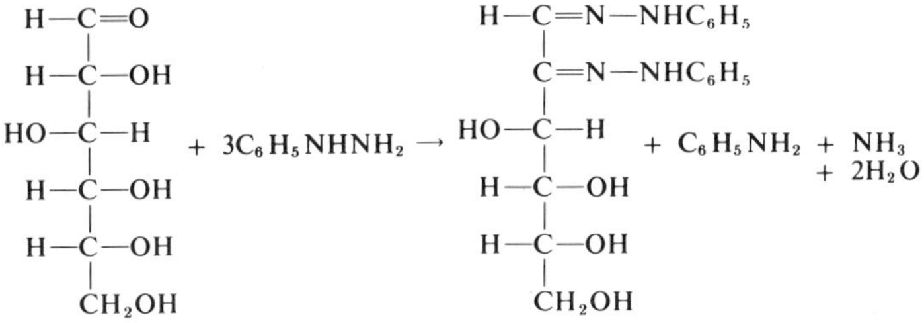

$$
\begin{array}{l}
\text{H}-\text{C}=\text{O} \\
\text{H}-\text{C}-\text{OH} \\
\text{HO}-\text{C}-\text{H} \\
\text{H}-\text{C}-\text{OH} \\
\text{H}-\text{C}-\text{OH} \\
\text{CH}_2\text{OH}
\end{array}
+ 3\text{C}_6\text{H}_5\text{NHNH}_2 \rightarrow
\begin{array}{l}
\text{H}-\text{C}=\text{N}-\text{NHC}_6\text{H}_5 \\
\text{C}=\text{N}-\text{NHC}_6\text{H}_5 \\
\text{HO}-\text{C}-\text{H} \\
\text{H}-\text{C}-\text{OH} \\
\text{H}-\text{C}-\text{OH} \\
\text{CH}_2\text{OH}
\end{array}
+ \text{C}_6\text{H}_5\text{NH}_2 + \text{NH}_3 \atop + 2\text{H}_2\text{O}
\qquad (16\text{-}5)
$$

and ammonia are formed as a result. An interesting point about the process is that it stops after two phenylhydrazine residues have been introduced, even though the structure at carbon three is the same as was previously present at carbon two. The high insolubility of the osazones and thus their removal from the field of action by precipitation have been offered as an explanation, but this reasoning is contradicted by the fact that some disaccharides form soluble osazones. Mester[2] has reviewed the facts in osazone formation and structure. He concludes that osazones exist in the stable, hydrogen-bonded chelate structure (see Chap. 18) shown below, and that it is the stability of this structure that limits further reaction.

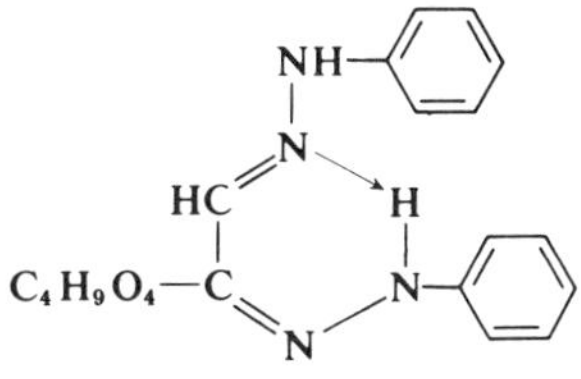

As can be seen from Eq. 5, osazone formation destroys the asymmetry at carbons one and two; therefore, sugars with the same configuration below carbon two will give identical osazones. This is very useful in structural work. Other points that make osazones useful in the identification of sugars are their melting point, crystalline form, and rate of formation. The latter, when used under standardized conditions, can very nicely serve to distinguish the various sugars. A sample of the sugar is heated with phenylhydrazine hydrochloride and sodium acetate, and the time is noted until a precipitate appears. This time is characteristic of the individual sugar and may be used to distinguish it; glucose, mannose, and fructose all form the same osazone but at different rates. With mannose, the precipi-

[2]L. Mester, *Advances in Carbohydrate Chemistry,* Vol. XIII (New York: Academic Press, 1958), p. 129.

tate that first appears is the slightly soluble, nearly colorless phenylhydrazone, and this is slowly converted to the yellow phenylosazone as the reaction proceeds. It should be borne in mind that the essential structure for osazone formation is a hydroxyl group alpha to a carbonyl; so the reaction is characteristic of all α-hydroxyaldehydes and ketones.

EXPERIMENTAL PROCEDURES

Isolation of Lactose from Milk

Sweet skimmed milk (Note 1), 200 ml, is warmed to about 40°, and dilute acetic acid (1 part glacial acetic acid to 10 parts water) is added dropwise from a pipette with continuous stirring. This process is continued until casein no longer separates. An excess of acid should be avoided, for it may cause some hydrolysis of the lactose. The casein is worked into a mass, removed with a stirring rod, and discarded. Immediately, 5 g of finely divided calcium carbonate (precipitated chalk) is added, and the mixture is stirred for a brief period and then heated to boiling for about 10 minutes. Heating causes almost complete precipitation of the albumin. The hot mixture is filtered by suction, and the filtrate is concentrated in a beaker to about 30 ml (Note 2). To the hot solution are added 175 ml of 95% ethyl alcohol (*NO FLAMES!*) and 1–2 g of decolorizing carbon; after it has been mixed well, the warm solution is filtered by gentle suction through a layer of filter aid wet with ethanol (cf. Chap. 14, Notes 2, 3, and 4). The clear filtrate (Note 3) is allowed to stand overnight or longer in a stoppered Erlenmeyer flask. In some cases, several days will be required for complete crystallization. Hard crystals of lactose separate, usually on the walls and bottom of the flask. The crystals are collected by suction filtration and washed with a few milliliters of 25% alcohol. The average yield is 5-7 g.

Taste the product. Any material not oxidized as below is turned in as a product.

NOTES

1. This material should not be allowed to stand too long before being used in this experiment. Even under refrigeration bacterial attack takes place, and the lactose is converted to lactic acid.

The most convenient form of starting material for this experiment is powdered skimmed milk. In the case of one brand termed "Instant Dry Milk (nonfat)," the manufacturer recommended 5 lbs. of the dried milk per gallon of water;

therefore, 23.9 g in 200 ml of water was used for isolation of lactose. The yield of lactose was about 6 g.

2. In some cases, precipitation of proteins during the concentration will cause bumping in the boiling solution. The solution may also tend to froth out of the beaker if boiling is quite vigorous. Blowing on the froth will break it and allow faster concentration. It is important that the final volume be rather accurately 30 ml (± 2 ml); otherwise, lowered yields result.

3. If the filtrate from the suction filtration is not brilliantly clear, especially if it has the dark appearance caused by traces of decolorizing carbon, it is desirable to add about 1 g of filter aid and refilter by gravity. Lactose is unlikely to crystallize unless the solution is brilliantly clear; however, *one may be deceived by cloudiness caused by rapid crystallization of lactose after the suction filtration.* If the cloudiness increases relatively rapidly on standing, especially if reflecting surfaces of crystals become evident, further filtration should be avoided since it will remove the product.

Mucic Acid

In a 400-ml beaker are placed 3 g of lactose, 40 ml of water, and 15 ml of concentrated nitric acid. The mixture is heated on the steam bath, with occasional stirring, until the volume has been reduced to about 10 ml. At the beginning of heating, care must be taken that the mixture does not froth over or spatter on the skin *(KEEP THE FACE BACK)*. The cooled mixture is allowed to stand at least 1 hour (preferably overnight); then the mucic acid is collected by suction filtration and washed with a little cold water. The product is dried, weighed, and turned in. The average yield is 1.5 g. Calculate the theoretical and percentage yield.

Pentaacetyl-β-R-Glucose

To a 125-ml Erlenmeyer flask is added a mixture, well-ground in a mortar, of 5 g of glucose and 5 g of anhydrous sodium acetate, followed by 25 ml of acetic anhydride. The flask is stoppered with a cork containing an 18-inch length of glass tubing and heated in a boiling water bath for $2\frac{1}{2}$ hours, with frequent shaking. A little sodium acetate may remain undissolved. After the heating period has been completed the solution is poured, dropwise and with stirring, into 250 ml of ice water, as the stirring is continued until all solid lumps have disintegrated. The mixture is filtered with suction, and the solid is washed on the filter with two 25-ml portions of cold 50 % (by volume) aqueous ethanol. After the precipitate has been sucked and pressed as dry as possible, it is recrystallized from about 25 ml of ethanol. The yield is about 7 g.

Osazone Formation

Ten ml of a 2 % aqueous solution of each of the following sugars are added to separate labeled test tubes: mannose, glucose, fructose, lactose, and maltose. To each is added 2 ml of a solution prepared by dissolving 1.5 g of phenylhydrazine hydrochloride and 1.1 g of sodium acetate in 10 ml of water. The contents of the tubes are well mixed and, with the time noted, the tubes are placed in a beaker of boiling water. Heating is continued for 20 minutes, as the tubes are shaken occasionally, and the times at which precipitation first takes place are noted. After the heating period, any tubes in which no precipitation took place are cooled and scratched with a stirring rod to induce crystallization. The time necessary for each sugar to yield a precipitate is recorded.

An unknown sugar is obtained from the storeroom and its identity is established by the rate of osazone formation, using the data collected above.

Bromination of Aromatic Compounds

17

The large group of organic compounds classified as *aromatic* was originally so named because of the odor of some members of the group; however, present-day application of the term has no connection with odor. *Aromatic compounds* are those stabilized by electron delocalization in a cyclic conjugated system of double bonds. The resonance energy characteristic of such a system is usually sufficiently large that addition of a reagent to one of the double bonds, which "breaks" the fully conjugated system, leads to a product of higher energy than the fully conjugated starting material. This is in contrast to the situation in an alkene or polyalkene which does not possess the cyclic system of conjugated double bonds which causes a large lowering of the energy of the molecule (resonance energy is energy the molecule does not have on account of the opportunity for electron delocalization). Thus, the alkene not stabilized by electron delocalization adds reagents to the double bond readily, for the resultant product is of lower energy. Resonance-stabilized aromatic compounds do not add reagents readily, for the product is of higher energy; however, many *substitution reactions* occur readily in aromatic compounds, under conditions where a positive species (electrophile) is generated in the reaction.

Benzene may be regarded as the parent compound in the aromatic series containing six-membered rings, and halogenation of benzene is a highly characteristic aromatic substitution. In order for the substitution to occur, positive halogen must be generated; heating of liquid bromine with benzene at the boiling point of the mixture (or considerably higher temperature) does not result in reaction. Addition of ferric bromide does cause a facile reaction, however, for positive bromine is generated (Eq. 1).

Chapter 17

$$Br-Br + FeBr_3 \rightarrow {}^-FeBr_4 + Br^+ \qquad (17\text{-}1)$$

This positive species attacks the aromatic system as depicted in Eq. 2, to give an intermediate of only slightly lower energy than the transition

$$(17\text{-}2)$$

state. This intermediate, by losing a proton, gives a product, bromobenzene, which has regained the fully conjugated system. The intermediate does *not* add a negative species to complete addition to the double bond, for the resultant product would not have the resonance-stabilized aromatic system, hence would be of relatively high energy. Since ferric bromide is regenerated (Eq. 3), only catalytic amounts of it are needed to

$${}^-FeBr_4 + H^+ \rightarrow FeBr_3 + HBr \qquad (17\text{-}3)$$

promote a rapid rate of reaction. Indeed, more than trace amounts of ferric bromide will promote a violent reaction between bromine and benzene, so it is common laboratory practice to use pieces of metallic iron, such as tacks, to catalyze the bromination. The iron is "activated" by pre-treatment with halogen acid, to give traces of ferric halide, then the hydrogen bromide generated during the reaction provides an adequate source of ferric bromide catalyst.

The *main reaction* for *bromination of benzene* is that in Eq. 4, where further bromination to isomeric dibromobenzenes is included. Dibromina-

$$(17\text{-}4)$$

tion yields the *ortho* and *para* isomers, because bromine is an *ortho, para*-director.[1] In contrast with other *ortho, para*-directors, halogen retards rate of substitution in benzene; however, benzene reacts only slightly more rapidly than bromobenzene, so disubstitution is a significant *side reaction*. Further substitution, resulting in 1,2,4- and 1,2,3-tribromobenzene, oc-

---

[1]An elementary textbook in organic chemistry should be consulted for discussion of the principles involved in *ortho, para-* or *meta*-direction; however, a general guide may be stated: if the substituent atom attached to the aromatic ring is a relatively negative group the substituent is *ortho, para*-directing; if the atom attached to the ring is relatively positive, the substituent is *meta*-directing.

curs so slowly as to constitute a minor side reaction. Still further substitution occurs at a significant rate only at higher temperatures.

Since the object of the experiment is to prepare bromobenzene, let us examine the various factors and how they might be modified to maximize the yield of bromobenzene. The first factor is the ratio of benzene to bromine. From Eq. 4, it is seen that after a molecule of bromobenzene has been formed, the bromine may then react either with benzene or bromobenzene; that is, there will be a competition between the two for unreacted bromine molecules. Naturally, a factor influencing this competition will be the relative amounts of benzene and bromobenzene. The one present to the greater extent will have the greater probability of reacting. Thus, a large excess of benzene will make it more likely that a bromine molecule will collide and react with a benzene rather than with a bromobenzene molecule. However, increasing the amount of benzene has its practical limits, since too great an excess will introduce difficulties and losses in the purification step. It is important, of course, that the bromine be added to the benzene, rather than vice versa, and addition should be slow enough to avoid local high concentrations of bromine and bromobenzene. Under these conditions, dibromination is not a serious side reaction, and higher bromination is insignificant.

A consideration of the preparative procedure reveals that the *purification* must separate bromobenzene from benzene, dibromobenzene, and higher-brominated benzenes. In order to accomplish this, the reaction mixture, after washing with water to remove any dissolved hydrogen bromide, is steam-distilled. Since volatility with steam is governed in part (cf. Chap. 6) by the vapor pressure of a substance, the higher-brominated benzenes do not distill to any significant extent. According to the principles of fractional steam distillation (cf. Chap. 6), the first distillate will be richest in benzene, the ratio of bromobenzene increases as distillation progresses, and the dibromobenzenes distill in significant amounts only towards the end of the steam distillation. Since *p*-dibromobenzene, which is a solid, is present in larger amount, appearance of solid in the distillate may be used as a signal to change receivers and start collecting a second fraction, which contains only small amounts of bromobenzene.

For isolation of bromobenzene, the water layer is separated from the first fraction from steam distillation, then the organic phase is dried over calcium chloride and fractionally distilled. Although bromobenzene boils about 75° above benzene and 65° below dibromobenzene, effective separation is not accomplished in an ordinary distilling flask. The simple fractionating column described in Chap. 5 (Fig. 5-4) effects an excellent separation, however. In Fig. 1 is reproduced the tracing obtained by a student in glpc of his preparation of bromobenzene.

For isolation of *p*-dibromobenzene, the residue from the fractional

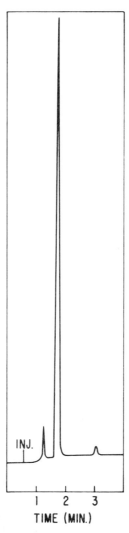

FIG. 1. Gas chromatography of 1.5 μl of bromobenzene, using "D" settings on the Carle instrument, 5-ft silicone column. Time of injection is
marked "inj." Attenuation: first peak (benzene) and last peak (dibromobenzene), 1; second peak (bromobenzene), 5. Assuming the same response
factor for the three compounds, this preparation of bromobenzene contained only 0.3% of benzene and 0.2% of dibromobenzene, thus is of 99.5%
purity.

distillation is combined with the solid from the final fraction in steam distillation. Since the molecular weights of the isomeric dibromobenzenes are
the same, similar volatilities are predicted, so fractional distillation is not
a promising method of separation. In contrast, crystallization should be

quite effective for separation of the p-isomer, the chief component, for it is known to be much higher melting, hence, should be less soluble. Ethyl alcohol proves to be a satisfactory solvent for the crystallization.

Calculation of the theoretical yield of the principal product, bromobenzene, is carried out in the usual manner, by calculating the maximum amount obtainable on the basis of the limiting reagent, if only bromobenzene is formed in the reaction. If desired, one can also calculate the theoretical yield of p-dibromobenzene as the maximum amount obtainable if it should be the only product of the reaction. Thus, percentage yields of each product can be calculated and reported.

Another method of preparing bromobenzene (Eq. 5) consists in treating

$$\underset{\text{Aniline}}{\underset{}{C_6H_5NH_2}} + HBr + HNO_2 \xrightarrow{0^\circ} \underset{\text{Benzenediazonium bromide}}{\underset{}{C_6H_5N_2Br}} + 2H_2O \tag{17-5}$$

$$\Big\downarrow \Delta \;\; CuBr$$

$$C_6H_5Br + N_2$$

aniline hydrobromide with nitrous acid to form benzenediazonium bromide, which is heated in the presence of cuprous bromide to form bromobenzene. This method is, of course, much more troublesome than direct bromination for the preparation of bromobenzene, but for more complicated compounds it is extremely useful. It is discussed in detail in Chap. 25.

Bromination of chlorobenzene is subject to the same considerations which have been discussed for bromination of benzene, except that the rate of reaction is slower. Chlorobenzene is brominated at about one-sixth the rate for benzene. The *main reaction* is shown in Eq. 6; further

$$C_6H_5Cl + Br_2 \xrightarrow[Fe]{80\text{-}90^\circ} \text{(p-bromochlorobenzene)} \;\; and \;\; \text{(o-bromochlorobenzene)} + HBr \tag{17-6}$$

bromination is a minor side reaction. The ratio of isomeric bromochlorobenzenes may be determined by glpc, and the more abundant *para* isomer may be separated by crystallization. For preparation of pure *o*-bromochlorobenzene by the diazotization route outlined in Eq. 5, refer to Chap. 25.

In addition to being prepared by methods quite different from those applied to the preparation of alkyl halides, the aromatic or aryl halides are also quite different in some of their reactions. An illustrative difference is their stability to ordinary alkaline hydrolysis. If bromobenzene is heated under reflux with aqueous alkali for several hours, the solution will not contain any bromide ion, whereas butyl bromide under the same conditions is hydrolyzed to a considerable extent. This marked difference in ease of hydrolysis may be used to distinguish alkyl from aryl halides.

EXPERIMENTAL PROCEDURES

Bromination of Benzene

An apparatus is assembled using the 500-ml flask (Note 1) with ground-glass center neck and side tubes. The center neck is attached to a reflux condenser, whose top is connected to a gas trap. The trap included in Fig. 8-1 may be used, but the large amount of hydrogen bromide evolved makes desirable the more efficient trap shown in Fig. 8-5. One side tube of the flask is fitted with a rubber connection for attachment of your smallest dropping (separatory) funnel, and the stem of this funnel is well lubricated with a drop of glycerol or a small amount of silicone grease (Note 2) so that it may be easily slipped into the side tube. The other side tube is closed with a short glass rod or sealed section of glass tubing. Make certain that the stopcock in the separatory funnel is lubricated carefully with silicone grease (Note 2) and works smoothly.

CAUTION. Bromine is very highly corrosive to the skin, and its vapors are highly obnoxious and dangerous. Be *especially cautious* always to keep the face in such a position that an accident will not result in bromine getting into the eyes. If bromine is spilled on the skin, it causes a painful burn that heals slowly unless it is washed off immediately. After immediate flooding of the area with water, scrub well with soap and water, and then apply glycerine. *Do not apply a burn ointment.* Grease facilitates the penetration of bromine into the flesh. If the washing is not done quickly enough to prevent a burn, report to the infirmary *immediately after* the thorough washing.

The reaction flask, with small separatory funnel attached, is unclamped and disconnected from the reflux condenser, then taken to the forced-draft hood where bromine is dispensed (Note 2). After 60 g (19 ml) of bromine has been placed in the properly prepared separatory funnel, the funnel is stoppered loosely by placing a strip of paper between the glass stopper and the ground surface. The flask is then returned to the desk, clamped in position, and charged with 33 g (40 ml) of benzene and 2–3 g of iron tacks or filings which have been previously etched with dilute hydrochloric acid and dried. Iron powder should *not* be used. After the condenser fitted with gas trap has been attached to the flask, 1–2 ml of bromine is allowed to flow into the benzene. If the reaction does not start after two or three minutes (as evidenced by evolution of HBr), the flask is warmed gently until reaction does start. After onset of the reaction, the remainder of the bromine is dropped in at such a rate that the reaction proceeds quietly (usually about a half-hour is required). When addition of bromine is complete, the mixture is warmed under reflux on a steam bath until the red vapors of bromine are no longer visible. Normally, this requires an additional half-hour.

After about 50 ml of water has been added to the cooled reaction mixture, it is shaken briefly in a separatory funnel, then the organic phase (which layer?) is separated. The organic layer is next washed with two portions of water, then indirectly steam-distilled from a 500-ml flask. The first fraction of steam distillate is collected until crystals of *p*-dibromobenzene begin to separate in the condenser tube. At this point, receivers are changed and the second fraction is collected until all the dibromobenzene has been distilled. Crystals are easily removed from the condenser by draining the water from the jacket before passage of steam is interrupted. Material that does not steam distill is rejected, and steam distillation should not be prolonged unduly because a slight cloudiness persists. Conditions have been adjusted to minimize dibromobenzene formation, so only a small amount should be anticipated.

Bromobenzene

From the first fraction of steam distillate, the heavy liquid is carefully separated in a separatory funnel and dried with 3–4 g of anhydrous calcium chloride. Drying is allowed to continue overnight or with frequent swirling until the liquid becomes clear. A small, round-bottomed flask is fitted with a fractionating column (Fig. 5-4), and the filtered mixture is distilled carefully. Benzene is collected, mostly at a boiling point of about 80°, then the heat input is increased until nearly all the benzene has been stripped out and bromobenzene is refluxing in the bottom of the column. At this point, the heat is temporarily removed and the column allowed to drain. The fractionating column is then replaced with a distilling head (Fig. 5-5), a new boiling chip is added, and the bromobenzene is collected in the range 150–160°. The actual boiling range is observed and reported. Any residue is added to the *p*-dibromobenzene obtained from the second fraction of steam distillate. The yield of bromobenzene is about 40 g.

p-Dibromobenzene

The solid *p*-dibromobenzene is removed from the second fraction of steam distillate by suction filtration and pressed as dry as possible on the funnel. (Thorough drying is not necessary, since water is miscible with ethanol, the solvent used for crystallization.) This solid is combined with the residue from the distillation of the bromobenzene, and the total is crystallized from ethanol. About 4 ml of ethanol is used per gram of material to be crystallized; if the solution is discolored, it is treated with a small amount of charcoal and filtered hot through a semifluted filter paper. The alcohol must not be heated over an open flame but in a bath of hot water after the flame has been extinguished, or on a steam bath. A flame may be used only if the alcohol is heated in a flask attached to a reflux condenser. After the solution has cooled to room temperature and crystallization has set in, cooling is continued for 10–15 minutes in an ice bath. The crystals are collected by suction filtration, pressed on the funnel with the flat surface of a glass stopper, and washed with two 2-ml portions of ice-cold ethanol. The wash solvent is first put into the flask and used to rinse out the last crystals, and the first wash is allowed to drain thoroughly before the second wash is used. The yield of recrystallized p-dibromobenzene is usually less than 2 g. After thorough drying, the melting point of the product is taken.

NOTES

1. If a flask with side tubes is not available, the reaction may be carried out in a 500-ml extraction flask. This flask has a sufficiently large neck that a cork may be bored to take both the condenser and the separatory funnel; however, a sound cork should be chosen, and it should be bored carefully. It is imperative that the apparatus be gas-tight so that bromine and hydrogen bromide will not escape into the laboratory. The flask is charged with the iron and benzene, then the cork with both condenser and separatory funnel attached is taken to the hood where bromine is dispensed. After bromine has been charged into the separatory funnel, the cork is seated carefully in the reaction flask.

2. Bromine tends to dissolve the stopcock grease in the separatory funnel, causing the stopcock to leak or stick. This may be prevented by the use of silicone stopcock grease; this is highly recommended. This stopcock grease is relatively expensive, and it should not be wasted nor used for purposes for which it is not needed. In order to make certain that the stopcock does not become dislodged, it should be held in place by a small rubber band placed over the stopcock, around the barrel of the stopcock, and back over the stopcock.

For safety, bromine should be measured either from a dispensing burette or a tilting dispenser. The latter device is especially convenient for such corrosive reagents as bromine, for no stopcock is involved. The flask with dispensing head is tilted in one direction to charge the desired volume (the pre-set capacity of the head), then it is tilted in the other direction to pour the charge into the vessel in which it is to be used.

Bromination of Chlorobenzene

The bromination is carried out in the apparatus described for bromination of benzene, using 60 g (19 ml) of bromine, 48 g (43.4 ml) of chlorobenzene, and 2–3 g of iron tacks or filings. The bromination procedure is the same except that the flask is heated on the steam bath before bromine addition is begun, and heating is continued during the addition. After all the bromine has been added, 0.5–1 hour of additional heating is required to discharge the bromine color.

After completion of the reaction, the warm, dark solution is poured into a separatory funnel containing 50 ml of water and 50 ml of benzene. The mixture is shaken for a minute or two (which discharges most of the color), then the organic phase (which layer?) is separated and washed with 50 ml of water. The washed organic phase is separated carefully, dried over 3–4 g of anhydrous calcium chloride, and distilled in a flask constructed from the 250-ml ground-jointed flask and distillation head (cf. Fig. 5-5). This gives a small amount of fractionation which would not be the case in an ordinary distilling flask. After much of the benzene solvent has been distilled, the boiling point will rise to that of chlorobenzene (b.p. 132°), then proceed to rise further as the small amount of remaining chlorobenzene distills. Careful distillation and fractionation of the low-boiling material are unnecessary. As the boiling point rises above that of chlorobenzene, at some point (usually in the range 140–160°) the content of *p*-bromochlorobenzene in the distillate will become sufficient to cause it to crystallize in the condenser. At this point, water is drained from the condenser, the steam line is connected to the condenser, and a new receiver is placed to catch the distillate. Distillation is continued, as steam is applied to the condenser whenever required to prevent its clogging. *Caution* must be exercised that clogging of the condenser does not occur, for this would give a closed system that would blow apart. The boiling point should rise fairly rapidly. At about 190°, receivers are changed again, using a tared flask, and the yield of bromochlorobenzene is collected over a range of about 10°. The weight of this product is determined, and reported as "crude" yield; about 0.1 g is reserved for glpc analysis.

The high-boiling intermediate fraction (except for 0.1 g reserved for glpc analysis) is combined with the final fraction, and the total is dissolved in about 50 ml (more or less as required) of hot 95% ethanol. Since the material has been distilled, a brilliantly clear solution should result. Crystallization is promoted by cooling to room temperature, then in an ice bath for 20–30 minutes. The crystals are collected, washed, and dried in the usual fashion. The filtrate from this first crop of crystals is distilled until its volume has been reduced to 35–40 ml. This residual hot solution is poured into an Erlenmeyer flask, then cooled to yield a second crop of crystals, which is collected in the usual manner. The weights and melting points of the two crops of crystals are determined, and the properly labeled products are turned in, after glpc analysis. The yield of *p*-bromochlorobenzene is in the range 55–65%.

Glpc Analysis

For glpc analysis of solids, an approximately 20% solution in benzene is prepared, if the substance is sufficiently soluble for that concentration, and enough of the solution is injected to give about 0.5 mg of the solute. Essentially all compounds that are solids will have sufficiently long retention times that the large amount of solvent will have cleared out of the column before the substance of interest appears. Of course the solvent peak will be off-scale unless a high attenuation is used. For analysis of the present materials on a 5-foot silicone column, c settings on the Carle instrument should give sufficiently good separation of the *ortho-* and *para-* bromochlorobenzenes. If the two peaks overlap, they may be extrapolated to baseline for estimation of area. Each tracing should be examined for chlorobenzene, as well as the isomeric bromochlorobenzenes. Analyze the following products (or those assigned):
1. High-boiling intermediate fraction.
2. Main fraction of distillate (b.p. > 190°).
3. First crop of crystallized product.
4. Second crop of crystallized product.
5. A sample of the mother liquor from the second crop.

Nitration

18

An important substitution reaction of aromatic compounds is nitration, replacement of a hydrogen by the nitro group ($-NO_2$). The importance of this reaction, especially in the benzene series, stems from at least three factors: the isomeric nitro compounds are relatively easily separated by fractional distillation, in contrast with most isomeric aromatic compounds; there is a minimal problem with disubstitution on account of the inactivating effect of a *meta*-director on rate of substitution in benzene; nitro is readily reduced to amino (cf. Chap. 20), which may be converted to numerous other groups (e.g., cf. Chap. 25).

The positive species active in nitration of benzene is the nitronium ion, $^+NO_2$, which is not the dominant ion formed when nitric acid ionizes in water. The nitronium ion is the principal nitrogen-containing cation when nitric acid ionizes in sulfuric acid solution (Eq. 1). Thus, in com-

$$HNO_3 + 2H_2SO_4 \rightleftarrows {}^+NO_2 + 2HSO_4^- + H_3O^+ \qquad (18\text{-}1)$$

pounds difficult to nitrate, sulfuric acid is an excellent solvent for the reaction. For especially difficult cases, fuming nitric and sulfuric acids may be used. For compounds more readily nitrated, acetic acid is a satisfactory solvent. For compounds very easily nitrated, where an extremely small concentration of the nitronium ion is permissible, or even desirable, aqueous nitric acid may be used. In the present chapter are included nitration of a compound rendered inert by presence of a *meta*-orienting substituent (nitrobenzene), by use of fuming nitric acid and concentrated sulfuric acid; nitration of unsubstituted benzene with concentrated nitric and sulfuric acids; and nitration of a highly reactive compound (phenol) with diluted nitric acid.

The net ionization shown in Eq. 1 may be profitably regarded as the addition of the two processes displayed in Eqs. 2 and 3. In Eq. 2 the reac-

$$HNO_3 + H_2SO_4 \rightleftarrows {}^+NO_2 + HSO_4^- + H_2O \qquad (18\text{-}2)$$

$$H_2SO_4 + H_2O \rightleftarrows H_3O^+ + HSO_4^- \qquad (18\text{-}3)$$

tion may be regarded as that between a base (nitric acid) and an acid (sulfuric acid) to give a salt and water. In turn, the water is consumed by ionization of a mole of sulfuric acid (Eq. 3). Since nitration of an aromatic compound results from attack of the nitronium ion (via an intermediate such as shown in Eq. 17-2) as in Eq. 4, it is convenient to write a net reac-

$$Ar{-}H + {}^+NO_2 \longrightarrow Ar{-}NO_2 + H^+ \qquad (18\text{-}4)$$

$$Ar{-}H + HNO_3 \xrightarrow{H_2SO_4} Ar{-}NO_2 + H_2O \qquad (18\text{-}5)$$

tion, which shows the stoichiometry, as in Eq. 5 (addition of Eqs. 2 and 4). Ionization of sulfuric acid (Eq. 3) is not involved in the stoichiometry, although it is important for removal of water and promotion of the ionization shown in Eq. 2.

The *main reaction* for preparation of *nitrobenzene* is given in Eq. 6.

$$\text{(benzene ring)} + HNO_3 \xrightarrow[H_2SO_4]{50\text{-}60^\circ} \text{(benzene ring)}{-}NO_2 + H_2O \qquad (18\text{-}6)$$

Although this reaction is not reversible, removal of water is necessary in order to prevent dilution of the nitric acid, as discussed above. The only side reaction is formation of *m*-dinitrobenzene (Eq. 7), which occurs at a

$$\text{(benzene ring)}{-}NO_2 + HNO_3 \xrightarrow{H_2SO_4} \text{(benzene ring)}{-}NO_2, NO_2 + H_2O \qquad (18\text{-}7)$$

slow rate under the conditions of the reaction.

It should be noted that the rate of substitution of the second nitro group is much slower than that of the first, also that this second group enters *meta* to the first. In halogenation (Chap. 17), dibromination was only slightly slower than monobromination, and the second bromine took a position *ortho* or *para* to the first. This strong inactivation of the nucleus is a characteristic effect of *meta*-orienting substituents. Another side reaction that might be suspected is sulfonation by the concentrated sulfuric acid (Chap. 19); however, this does not occur, for sulfonation of benzene is a reversible reaction, and nitration is not.

The nitrobenzene may be obtained in a pure condition by washing it with water to remove acid, then distilling. No fractionating equipment is needed, for nitrobenzene (b.p. 211°) boils about 130° above benzene and about 90° below the solid dinitrobenzene. Gas chromatography of a sample properly distilled in an ordinary distilling flask reveals no contamination with either benzene or dinitrobenzene.

For the preparation of *m-dinitrobenzene*, Eq. 7 becomes the *main reaction*. The conditions necessary are more drastic—fuming nitric acid and a temperature of 100°. Under these conditions, the *side reaction* becomes formation of 1,3,5-trinitrobenzene (Eq. 8); however, this reaction

$$\underset{NO_2}{\overset{NO_2}{\bigcirc}} + HNO_3 \ \underset{(fuming)}{\xrightarrow[100°]{H_2SO_4}} \ \underset{NO_2}{\overset{O_2N \qquad NO_2}{\bigcirc}} + H_2O \qquad (18\text{-}8)$$

takes place to only a very slight extent. To form appreciable amounts of 1,3,5-trinitrobenzene (TNB), it is necessary to heat the reaction mixture for several days at higher temperatures.

Purification is easily effected by crystallizing the crude product from ethanol. Although the trinitrobenzene is the less soluble, it is present in such small amounts that cooling to room temperature causes only the *m*-dinitrobenzene to crystallize, if the nitration was carried out properly.

The *nitration of phenol* results in a mixture of *o-* and *p-nitrophenols* as the *main products* (Eq. 9). In this case, the presence of a strong *ortho*,

$$\overset{OH}{\bigcirc} + HNO_3 \ \xrightarrow{20°} \ \underset{NO_2}{\overset{OH}{\bigcirc}} \text{ and } \underset{O_2N}{\overset{OH}{\bigcirc}} + H_2O \qquad (18\text{-}9)$$

para-orienting group (the hydroxyl)'makes further substitution extremely easy, and dilute nitric acid at 10–20° is sufficient to introduce the nitro group. In fact, the hydroxyl so labilizes the nucleus that it is frequently difficult to prevent more extensive substitution. For instance, when phenol is treated with aqueous bromine at room temperature, the only isolable product is 2,4,6-tribromophenol (Eq. 10). When it is recalled that

$$\overset{OH}{\bigcirc} + 3Br_2 \ \rightarrow \ \underset{Br}{\overset{Br}{\underset{Br}{\bigcirc}}}{}^{OH} + 3HBr \qquad (18\text{-}10)$$

a bromine has only a slight retarding influence on the reactivity of the nucleus, this reaction can be logically explained. In contrast, the marked general inactivation of the nucleus by the nitro group counterbalances the effect of the hydroxyl, and only a slight amount of dinitration takes place as a side reaction (Eq. 11). This dinitration product is mostly the 2,4-

$$(18\text{-}11)$$

isomer, but a small amount of the 2,6-isomer is found. No trinitrophenol is formed.

The hydroxyl group also makes the molecule much more susceptible to oxidation, and tarry oxidation products are formed by the action of the nitric acid. Controlling the temperature below 25° reduces this side reaction.

The *purification* problem in this experiment includes isolation of both the *ortho* and *para* isomers. First, the excess nitric acid is separated and the organic layer steam-distilled. The *ortho* isomer is quite volatile with steam and is readily obtained pure by filtering the distillate and crystallizing the yellow solid from an alcohol-water mixture. The *para* isomer, on the other hand, is completely nonvolatile with steam and remains behind with most of the dinitro compounds and the tarry oxidation products. Since the dinitro isomers are also *ortho* nitrophenols, they are somewhat steam-volatile. However, the small amount in the distillate is removed by the crystallization.

Obviously, the explanation for this vivid difference in steam volatility between *ortho* and *para* isomers must lie in the geometry of the molecules, since they differ only in the proximity of the nitro to the hydroxyl group. In the *ortho* isomer, the hydrogen is held *between* one oxygen in the nitro group and the oxygen attached to the aromatic ring. Such a structure is described as *chelated*, and the resultant ring is termed a *chelate ring*. This type of bonding is similar to hydrogen bonding in the sense that the hydrogen is effectively bound to two oxygens; however, hydrogen bonding is a polar attraction directed in line with the oxygen-hydrogen bond. As the second oxygen is held to one side of the line extending along the oxygen-hydrogen bond direction, the strength of the hydrogen bonding is reduced. In *o*-nitrophenol, it is apparent (formula A) that classical hydrogen bonding must be insignificant, for the second oxygen is far out of line with the oxygen-hydrogen bond direction. A more adequate explanation attributes the stability of the chelate ring to electron delocalization, as indicated in

(A)   (B)   (C)

the resonance forms B and C. The resultant lowering of energy would tend to hold the *o*-nitrophenol in the chelated form, and this in turn would prevent intermolecular hydrogen bonding, either with water or another molecule of nitrophenol. This would increase the volatility of the *ortho* isomer and, more importantly, decrease its solubility in water. Thus, the insoluble, more volatile *ortho* isomer steam-distills readily, while the *para* isomer remains behind in solution in the hot water. Essentially none of the soluble, less volatile nitrophenol fractionally distills in water solution.

By filtering the hot residual solution from steam distillation through filter aid, most of the tarry material is removed. The *p*-nitrophenol is then further purified by formation of its sodium salt with sodium hydroxide and crystallization of the salt from water after the addition of sodium chloride. Recrystallization yields the pure sodium *p*-nitrophenolate from which the free phenol is obtained by acidification and crystallization from water.

There are *two alternative methods of preparation*, both of which introduce the hydroxyl group as the last step. In one, the corresponding nitroaniline is prepared and the amino group then replaced by hydroxyl (Eq. 12). This method of preparing phenols is discussed in detail in Chap. 25.

$$(18\text{-}12)$$

The second method takes advantage of the fact that aryl halides in which the halogen is *ortho* or *para* to a nitro group are exceptions to the usual rule and can be hydrolyzed with aqueous alkali to the nitrophenol (Eq. 13). The latter method is used for the commercial preparation of nitrophenols.

$$(18\text{-}13)$$

EXPERIMENTAL PROCEDURES

Nitrobenzene

To 195 g (110 ml) of concentrated sulfuric acid in a 250-ml flask, 120 g (85 ml) of concentrated nitric acid is added in portions with shaking and cooling. After this mixture has been cooled to room temperature, it is placed in a 250-ml separatory funnel supported on a padded ring. In a 500-ml Erlenmeyer flask is placed 65 g (75 ml) of benzene, and to this is added about 20 ml of the mixed acid. A thermometer is placed in the reaction mixture in the flask and left there during the nitration. The mixture is agitated by swirling, and when the temperature has risen to 50°, the flask is cooled in a pan of water sufficiently to maintain the temperature at 50–60°. When the exothermic reaction has abated somewhat, another portion of mixed acid is added; this process is continued until all the acid has been added (usually 30–40 minutes). After addition is complete, swirling is continued without cooling until the temperature drops to 40° (about 5 minutes). At the end of this period, the flask is cooled, the contents transferred to a separatory funnel, and the lower layer of mixed acid drawn off. The organic layer is washed with 100 ml of water, 100 ml of 0.5N sodium hydroxide, and another 100 ml of water. The aqueous washings (which layer?) are discarded. After the nitrobenzene is transferred to an Erlenmeyer flask, it is dried by adding about 10 g of calcium chloride and warming in a water bath with swirling until the original cloudiness has disappeared. The dried liquid is filtered into a 125-ml distilling flask and distilled. The boiling point rises rapidly, and the product is collected at 205–212°. If drying was incomplete, the first distillate is cloudy and should be collected separately for re-drying. *It is important not to distill quite to dryness, as the residue (mostly m-dinitrobenzene) may decompose violently if heated much above the boiling point of the nitrobenzene.* The yield is about 85–88 g.

Gas chromatography of this product may be accomplished on a 5-foot silicone column at D settings on the Carle instrument. Retention times have been observed as 26 seconds for benzene, 2 minutes 10 seconds for nitrobenzene, 7 minutes 44 seconds for *m*-dinitrobenzene.

m-Dinitrobenzene

In a 125-ml Erlenmeyer flask is placed 14 ml (25 g) of concentrated sulfuric acid, and to this is added *cautiously* 10 ml (15 g) of *fuming* nitric acid. To this mixture is added (in the hood), during about 5 minutes, 8 ml (9.6 g) of nitrobenzene. During the addition the flask is cooled in water sufficiently to prevent the temperature from rising above 50°, and the flask is swirled constantly. Toward the end of the addition the mixture separates into two phases. After addition is complete, the flask is placed in a cold-water bath, and the water is heated to boiling in the course of 5–10 minutes. Heating is then continued on the boiling-water bath for 10 minutes. During the heating period the flask is swirled frequently.

At the end of the heating period the flask is cooled in water to about room temperature, and then the reaction mixture is poured slowly into 200 ml of cold water with continuous stirring. The flask is rinsed with a little water, and this is added to the main portion. The finely divided dinitrobenzene is collected by suction filtration and washed thoroughly with water (at least 200 ml). The moist product is then dissolved in 30–35 ml of hot 95% alcohol in a 125-ml Erlenmeyer flask. Heating of the alcohol over an open flame must be avoided unless the flask is attached to a reflux condenser. It is convenient to heat a pan of water to boiling, extinguish the burner, and then heat the alcohol in the hot water if a steam bath is not available. When the crude dinitrobenzene is completely in solution, the flask is removed from the bath, corked loosely, and allowed to stand without artificial cooling or agitation. The product separates as long flat needles. After the solution has cooled to room temperature, it is allowed to stand for about 30 minutes; then the mass of crystals is broken up with a stirring rod and collected by suction filtration. For washing the crystals with two or three *small* portions of cold alcohol, the wash solvent is first put into the flask and used to rinse out the last traces of crystals. The product should be practically colorless. After the crystals have been dried, the melting point is determined. Pure *m*-dinitrobenzene melts at 90°. The average yield is 8–10 g.

o- and *p*-Nitrophenol

To a 500-ml Erlenmeyer (or round-bottomed) flask are added 60 g (42 ml) of concentrated nitric acid and 145 ml of water. A thermometer is placed in the liquid, which is cooled to about 10°. From a separatory funnel, supported above the flask, is then added dropwise and continuously, during about 20 minutes, a mixture of 35 g of phenol *(CAUTION! Corrosive and poisonous)* and 10 ml of water. (This mixture is obtained from the stock room.) During the addition the temperature is kept at 10–20° by swirling and external cooling if necessary. After addition is complete, the mixture is allowed to stand at room temperature for 1 hour, with frequent swirling, and cooling if necessary to keep the mixture below 25°. At the end of this time, the tarry mixture is poured into a separatory funnel and allowed to stand for a few minutes. Next the lower layer is carefully drawn off into a 500-ml round-bottomed flask that has been fitted for indirect steam distillation. After most of the lower layer has been drawn off, it is important to swirl the funnel gently and allow a minute or two for the oil to drain from the sides of the flask before the final careful separation of the layers. To the flask is added 20 ml of water, and the contents are steam-distilled by indirect steam distillation as rapidly as possible. Care must be taken that the condenser does not become plugged (see "Steam Distillation," p. 69). Steam distillation is continued until the yellow *o*-

nitrophenol ceases to distill or until a 100-ml portion of steam distillate yields less than 0.5 g of insoluble material.

Isolation of *o*-Nitrophenol

The steam distillate is cooled in water, and the crystallizate collected by suction filtration. The crystals are dissolved in 75 ml of 95% ethanol at about 40° (*USING HOT WATER or STEAM BATH, NO FLAMES!*); at this temperature water is added until the solution becomes cloudy, followed by alcohol until it becomes clear again. On cooling, *o*-nitrophenol crystallizes as yellow needles. If the substance tends to separate as an oil, a stirring rod is dipped into the solution, withdrawn, and the product allowed to crystallize as the solvent evaporates from the rod. The solution may then be "seeded" by dipping the stirring rod into it. Scratching the inside of the vessel with the stirring rod just above the liquid is sometimes helpful. It is very important that the substance not separate as an oil, which later crystallizes. The impurities become dissolved in the oil and thus appear in the crystals. If "oiling out" persists, it may be necessary to add a little more ethanol. After crystallization is well under way, the solution is cooled, without shaking, in an ice-salt bath for at least 30 minutes. The yellow needles are collected by suction filtration, washed with a little ice-cold 75% aqueous alcohol, and sucked as dry as possible on the funnel, after pressing down with the bottom of a small beaker. The air-drying process should not be prolonged more than two days (one day is preferable), and the product should not be dried in an oven, since it is rather volatile and is lost at an appreciable rate by sublimation. After the product is dry, the melting point and weight are taken. The average yield is 9–11 g.

Isolation of Sodium *p*-Nitrophenolate

To the residual mixture from steam distillation, 100 ml of water is added. After the mixture has been heated at the boiling point for a few minutes, it is filtered by suction through a Büchner funnel that contains 10–15 g of wet filter aid (for preparation of a filter-aid mat, see Chap. 14, Notes 2, 3, and 4). The vessel and filter aid are washed with a little hot water. To the dark filtrate, transferred to a 500-ml Erlenmeyer flask, are added 20 ml of 12N sodium hydroxide and 20 g of clean sodium chloride. The solution is concentrated over a burner (care against frothing!) until crystallization of sodium *p*-nitrophenolate from the boiling solution begins. After the concentrated solution has been cooled in water to room temperature, the crystals are collected by suction filtration and washed with saline solution (two parts saturated sodium chloride and one part water). For recrystallization, the light brown crystals are dissolved in about 150 ml of hot water, and 20 g of clean salt is dissolved in the dark red solution. If the solution is not clear, it is filtered hot; then crystallization is carried out as previously described. After the product has been collected and washed with salt solution, it is washed with 10 ml of 95% ethanol and 25 ml of ether (*CAUTION! NO FLAMES!*). After the salt has been dried on the filter for a few minutes, it may be weighed. It should be a dark golden yellow. The average yield is 10–12 g.

Isolation of *p*-Nitrophenol

For isolation of *p*-nitrophenol, the above salt is dissolved in about 200 ml of warm water (if the yield of salt was not 10–12 g, the amounts of reagents are adjusted proportionately), and 10 ml of concentrated hydrochloric acid is added. (Why does the color change?) A small amount of charcoal is added to the warm solution, which is then filtered by gravity. The clear filtrate is cooled with seeding, as described above. If an oil tends to separate even after some crystals have separated, the solution is warmed very slightly. If necessary, a little more water is added. This is a slow and difficult crystallization. After the solution has cooled to room temperature and considerable crystallization has occurred (standing overnight is satisfactory), the solution is cooled in an ice-salt bath for an hour, as care is taken not to freeze out water. The product, which should be nearly white, is collected, washed with ice water, and dried. The average yield is 7–9 g.

Calculate the theoretical yield of nitrophenols and report the actual and percentage yields of *o*-nitrophenol and *p*-nitrophenol.

Sulfonation

19

Another characteristic substitution reaction of aromatic systems is sulfonation, in which a hydrogen atom attached to the aromatic nucleus is replaced by the sulfonic acid group, $-SO_3H$. This substitution is nearly always accomplished with sulfuric acid. The mechanism which supplies the positive sulfonium ion is probably analogous to that shown in Eq. 18-1, but involving three moles of sulfuric acid. By varying the temperature and concentration of the acid, suitable conditions can be attained for sulfonating a large variety of compounds differing greatly in their reactivity. For example, phenol is readily sulfonated by dilute acid, whereas benzene requires fuming sulfuric acid. In contrast to bromination and nitration—the two typical aromatic substitution reactions discussed previously—sulfonation is a reversible process. The considerations involved in obtaining a good yield of sulfonic acid will be examined in detail in the case of toluene.

The *main reaction* for the preparation of *p-toluenesulfonic acid* is shown in Eq. 1. Actually, the product is isolated as the sodium salt so that

$$\text{CH}_3\text{-C}_6\text{H}_5 + H_2SO_4 \underset{(HO-SO_2-OH)}{\overset{85-95°}{\rightleftharpoons}} HO_3S\text{-C}_6\text{H}_4\text{-CH}_3 + H_2O \qquad (19\text{-}1)$$

Eq. 3 represents part of the main reaction. In addition to the desired *para* compound, the other two monosulfonation products, the *ortho* and *meta* isomers, are formed in small amount. Another *side reaction* is disulfonation, which occurs to only a very slight extent under the conditions of the experiment. For the *para* and *ortho* isomers, which constitute nearly all the

188

product, disulfonation takes the course shown in Eq. 2. Of course the toluene-2,6-disulfonic acid is formed in very small amount.

$$\text{(19-2)}$$

An inspection of the main and side reactions reveals that there are three factors that must be taken into account in formulating means for maximizing the yield of p-toluenesulfonic acid: (1) the reversibility of the reaction, (2) the distribution of monosulfonation products among the o-, m-, and p-isomers, and (3) the degree of disulfonation.

Considering first the reversibility of the reaction, it is obvious that in order to drive the sulfonation more completely to the right, the water must be removed as it is formed. This could be accomplished by a distillation process, but, at the same time, unsulfonated toluene would also be removed because of its steam volatility. Thus, a special apparatus would be required so that the distillate could be separated into its components and the toluene returned to the reaction flask. In some cases, this is actually done, but only when the expense of the aromatic starting material justifies this complication. In the present case, it is more economical to accept the lower yield. Another possible scheme for water removal would be to use fuming sulfuric acid (containing sulfur trioxide), and thus convert any water to sulfuric acid, but then the initial acid concentration would be sufficiently high to cause a serious amount of disulfonation.

The second factor, the relative amounts of o-, m-, and p-isomers, has been found to be a function of the temperature of sulfonation. Since orientation is controlled by the methyl group, which is a moderately strong o-, p-director, the quantity of m-isomer is always quite small. By careful analysis of mixtures sulfonated at various temperatures, it has been found that higher temperatures favor the p-isomer, so the present sulfonation is carried out at about 85–95°.

Higher temperatures might be even more favorable toward formation of the p-isomer, but here the third factor, disulfonation, enters into the picture. At higher temperatures, disulfonation would become appreciable; therefore, 85–95° is chosen as the optimum temperature for maximizing the production of the p-toluenesulfonic acid. In addition to temperature control, frequent and thorough mixing of the toluene and sulfuric acid layers is an aid in decreasing disulfonation. Without this mixing, contact between the two reactants would be much less intimate, and the reaction would require a longer period of time. The sulfonic acid, being soluble in sulfuric acid, is continuously exposed to further sulfonation. Thus, reducing the duration of the reaction helps suppress disulfonation.

After the most favorable conditions for the formation of *p*-toluenesulfonic acid have been established, the next problem is to isolate the product in a pure form. Like most sulfonic acids, the product is a nonvolatile solid and cannot be distilled. Also, extraction is of no use because of its high solubility in water. This water-solubility makes direct crystallization from water quite wasteful; however, in some instances it has been used to obtain the free sulfonic acid. In these cases, filtrations must be carried out with sintered-glass filters, since the free acid is comparable in strength to sulfuric acid and rapidly attacks filter paper.

Because of the considerations above, most sulfonic acids are isolated in the form of a salt. With the present compound, this is accomplished conveniently through the *sodium p-toluenesulfonate.* When sodium chloride is added to the reaction product, the equilibrium shown in Eq. 3 is established. This is possible because the sulfonic acid and hydrochloric acid are of comparable strength. Sodium chloride, of course, does not lead to salt formation with a carboxylic acid because in this case the weaker, less dissociated organic acid causes the equilibrium to lie far to the left. The

$$HO_3S{-}\langle\rangle{-}CH_3 + NaCl \rightleftharpoons NaO_3S{-}\langle\rangle{-}CH_3 + HCl \qquad (19\text{-}3)$$

$$H_2SO_4 + NaCl \rightleftharpoons NaHSO_4 + HCl \qquad (19\text{-}4)$$

unreacted sulfuric acid also forms some salt (Eq. 4), as do all the other sulfonic acids present.

Addition of a large excess of sodium chloride will then cause the least soluble substance to precipitate due to the common ion (sodium) effect, and this proves to be the sodium *p*-toluenesulfonate. The same result could be attained with sodium hydroxide, but the concentrations necessary to produce the desired sodium-ion strength would result in a very strongly alkaline solution with the concomitant difficulties in filtration. Recrystallization from a sodium chloride solution followed by washing with ethanol (to remove water) and drying affords pure sodium *p*-toluenesulfonate.

An alternative method for sulfonating aromatic compounds is with chlorosulfonic acid. In a number of instances this is preferable to the use of fuming sulfuric acid since it results in less oxidative breakdown. This method is especially useful if the sulfonyl chloride is desired, for this derivative may be isolated directly from the chlorosulfonation reaction (cf. Chap. 21).

EXPERIMENTAL PROCEDURE

Sodium *p*-Toluenesulfonate

To a 125-ml Erlenmeyer flask provided with an air condenser are added 11 ml (9.3 g) of toluene (sulfur-free) and 10 ml (18.5 g) of c.p. (chemically pure) concentrated sulfuric acid. The mixture is heated in a boiling-water bath or on a steam bath, with frequent vigorous shaking, as care is taken not to get acid on the cork. The ground-jointed equipment is quite useful here. When all the toluene has reacted (about one-half hour), as indicated by a homogeneous solution, the mixture is poured slowly, with stirring, into a beaker containing 75 ml of water. After 25 g of well-ground sodium chloride has been added, the beaker is covered with a watch glass and heated until all the salt has dissolved. The hot solution is filtered by gravity into an Erlenmeyer flask, and the filtrate is cooled to induce crystallization of the sodium *p*-toluenesulfonate. Supersaturation (cf. Chap. 3) is very common in this crystallization, and scratching the wall of the flask at the surface of the liquid may be needed to induce crystallization. After crystallization begins, the flask is allowed to stand for at least one-half hour at room temperature, then the crystals are collected by suction filtration. Some of the filtrate is used to transfer the last of the crystals onto the Büchner funnel. After the filter cake has been pressed well with the bottom of a small beaker, it is washed with 15–20 ml of ethanol. Drying of the crystals may be accelerated, if desired, by placing them on a watch glass over a radiator or steam bath.

If the product is discolored, or its form indicates presence of large amounts of sodium chloride, it should be purified by recrystallization. For this purpose, the material is dissolved in 30 ml of water, 10 g of ground sodium chloride is added, and solution is effected by heating and stirring. A very little more water may be added if necessary. The solution is stirred with about 0.5 g of decolorizing carbon, then filtered by gravity. The minimum amount of hot water is used as a rinse for the flask and funnel (see Chap. 3). Concentration of the clear filtrate to about 30–35 ml and cooling gives 6–8 g of crystals, collected and dried as described above. This product is sodium *p*-toluenesulfonate dihydrate, so the theoretical yield should be calculated on the basis of this formula.

Reduction of Nitro Compounds

20

The reduction of nitro compounds is a very important synthetic process, especially in the aromatic series, for it constitutes the principal source of aromatic primary amines. The amino group, in turn, may be converted to various other substituents, as illustrated in part by the procedures in Chap. 25. The nitro group may be reduced to amino in a surprisingly large number of ways. These include catalytic hydrogenation, electrolytic reduction, and reduction by chemical agents in either acid or alkaline solution. Although catalytic hydrogenation is probably the most widely used process, chemical reduction in acid solution is also a very important method. The chemical reduction employed in the present chapter, which is carried out under weakly acidic conditions, offers the advantage of limiting side reactions to a minimum.

The reduction of nitro to amino has been shown to proceed through several intermediates, and the sequence of intermediates in acid solution is rather different from that in basic solution.[1] Certain of these intermediates, which are discussed below in connection with side reactions, have some importance and may be obtained, under suitable conditions, as the principal end products of the reaction. For example, N-phenylhydroxylamine (cf. Eq. 4) may be obtained in moderately good yield by chemical reduction with zinc and aqueous ammonium chloride solution. The very

---

[1]Although some comment on intermediate reduction products is included in the present discussion, in connection with the consideration of side reactions, a more adequate treatment of this interesting topic should be sought in elementary textbooks for lecture courses in organic chemistry.

unstable[2] *N*-phenylhydroxylamine is used chiefly for rearrangement to *p*-aminophenol (Eq. 6). Electrolytic reduction, in which the extent of reduction may be determined by control of cathode potential, is quite useful for obtaining intermediate reduction products in many sequences. In Chap. 39 is illustrated the preparation of an *N*-phenylhydroxylamine by electrolytic reduction in acid solution, under which conditions the rearrangement to the desired *p*-aminophenol proceeds immediately.

It should be emphasized that, although the steps in a sequence such as that in Eq. 4 may proceed at different rates, it is also the case that the product obtained depends on the strength of the reducing agent. For example, reduction of nitrobenzene with tin and hydrochloric acid gives aniline, and it is not possible to isolate significant amounts of *N*-phenylhydroxylamine, even if less than an equivalent amount of reducing agent is used. On the other hand, reduction with zinc and ammonium chloride gives *N*-phenylhydroxylamine, and no aniline is obtained, even if a large excess of reducing agent is used. This effect applies to oxidations and reductions and can be very useful in synthesis. The key factor is the opportunity to control the intensity of the oxidation or reduction by use of different reagents to supply the oxidizing or reducing power. Such an effect cannot be secured in other types of reactions such as additions to multiple bonds or displacement reactions, for there is no opportunity to selectively control the intensity of a given addition or displacement reaction. In these latter types of reactions, an intermediate product can be obtained in satisfactory yield only if the second step is slower than the first. Such a situation is discussed in Chap. 13 (cf. Eqs. 13-4, 13-5). A preparation in which an intermediate product is actually isolated is described in Chap. 35 (6-chlorohexanenitrile).

The *preparation of aniline* is accomplished by reducing nitrobenzene with iron powder in the presence of a small amount of hydrochloric acid. As with other organic oxidation-reduction reactions, the equation is most conveniently balanced by adding the necessary number of hydrogen atoms (Eq. 1) and then considering the source of this reducing power. In this case,

$$\text{C}_6\text{H}_5\text{NO}_2 + 6[\text{H}] \rightarrow \text{C}_6\text{H}_5\text{NH}_2 + 2\text{H}_2\text{O} \qquad (20\text{-}1)$$

the reducing action is supplied by iron according to Eq. 2, which is the sum of (a), (b), and (c). The hydrochloric acid serves to initiate the reaction

---

[2]This hydroxylamine is so unstable that it alters rapidly on storage at room temperature, even in absence of air. At 100°, there is an almost instantaneous disproportionation to an equimolar mixture of nitrosobenzene and aniline.

$$Fe \quad + 2H^+ \quad \rightarrow Fe^{++} \quad + 2[H] \qquad (a)$$

$$Fe^{++} \quad + H^+ \quad \rightarrow Fe^{+++} \quad + [H] \qquad (b) \qquad (20\text{-}2)$$

$$Fe^{+++} + 3H_2O \rightarrow Fe(OH)_3 + 3H^+ \qquad (c)$$

$$Fe \quad + 3H_2O \rightarrow Fe(OH)_3 + 3[H]$$

by giving ferrous ion and two hydrogens (a). In the presence of a hydrogen-acceptor (nitrobenzene), the ferrous ion is oxidized to ferric (b), and the latter, by hydrolysis, forms ferric hydroxide and hydrogen ions. Thus the acid consumed in (a) and (b) is regenerated by (c), and the over-all effect (Eq. 2) is the consumption of iron and water. This affords a very economical process for carrying out the reduction, and only a small amount of acid is required. The main reaction is then the sum of Eqs. 1 and 2 (Eq. 3).

$$+ 2Fe + 4H_2O \xrightarrow{H^+} \qquad + 2Fe(OH)_3 \qquad (20\text{-}3)$$

The reduction proceeds through a series of intermediates as shown in Eq. 4. Nitrosobenzene, the first intermediate, cannot be prepared by a

$$\xrightarrow{2[H]} \qquad \xrightarrow{2[H]} \qquad \xrightarrow{2[H]} \qquad (20\text{-}4)$$

Nitrosobenzene   N-Phenylhydroxylamine

chemical reduction of nitrobenzene because it is much more rapidly reduced than the latter in all processes that have been investigated; however, its presence in the reduction sequence has been rather well established. The occurrence of these intermediates in the reaction mixture is responsible for two *side reactions*, neither of which is significant in the weakly acid solution that is employed.

One sequence of side reactions results from the condensation of nitrosobenzene and aniline, as shown in Eq. 5. The initial product, azobenzene, is further reduced to hydrazobenzene, which is rearranged to the final

$$+ \rightarrow H_2O +$$

Azobenzene

$$\downarrow 2[H] \qquad (20\text{-}5)$$

$$\xleftarrow{H^+}$$

Benzidine   Hydrazobenzene

product, benzidine. This sequence of reactions is minor in acid solution, for the initial condensation is quite slow in acid. In basic solution, this condensation is quite rapid, and aniline may be obtained eventually by further reduction of hydrazobenzene. Proper choice of an alkaline reducing agent will yield either azobenzene or hydrazobenzene as the final product. Benzidine, of use as a dye intermediate, is obtained industrially by rearrangement of hydrazobenzene.

The second side reaction also involves a rearrangement, as illustrated in Eq. 6. This reaction is suppressed by the weakly acidic conditions but may become the main reaction under strongly acidic conditions (cf. Chap. 39).

$$\text{C}_6\text{H}_5\text{NHOH} \xrightarrow{\text{H}^+} \text{HO-C}_6\text{H}_4\text{-NH}_2 \qquad (20\text{-}6)$$

The *purification* problem thus becomes that of separating aniline from small amounts of nitrobenzene (unreduced because of the coating of the iron by ferric hydroxide), benzidine, and *p*-aminophenol. Since the aniline is present in part as the water-soluble, nonvolatile hydrochloride, the reaction mixture is first made distinctly alkaline and then steam-distilled. The *p*-aminophenol, now present as the soluble sodium phenolate, will remain in the residue along with the high molecular weight, nonvolatile benzidine and inorganic material. To separate the nitrobenzene from the aniline in the steam distillate, the aniline is converted to the water-soluble hydrochloride by adding hydrochloric acid. The neutral nitrobenzene remains unaffected by this addition of acid, and direct steam distillation removes it in the volatile fraction. The aqueous residue, now containing only aniline hydrochloride, is basified and the liberated aniline is extracted into benzene. Sodium hydroxide pellets are used to dry the benzene solution, which is then decanted and distilled to give pure aniline as the high-boiling fraction.

Aniline, being an organic base, has the property of forming salts with acids. It should be noted that the water-solubility of such salts is utilized to good advantage in the above purification. In addition, since there are hydrogen atoms on the nitrogen in aniline, it will form amides with acid derivatives such as acid chlorides, acid anhydrides, and esters (cf. Chap. 13). When a sulfonyl chloride is used, the product is a sulfonamide, which is an important type of compound. In addition to the uses of sulfonamides in synthesis and as therapeutic agents (cf. Chap. 21), they may also function as derivatives for the characterization of amines, for they are nearly always easily crystallized solids (cf. Chap. 30). The sulfonamides can also serve to distinguish among and to separate primary, secondary, and tertiary amines (cf. the Hinsberg procedure, Chap. 30).

Although aromatic nitro compounds may be reduced to the corresponding amines by numerous reagents, as has been mentioned, primary aromatic amines are rarely obtained by *other methods of preparation.* Occasionally, it is convenient to prepare an aromatic amine from the corresponding carboxylic acid. This can be accomplished by treatment of the amide of the acid with sodium hypobromite, according to the net reaction shown in Eq. 7. The mechanism of this remarkable conversion, known as the Hofmann hypobromite reaction, is rather well understood and is discussed in lecture texts on organic chemistry.

$$R-C \overset{O}{\underset{NH_2}{\diagdown}} + NaOBr \rightarrow R-NH_2 + CO_2 + NaBr \qquad (20\text{-}7)$$

EXPERIMENTAL PROCEDURE

Aniline

To a 500-ml round-bottomed flask are added 30 g of iron powder, 25 g (21 ml) of nitrobenzene, and 75 ml of water; then a reflux condenser is attached. Through the top of the condenser is added 0.5 ml of concentrated hydrochloric acid, and the mixture is shaken vigorously. If an exothermic reaction does not ensue within a few minutes, the flask is heated carefully with a small flame. When the reaction has started, the flame is withdrawn, and shaking is continued until the reaction has moderated. If the reaction becomes so vigorous as to threaten getting out of control, the flask is cooled briefly in a pan of water. If the iron powder is not of a good grade (Note 1), there may be no exothermic reaction. After the initial reaction has subsided, another 0.5-ml portion of concentrated hydrochloric acid is added and the mixture shaken as before. When the exothermic reaction has subsided, the mixture is heated to boiling under reflux with a small flame. After 15 minutes an additional 1-ml portion of concentrated hydrochloric acid is added; heating is continued for about 45 minutes after this addition. If the reaction was not exothermic at the beginning, the heating period should be extended to at least 1½ hours.

At the end of the heating period, 2 ml of 12N sodium hydroxide is added to the reaction mixture, then it is indirectly steam-distilled until no more immiscible liquid collects. This point is tested by collecting a portion of distillate separately in a test tube. The distillate may continue to run slightly cloudy, but when no oily droplets are visible in the test tube, distillation is discontinued (Note 2). To the distillate is added 17 ml of concentrated hydrochloric acid, and the distillate is heated to boiling, while being mixed. If any water-insoluble nitrobenzene is present (Note 3), the mixture is *directly* steam-distilled until a clear solution, free from oil, remains in the distilling flask. Since nitrobenzene is somewhat toxic, this mixture must be distilled, using a condenser, *not merely boiled in an open flask.*

The acidic solution is made alkaline with sodium hydroxide (*CAU-TION! Heat evolution*) in order to liberate the aniline from its salt. In the mixture is dissolved 25 g of clean sodium chloride per 100 ml of solution (Note 4); the mixture is cooled somewhat and transferred to a separatory funnel; then the aniline is extracted with two 40-ml portions of benzene. The water is separated carefully from each extract. The combined extracts are dried with a few sodium hydroxide pellets until the solution becomes clear; then it is carefully decanted into a 125-ml distilling flask from which the benzene is distilled with a small flame. (*CAUTION! Benzene is highly inflammable.*) After most of the benzene has been distilled, the mole fraction of aniline becomes sufficiently high that the distillate contains enough aniline so that the boiling point rises above that of benzene. As the temperature rises rapidly to the boiling point of aniline, the small intermediate fraction should be distilled slowly in order to keep loss of aniline to a minimum. If this fraction is properly distilled, it is so small that its redistillation is hardly worthwhile. The aniline is collected at 180–185°, and the average yield is about 15 g (Note 5). The product is usually nearly colorless immediately after distillation but will darken on standing. Darkening is due to air oxidation to quinonoid-type compounds of high molecular weight. Dark samples of aniline are often redistilled from a pinch of zinc dust before use in chemical reactions.

NOTES

1. Unless the iron powder is finely divided and free of an oxide coating, poor results are obtained in this reduction. The importance of a large surface for attack in the heterogeneous reaction is magnified by the fact that the iron tends to become coated with the sludgy ferric hydroxide. The grade of iron powder termed "reduced with hydrogen" is recommended, and it should be stored in tightly closed bottles.

2. The flask in which the reduction was carried out, and from which steam distillation is usually done, is likely to become coated with ferric oxide. This oxide is removed with difficulty, whether by scrubbing or use of acid, but if a little concentrated hydrochloric acid and a small piece of mossy zinc are heated in the flask, the iron is reduced to the ferrous state and is readily dissolved by the hot acid.

3. The principal factor determining the amount of unreduced nitrobenzene is the quality of the iron powder (cf. Note 1). Sometimes there is no nitrobenzene observed at this point, so the distillation is unnecessary. If only a few drops are

present, it may be removed by filtration through a previously wetted filter paper (cf. Chap. 14, page 144).

4. Since aniline has appreciable solubility in water, its extraction is facilitated by addition of an electrolyte to the water. Organic compounds (except salts) are covalent, therefore are much less soluble in water containing a high concentration of an electrolyte. Even organic salts are less soluble in concentrated solutions of electrolytes (cf. Chap. 19).

5. Purification of a base via its water-soluble salt is so effective in removing nonbasic compounds that aniline purified in this way should be an excellent sample. Gas chromatography on silicone may be used to assess the effectiveness of the distillation in removing the benzene used as solvent.

Sulfanilamides

21

A rather large number of sulfanilamides, commonly known as "sulfa drugs," have been prepared for the study of their chemotherapeutic activity, and some of them became our most effective bacteriostatic agents for several years. Following World War II, introduction of the so-called "antibiotics" (antibacterial agents made by microorganisms) caused a sharp reduction in use of the more toxic sulfa drugs; however, certain infections have continued to be controlled by sulfa drugs more effectively than by other agents. The most simple sulfa drug, which may be regarded as the parent compound to the more elaborate ones, is p-aminobenzene-sulfonamide, usually called sulfanilamide. The sulfa drugs contain both

p-Aminobenzenesulfonamide (sulfanilamide)

an amino nitrogen (4) and an amido nitrogen (1). In the present chapter, we shall discuss the preparation of sulfanilamide as well as that of sulfa-thiazole, the analogous compound in which one of the hydrogens on the amido nitrogen is replaced by the thiazole group.

An obvious way to prepare various sulfanilamides would be to allow p-aminobenzenesulfonyl chloride to react with ammonia or the appropriate primary or secondary amine; however, this is not possible because the necessary sulfonyl chloride cannot exist as such. It would immediately react with the free amino group in the *para* position of another molecule, and a chain polymer would result. Therefore, it is necessary to "protect" the *p*-amino group so that it will not interfere by reacting with the sulfonyl chloride. After the sulfonamide has been formed, the protecting group is removed to give the free amine. This is a common procedure when carrying out reactions on difunctional molecules in which the functional groups are reactive towards each other. It is necessary, of course, that the protecting device be so chosen that removing it does not alter the other modifications introduced into the molecule.

A very convenient method for protecting the amino group in preparing sulfanilamides is to form the acetyl derivative. The sulfonyl chloride group may then be introduced and converted to the sulfonamide, after which the acetyl group may be removed without affecting the sulfonamide (Eq. 1). The individual steps in this sequence will be discussed in detail below.

$$(21\text{-}1)$$

Acetanilide

The first step in the process is conversion of aniline to acetanilide, as shown in Eq. 2. Since the acetylation is carried out in aqueous solution,

$$+ \; 2CH_3CO_2H \; + \; NaCl$$

$$(21\text{-}2)$$

hydrochloric acid is added to change the water-insoluble aniline into the readily soluble hydrochloride salt. Acetic anhydride is now added, followed immediately by sodium acetate. The sodium acetate neutralizes the hydrochloric acid to form sodium chloride and acetic acid, and thus liberates the aniline, which is acetylated by the acetic anhydride.

This method of acetylating amines in aqueous solution is extremely convenient and eliminates diacetylation (Eq. 3), a troublesome side reac-

$$(21\text{-}3)$$

tion encountered when some amines are acetylated directly in acetic anhydride. The only side reaction in the aqueous procedure is the competing reaction of acetic anhydride with water (Eq. 4), which may dissipate some

$$(CH_3CO)_2O + H_2O \rightarrow 2CH_3CO_2H \qquad (21\text{-}4)$$

anhydride. The reaction with aniline is so very much more rapid than the hydrolysis that little anhydride is lost. Also, excess acetic anhydride is added as a safety factor. This can be done without complicating the purification procedure, since excess anhydride will be hydrolyzed to acetic acid. Thus, all the products are soluble except the acetanilide, which is filtered and crystallized from water.

Alternate methods for the preparation of amides have already been discussed in Chap. 13.

Chlorosulfonation

This term is used for the one-step reaction in which a sulfonyl chloride group is introduced directly into the aromatic nucleus. As applied to acetanilide, the over-all reaction is shown in Eq. 5. A slight excess over two

$$\text{(21-5)}$$

moles of chlorosulfonic acid is used, because the course of the reaction has been shown to proceed through formation of the sulfonic acid and conversion of this to sulfonyl chloride by the further action of chlorosulfonic acid (Eq. 6). It should be noted that the acetamino group orients almost ex-

$$\text{(21-6)}$$

clusively to the *para*-position. In general, the orientation of the acetamino group is similar to that of the amino group (*o,p*); however, in acid solution as in Eq. 5, the amino group would be converted to the salt, which is *meta*-directing.

The product is isolated by cautiously pouring the reaction mixture into ice water. This decomposes any excess chlorosulfonic acid and precipitates the *p*-acetaminobenzenesulfonyl chloride, which is filtered and washed free of acid. For the preparation of sulfanilamide, this moist acid chloride is used directly. If the product is to be stored or used for preparing sulfathiazole, it must be made anhydrous. Although sulfonyl chlorides are far less reactive than are carboxylic acid chlorides, nevertheless, slow hydrolysis does occur on standing in presence of water (Eq. 7). For this reason

$$\underset{CH_3CONH}{\bigotimes}\!\!-SO_2Cl \;+\; H_2O \;\rightarrow\; \underset{CH_3CONH}{\bigotimes}\!\!-SO_2OH \;+\; HCl \qquad (21\text{-}7)$$

a sulfonyl chloride cannot be dried merely by exposure to air or at elevated temperatures. Drying is best accomplished by dissolving the moist product in chloroform, separating the aqueous layer, and crystallizing the sulfonyl chloride from its chloroform solution.

This slow hydrolysis (Eq. 7) is the only side reaction of consequence in preparation of the sulfonyl chloride, and this is minimized by limiting the duration of contact with water, as described above. There is no danger of hydrolysis of the acid chloride by presence of water during its preparation, for chlorosulfonic acid reacts violently with water, to yield sulfuric acid and hydrogen chloride. For this latter reason, however, thoroughly dried equipment must be used for the reaction. Not only would water consume chlorosulfonic acid, but it would also create a hazard on account of the violent reaction between these two compounds. *Special care must always be exercised in handling the corrosive and highly reactive chlorosulfonic acid.*

Sulfanilamide

To form the amide, the moist sulfonyl chloride prepared above is *immediately* warmed with excess aqueous ammonia. The last step in the process is the removal of the protecting acetyl group. This can be easily accomplished, using either acid or alkaline hydrolysis, without affecting the sulfonamide group, for the latter is much more resistant to hydrolysis. In this instance, acid hydrolysis is convenient, for the liberated amino group forms the water-soluble amine salt. To obtain the free base, the acid must be neutralized with alkali which is stronger than the amino but not strong enough to form a salt with the weakly acid sulfonamide group. Alkali of such strength is conveniently furnished by sodium bicarbonate, and its addition after hydrolysis precipitates the sulfanilamide. The sequence of reactions representing these conversions is shown in Eq. 8. Final purification is effected by crystallization from water. The only side reaction is hydrolysis of the acid chloride (Eq. 7).

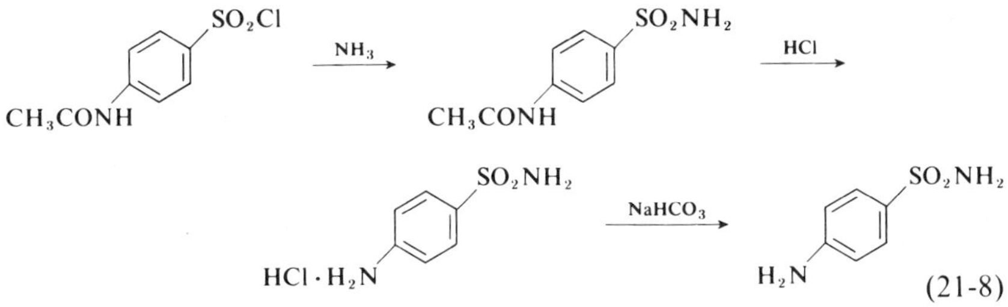

(21-8)

Sulfathiazole

In the condensation to form sulfanilamide, excess ammonia neutralized the hydrogen chloride formed. In preparing sulfathiazole, the 2-aminothiazole (Chap. 27) is the more valuable reagent, so other means must be found for neutralizing the hydrogen chloride and preventing it from inactivating the 2-aminothiazole through salt formation. This is conveniently done by carrying out the reaction in pyridine, an organic base, which forms a salt with hydrogen chloride and also serves as a solvent (Eq. 9). Since the sulfonyl chloride reacts with water very rapidly in pyridine solution, all reagents must be completely dry.

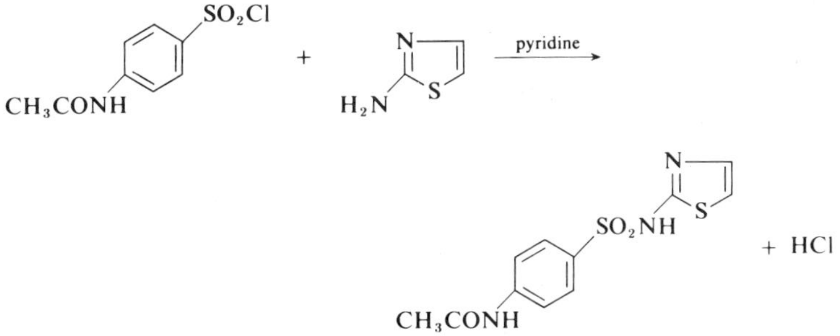

(21-9)

The *side reactions* that occur do so because of the tautomerism of the amino hydrogen between the exocyclic nitrogen and the ring nitrogen. Thus, 2-aminothiazole contains some of form B, which can also react with *p*-acetaminobenzenesulfonyl chloride, designated as R—SO$_2$Cl (Eq. 10).

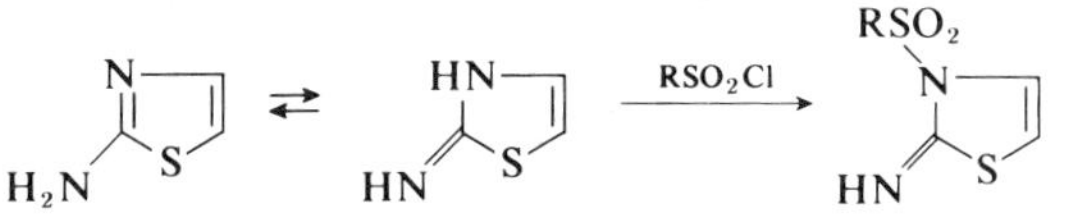

(21-10)

In the same way, the product of reaction 9 can exist in tautomeric forms of which B can undergo further reaction with the sulfonyl chloride (Eq. 11).

$$(21\text{-}11)$$

In both cases (Eqs. 10 and 11), however, the final product will be insoluble in alkali because of the absence of any hydrogen atoms on the sulfonamide nitrogen (see Hinsberg reaction, Chap. 30). The reaction product that precipitated when the mixture was decomposed with water is treated with alkali and filtered. Since the desired product (Eq. 9) is alkali-soluble, impurities originating by reactions 10 and 11 may be removed by filtration.

Alkaline hydrolysis is used to remove the protecting acetyl group. The alkaline reaction mixture is finally treated with hydrochloric acid followed by sodium acetate. The sulfathiazole precipitates from this solution, for the resulting acetic acid-sodium acetate buffer is too weakly acidic to form a salt with the *p*-amino group.

There are *two other general methods for preparing sulfanilamides* in which the *p*-amino group is introduced in the last step by a reductive process (Eqs. 12, 13). These alternatives are useful when the sulfonamide

$$(21\text{-}12)$$

$$(21\text{-}13)$$

nitrogen contains a residue unstable to hydrolytic conditions. They also illustrate possible methods for carrying along a potential amino group. Another point of interest is the *para*-directing influence of the azo grouping, which is illustrated in Eq. 13.

EXPERIMENTAL PROCEDURES

Acetanilide

To a solution of 12 ml of concentrated hydrochloric acid in 350 ml of water is added 13 g of aniline. The aniline is brought into solution by swirling and, if the solution is dark colored, 2–3 g of decolorizing carbon is added and the solution filtered by gravity. A clear solution of 22 g of crystalline sodium acetate in 75 ml of water is now prepared. After the aniline hydrochloride solution has been warmed to 50°, 16.6 ml of acetic anhydride is added to it and dissolved by stirring very briefly, followed by the immediate addition of the sodium acetate solution. The acetanilide that separates after stirring and cooling in an ice bath is collected by suction filtration, washed with a small amount of cold water, and dried. The yield is about 16 g, and the melting point of the pure material is 114°. If necessary, the product may be purified by recrystallization from water (see Chap. 3).

p-Acetaminobenzenesulfonyl Chloride

In a 500-ml Erlenmeyer flask is placed 13.5 g of pure, dry acetanilide. It is melted by gentle heating with a free flame and obtained as a solid cake on the lower walls of the flask by moderate swirling to cool. If droplets of water have formed on the neck of the flask (because of incompletely dried acetanilide), these are removed by gentle flaming. The flask is fitted with a gas trap (Note 1), then cooled in an ice bath before 35 ml of chlorosulfonic acid (measured in a *dry* graduate) is added in one portion. The flask is now removed from the ice bath and the reaction allowed to proceed with moderate swirling, with occasional cooling if the evolution of hydrogen chloride becomes too vigorous. After the reaction has subsided and only a small amount of acetanilide remains undissolved (about 10 minutes), the reaction mixture is heated on the steam bath for an additional 10 minutes to complete the reaction. It is then cooled and poured slowly in a thin stream with vigorous stirring into a mixture of 125 g of ice and 50 ml of water in a 600-ml beaker. The contents of the flask are rinsed into the beaker with cold water, and the precipitated *p*-acetaminobenzenesulfonyl chloride, after being stirred to break up any lumps, is filtered with suction. The solid is washed with cold water and pressed dry.

For purification (Note 2), the sulfonyl chloride is dissolved in the minimum amount (plus 10% excess) of boiling chloroform (100–125 ml) and transferred to a separatory funnel previously warmed on the steam bath. The lower chloroform layer is rapidly drawn off from any water layer (careful separation of layers!), and a 25-ml portion of hot chloroform is used to rinse the funnel. The combined chloroform solutions are cooled, and the crystalline *p*-acetaminobenzenesulfonyl chloride is filtered with suction. A second crop is obtained by concentrating (Note 3) the mother liquor to one-fourth or one-fifth the original volume. The total yield is about 12–14 g of pure material (m.p. 149°). As soon as dry (less than 1 hour in a well-ventilated location), it should be stored in a tightly stoppered bottle.

Sulfanilamide

The preparation of *p*-acetaminobenzenesulfonyl chloride is carried out as described above, with *all* quantities adjusted to 4 g of acetanilide as starting material. The moist sulfonyl chloride, after suction filtration and washing, is transferred immediately to a 125-ml Erlenmeyer flask. Without delay, 12 ml of concentrated ammonium hydroxide diluted with an equal . volume of water is added slowly with swirling *(CAUTION! There may be heat evolution)*. The resultant mixture is heated under gentle reflux, with frequent swirling, for about 5 minutes, then cooled in an ice bath.

The precipitated amide is collected by suction filtration, then pressed on the funnel under suction to remove as much liquid as possible. If excess ammonia is left on the amide, this will neutralize enough hydrochloric acid to prevent effective hydrolysis in the next step. For hydrolysis, the amide is returned to the Erlenmeyer flask and heated under reflux with an acid solution prepared by diluting 2 ml of concentrated hydrochloric acid (Note 4) with 8 ml of water. Heating under reflux is continued for about 10 minutes after the hot solution becomes homogeneous (usually a total of about 20 minutes), then extent of hydrolysis is tested by cooling the solution in water to about room temperature. Precipitation of a solid indicates incomplete hydrolysis (Note 4); if this occurs, heating under reflux is continued until cooling of the hydrolysate gives no precipitate. If excess hydrochloric acid was used, the hydrochloride of the product will continue to precipitate on cooling. Decolorizing carbon is added to the cooled solution, which is then shaken for several minutes and filtered by gravity into a 200-ml beaker. Sodium bicarbonate (3.5 g) is next added very cautiously *(FOAMING!)* with stirring. If the solution is still acidic to litmus, additional bicarbonate is added. The very slightly alkaline suspension is finally cooled thoroughly and filtered. Pure sulfanilamide is obtained by recrystallizing the precipitate from water (about 25 ml). It melts at 163–164°, and the yield is about 2–3 g.

Sulfathiazole

Five g of 2-aminothiazole (Chap. 27) is dissolved in 20 ml of pyridine (dried over potassium hydroxide), and 12.9 g of pure *p*-acetaminobenzenesulfonyl chloride is added in portions, with swirling, at such a rate that the temperature does not rise above 40° without any external cooling. The reaction is completed by heating for 30 minutes on the steam bath, then the mixture is cooled and poured into 125 ml of water. The oil should solidify on working with a stirring rod; it is then filtered, washed with water, and dissolved in 25 ml of 2N sodium hydroxide by warming for a few minutes on the steam bath. The solution is cooled, and any insoluble material is filtered and washed with a little water. The filtrate is acidified to litmus with about 3.0 ml of glacial acetic acid to give a precipitate, which is filtered, pressed dry, and heated under reflux for 1 hour in ten times its weight of 2N sodium hydroxide. After this solution has been cooled, concentrated hydrochloric acid is added until the precipitate that first appears has redissolved. Excess acid should be avoided. After the solution has been treated with charcoal and filtered, it is brought nearly to neutrality with 2N sodium hydroxide (Note 5); then solid sodium acetate is added in portions until the mixture no longer turns blue litmus to red. To facilitate filtration, the mixture is heated to a boil, cooled thoroughly in an ice bath, and filtered. The insoluble sulfathiazole is washed with water and recrystallized from water to give a yield of 5–7 g, m.p. 201–202°.

NOTES

1. Evolution of HCl is so vigorous that the simple gas trap (Fig. 8-1) is usually ineffective in preventing escape of the corrosive HCl into the laboratory. Unless the improved gas trap (Fig. 8-5) is available, the reaction should be carried out in a forced-draft hood.

2. Since chloroform has a moderate toxicity, it is preferable to handle the hot solution in a forced-draft hood. If a hood is not used, heating for solution of the sulfonyl chloride should be under reflux.

3. Although the chloroform solution contains some water (since it was separated from an aqueous phase), there is no danger of this hydrolyzing a significant amount of the sulfonyl chloride during heating for concentration of the solution. The water is removed during the early stages of the distillation as the minimum-boiling azeotrope with chloroform. This azeotrope boils at 56° and contains 2.8% water.

Since chloroform is a rather expensive solvent, the distilled chloroform should be collected and returned to the bottle marked "Recovered Chloroform."

4. It is important that this acid be measured carefully. Too little gives slow or incomplete hydrolysis, while too much causes salting out of the hydrochloride of sulfanilamide. If the acid is measured carefully but precipitate separates from the solution after 20–25 minutes under reflux, there was probably an excessive amount of ammonia left in the amide; so it is well to add an additional 0.5 ml of acid before heating is continued.

5. Unless a part of the acid is neutralized with sodium hydroxide, a very large amount of sodium acetate is required to raise the pH of the buffered solution to the desired value. This is especially true if an excessive amount of acid was used for solution of the sulfathiazole.

Friedel and Crafts Reaction

22

The Friedel and Crafts reaction is of considerable utility for preparation of ketones in the aromatic series. The reaction is carried out by treating the aromatic compound with an acid chloride or anhydride in presence of a strong Lewis acid such as aluminum chloride. Of course the solvent must be inert to the acid chloride or anhydride, as well as to the Lewis acid. Satisfactory solvents are nitrobenzene, carbon disulfide, and tetrachloroethane. If the aromatic component in the reaction is an inexpensive liquid hydrocarbon, such as benzene, it is frequently used as both reactant and solvent. Such an application is discussed in the present chapter.

The *main reaction* for the preparation of *β-benzoylpropionic acid* is that between benzene and succinic anhydride in the presence of anhydrous aluminum chloride (Eq. 1). Although the aluminum chloride is a catalyst,

$$\text{(22-1)}$$

it must be used in at least two molecular proportions in order to obtain a good yield of the propionic acid. This is because the aluminum chloride serves a dual role by forming addition complexes with both the reactants and the product. Its catalytic function is not completely understood, but it is known that aluminum chloride will form complexes with both benzene and succinic anhydride. With the anhydride (or with an acid chloride),

209

this results in the formation of the reactive acylonium ion, $R-C_+^{\nearrow O}$, which then reacts with the aluminum chloride-benzene complex to give the product.

The addition complex with the product is very likely of the form shown in Eq. 2. One mole of aluminum chloride is coordinated with the keto

$$
\text{C}_6\text{H}_6 + \underset{\text{CH}_2-\text{C}}{\overset{\text{CH}_2-\text{C}}{\big|}}\overset{\nearrow O}{\underset{\searrow O}{\diagdown}}O + 2\text{AlCl}_3 \rightarrow \text{C}_6\text{H}_5-\overset{\overset{\text{AlCl}_3}{\uparrow}}{\underset{\|}{\text{O}}}\text{C}-\text{CH}_2\text{CH}_2\text{CO}_2\text{AlCl}_2 + \text{HCl}
$$

$$\downarrow \text{H}_2\text{O, H}^+$$

$$\text{C}_6\text{H}_5-\text{CO}-\text{CH}_2\text{CH}_2\text{CO}_2\text{H}$$

(22-2)

group, and the second mole is consumed by the carboxyl. Thus, if only a catalytic amount were used, the aluminum chloride would soon be inactivated because of this complex formation with the product, and the reaction would stop. It may be stated as a general rule that at least one mole of aluminum chloride should be used per mole of carbonyl group present in the reagent; therefore, when anhydrides are used, at least two moles of aluminum chloride are required. This situation should be contrasted with the case of alkylation, where only catalytic quantities are required because the resulting alkyl benzene does not inactivate the aluminum chloride. Since the activity of the aluminum chloride is retained, and since alkyl groups have a slight activating effect on further substitution in the benzene ring, alkylations invariably lead to polyalkylated side products.

A major advantage of the Friedel and Crafts method for preparing ketones from benzene is the absence of any serious side reaction. Only one acyl group is introduced, since the deactivating influence of a *meta*-orienting group on the benzene ring prevents further acylation. When thiophene-free benzene is used, even the small amount of tar formation that usually occurs when organic substances are heated in the presence of aluminum chloride is kept to a minimum.

In view of the above considerations of the main and side reactions, the chief function of the purification procedure is to remove the excess benzene and the large amount of aluminum salts. The reaction mixture is first treated with aqueous hydrochloric acid to break up the addition complex and dissolve any basic aluminum salts. Steam distillation then removes the easily volatile benzene, and the precipitated β-benzoylpropionic acid is filtered from the residue.

Since the water-insoluble acid was precipitated almost instantaneously when the reaction mixture was decomposed, the insoluble conglomeration contains an appreciable amount of occluded material. For removal of entrained aluminum salts, the crude acid is dissolved in sodium carbonate solution and filtered from the insoluble aluminum hydroxide. Careful acidification of the filtrate precipitates the β-benzoylpropionic acid.

EXPERIMENTAL PROCEDURE

β-Benzoylpropionic Acid

In a dry 500-ml round-bottomed flask (or the ground-jointed flask with side tubes, Appendix I) is placed 100 ml of thiophene-free benzene. A condenser is arranged for distillation, and 25 ml of benzene is distilled slowly, in order to dry both solvent and equipment by azeotropic distillation. To the residual benzene is added 10 g of succinic anhydride, and the condenser is placed in the reflux position. To the top of the condenser is attached a calcium chloride drying tube, which is in turn attached to a gas trap (Fig. 8-1 or 8-5). The mixture in the flask is cooled, with swirling, to about room temperature with the drying tube and condenser attached, then the condenser is removed briefly, and there is added in one portion 30 g of anhydrous aluminum chloride (Note 1). If an exothermic reaction, with evolution of hydrogen chloride, does not set in, the mixture may be warmed cautiously. A pan of cold water should be available for cooling, in case the reaction threatens to get out of control. After the exothermic reaction has subsided, the mixture is heated under reflux, with frequent shaking, in a boiling-water bath for 30 minutes.

At the end of the heating period the mixture is cooled in an ice-water bath, and there is added slowly from a dropping funnel (Note 2) about 75 ml of water followed by 15 ml of concentrated hydrochloric acid. The condenser is then arranged for distillation, and the mixture is directly steam-distilled until all the excess benzene has passed over. The hot residue is poured into a 250-ml beaker. After this mixture has been cooled in an ice bath, the solidified β-benzoylpropionic acid is collected by suction filtration and washed, first with a cold mixture of 10 ml of concentrated hydrochloric acid and 30 ml of water, and then with 50 ml of cold water.

The crude acid is dissolved in 75 ml of 15 % aqueous sodium carbonate by boiling under reflux in a one-liter flask for a few minutes. The insoluble aluminum hydroxide is removed from the hot solution by suction filtration (gentle suction) and washed with about 15 ml of hot water. About 1 g of charcoal is added to the filtrate (which is kept hot in an Erlenmeyer flask); after the solution has been stirred briefly, it is filtered by gravity into a 500-

ml beaker. The filtrate, which should be clear and nearly colorless, is cooled to about 50°, and acidified *(CAUTION, FOAMING!)* with about 20 ml of concentrated hydrochloric acid. After the mixture has been cooled with stirring for about a half-hour in an ice bath, it is collected by suction filtration, washed with cold water, and dried to constant weight. This acid tenaciously holds water and is best dried in a current of warm air. For this purpose, the radiator is quite convenient. The material should be placed on a watch glass at some distance from the radiator's surface since the wet material may melt well below 100°. The yield is about 15 g and the product should melt at about 114–115°.

NOTES

1. Anhydrous aluminum chloride is highly hygroscopic and, on absorption of water, evolves hydrogen chloride. This may cause the development of hydrogen chloride pressure in a closed bottle, so the bottle should be opened cautiously, with the face well back. It is recommended that a towel be thrown over the top of the bottle as it is being opened. Since hydrated aluminum chloride is worthless in this reaction, it is important that the *bottle be kept tightly closed except when material is being removed.* Also, the substance should not be left exposed to the air before it is put into the reaction. If it is lumpy, it may be rapidly ground in a mortar. If the aluminum chloride is discolored, this is caused primarily by anhydrous ferric chloride, which is no disadvantage.

2. Considerable hydrogen chloride is evolved during the water addition; so it should be carried out in a hood unless the side-tube flask is being used. If this ground-jointed flask is being used, then the separatory funnel may be attached to a side tube and the water added as the flask remains connected to the gas absorption trap via the top of the condenser.

Reduction of the Carbonyl Group

23

Reduction of the carbonyl group is an important process in synthetic organic chemistry, which may be carried out under different conditions so as to yield three different products. Proper choice of conditions can give a good yield of bimolecular reduction to a diol (Eq. 1), reduction to an alcohol (Eq. 2), or reduction to a methylene group (Eq. 3).

$$2R-\overset{\parallel}{\underset{O}{C}}-R' + 2[H] \rightarrow R-\overset{\overset{R'}{\mid}}{\underset{\underset{OH}{\mid}}{C}}-\overset{\overset{R'}{\mid}}{\underset{\underset{OH}{\mid}}{C}}-R \qquad (23\text{-}1)$$

$$R-\overset{\parallel}{\underset{O}{C}}-R' + 2[H] \rightarrow R-\overset{\underset{OH}{\mid}}{CH}-R' \qquad (23\text{-}2)$$

$$R-\overset{\parallel}{\underset{O}{C}}-R' + 4[H] \rightarrow R-CH_2-R' \qquad (23\text{-}3)$$

Bimolecular reduction (Eq. 1), which is nearly always applied to ketones (neither R nor R' is H), may be accomplished by certain special chemical reducing agents; however, electrolytic reduction is probably the best and most general procedure for effecting this type of conversion. Reduction to an alcohol (Eq. 2) may be applied to either aldehydes or ketones and can be accomplished with numerous chemical agents or by catalytic hydrogenation. Reduction to methyl (Eq. 3, R' = H) may be applied to aldehydes, but this procedure is most widely applicable to reduction of the keto group to methylene. This complete elimination of the functional group may seem a rather futile procedure at first consideration; however, it proves to be quite useful. Many of the procedures for extending a chain of carbon atoms involve synthesis of ketones, and these syntheses may often be accomplished with other functional groups present in the molecules. Subsequent elimination of the carbonyl group, as in Eq. 3, leads to the higher molecular weight compounds containing the other functional groups. An example of such a sequence is synthesis of β-benzoylpropionic acid, as in Chap. 22, followed by reduction to γ-phenylbutyric acid, as will be studied in the present chapter. Interestingly enough, methods useful for accomplishing the conversion indicated in Eq. 3 will not reduce an alcohol; therefore, the alcohol is not an intermediate in these reductions.

Although the reduction of carbonyl to methylene may be accomplished by catalytic hydrogenation if at least one group attached to carbonyl is aromatic,[1] in the general case rather special chemical methods must be used. One of the few chemical reagents that will accomplish such a reduction directly is zinc amalgam and hydrochloric acid, according to the procedure known as *Clemmensen reduction*. Although the Clemmensen reduction has been applied successfully to many hundreds of compounds, and is easily carried out, it suffers from serious interference by steric hindrance. Even a structure with a single adjacent branch, as in the formula below, is reduced with great difficulty.

$$R-\underset{\underset{O}{\|}}{C}-\underset{\underset{C_2H_5}{|}}{CH}-R'$$

The indirect method of reduction of carbonyl to methylene, known as the *Wolff-Kishner reduction*, in contrast to the Clemmensen method, is able to overcome a great deal of steric hindrance. For this reason, the method has become of much wider utility than the Clemmensen reduction. Until somewhat later than 1945, the Wolff-Kishner reduction was commonly accomplished in two steps. First, the hydrazone (occasionally, the semicarbazone) of the carbonyl compound was synthesized by simply mixing and heating the reagents, as usual in formation of hydrazones as derivatives (Eq. 4). The isolated and purified hydrazone was then subjected

$$R-\underset{\underset{O}{\|}}{C}-R' + H_2N-NH_2 \rightarrow R-\underset{\underset{N-NH_2}{\|}}{C}-R' + H_2O \qquad (23-4)$$

[1]Catalytic hydrogenation of a ketone ordinarily yields an alcohol, as mentioned previously; however, in the case of an aromatic ketone, this alcohol is a benzyl alcohol. Since benzyl alcohols are readily hydrogenated catalytically, in contrast to other types of alcohols, they do not appear as the final products from hydrogenation of aromatic ketones; the benzyl alcohol grouping is further reduced to methylene. In case an aromatic aldehyde is hydrogenated, of course the methyl group is formed. Even if stopping at the benzyl alcohol stage in the hydrogenation is desired, this usually proves to be very difficult or impossible. It should be specifically noted that the alcohol is an intermediate in catalytic hydrogenation of an aromatic ketone, although the alcohol is not an intermediate in Clemmensen reduction of ketones.

to high temperature, under pressure, in presence of sodium ethoxide in ethanol solution, to accomplish the decomposition illustrated in Eq. 5. This

$$\underset{\underset{N-NH_2}{\overset{\|}{}}}{R-C-R'} \xrightarrow[\text{ethanol, 200°}]{\text{NaOC}_2\text{H}_5 \text{ in}} R-CH_2-R' + N_2 \qquad (23\text{-}5)$$

two-step operation is still effectively used in instances where the starting ketone contains a structure sensitive to alkali, or anhydrous conditions are necessary in the second step; however, in most instances there is used a procedure, first reported by Huang-Minlon, wherein a high-boiling solvent is used to eliminate the necessity for pressure, and the two steps are carried out in the same reaction mixture. Such a reaction is used in the presently studied experimental procedure.

The *main reaction* for reduction of β-benzoylpropionic acid by the Huang-Minlon modification of the Wolff-Kishner reduction is shown in Eq. 6. The first step is accomplished by heating a diethylene glycol[2] solution of

$$(23\text{-}6)$$

the keto acid, potassium hydroxide, and hydrazine; then water is boiled from the solution until there is reached the temperature required for the second step. The reaction is then completed by a period of heating under reflux. After completion of the reaction, the free acid is liberated from its salt by addition of a strong mineral acid to the solution. The yield in the reaction is excellent, and the product is easily purified.

Side reactions are rather minor, and the principal by-products are neutral substances easily separated by extraction of an aqueous alkaline solution of the acid. It will be recalled that this device for separation of neutral material from the salts of acids or bases is used to advantage on many occasions. One side reaction is azine formation, shown for a general formula in Eq. 7.

---

[2]Various high-boiling solvents have been used, but technical diethylene glycol

$$HOCH_2CH_2-O-CH_2CH_2OH$$

is relatively cheap and quite satisfactory. The technical solvent, as well as the hydrazine that is used, contains some water; so the reaction mixture may be distilled slowly until enough water has been removed to give a boiling point of about 200° for the residual solvent.

$$R-\underset{\underset{R'}{|}}{C}=N-NH_2 + O=\underset{\underset{R'}{|}}{C}-R \xrightarrow{\text{heat}} R-\underset{\underset{R'}{|}}{C}=N-N=\underset{\underset{R'}{|}}{C}-R + H_2O \qquad (23\text{-}7)$$

This will be recognized as a repetition of the reaction forming the hydrazone. With phenyl ketones, as in the present preparation, this reaction occurs to an insignificant extent.

At the temperatures used for the hydrazone decomposition, there is slow formation of a ketone from the salt of the acid, as shown in Eq. 8.

$$2 \ \text{C}_6H_5{-}(CH_2)_3{-}CO_2K \xrightarrow{\text{heat}} C_6H_5{-}(CH_2)_3{-}\underset{\underset{O}{\|}}{C}{-}(CH_2)_3{-}C_6H_5 + K_2CO_3$$

$$(23\text{-}8)$$

Since excess hydrazine is boiled out of the solution, the ketone formed in Eq. 8 is unlikely to be reduced to 1,7-diphenylheptane.

Alternate methods of preparation of γ-phenylbutyric acid usually involve multiple chain extensions of a benzene derivative. For example, one may start with benzyl chloride, convert it to the cyanide, and alcoholize this to ethyl phenylacetate. The ester is reduced to β-phenylethyl alcohol, which is converted to the bromide and thence to the Grignard reagent. Reaction of the Grignard reagent with formaldehyde yields 3-phenyl-1-propanol. This alcohol is converted to the bromide, which is treated with potassium cyanide, and the cyanide is hydrolyzed to the desired acid. Other sequences may be used in which two carbons are added in one operation; however, they remain sufficiently laborious to illustrate the utility of the chain extension which introduces the keto group that is subsequently removed.

EXPERIMENTAL PROCEDURE

γ-Phenylbutyric acid

A mixture of 15 g of β-benzoylpropionic acid (Note 1), 16 g of potassium hydroxide pellets (Note 2), 11.5 ml of 85% hydrazine hydrate (Note 3), and 110 ml of diethylene glycol is placed in a 250-ml round-bottomed flask (Note 4) and heated carefully to boiling with a small flame. (*CAUTION!* When the potassium hydroxide dissolves, a large amount of heat is evolved, and unless the flame is temporarily removed the very hot alkaline solution is likely to be driven out the top of the condenser.) After the mixture has been boiled under reflux for about one hour, the condenser is attached to the flask with a bent tube and set downward for distillation, and a thermometer is also attached (Note 4) to the flask so that its bulb is immersed in the liquid. The mixture is distilled sufficiently slowly that it does not froth over, until the liquid reaches a temperature of 205–210°. The thermometer is then removed, the condenser is returned to reflux position, and the mixture is heated under reflux for an additional three hours (Note 5).

While the reaction mixture is still warm, but below 100°, it is added to a solution of 45 ml of 12N hydrochloric acid in 140 ml of water. The resultant mixture is cooled to room temperature and extracted with two 30-ml portions of benzene. After the benzene extract has been washed with water, the γ-phenylbutyric acid is extracted with two portions (100 ml, then 25 ml) of 1N sodium hydroxide. The combined alkaline extracts are washed once with a 30-ml portion of fresh benzene, then the aqueous alkaline solution is treated with about 1 g of decolorizing charcoal. After a boiling chip has been added, this mixture is heated to boiling for a few minutes on a steam bath in a forced-draft hood (*NO FLAMES!* Benzene is given off; *CAUTION!* Note 6). After the heating period, the solution is filtered by gravity through a semifluted paper and allowed to cool during the filtration. The filtrate is acidified to Congo red with 6N hydrochloric acid, then cooled with swirling in an ice bath. The product, which separates as an oil in the warm solution, sets to a crystalline mass as it is cooled. After thorough cooling, the light-colored product is collected by suction filtration and washed with two portions of ice water. It is dried on a watch glass or in a small beaker at room temperature, and weighed. This substance is low-melting and also polymorphic, so it may become semisolid while being dried; therefore, it should not be placed on a paper for drying. The weight and melting point are determined.

The γ-phenylbutyric acid prepared in this manner is pure enough for most purposes. On account of its low melting point and polymorphic character, it is purified by crystallization with great difficulty. If further purification is desired, distillation at reduced pressure (Chap. 31) is the recommended procedure.

NOTES

1. It may be desirable to use all the acid prepared according to the procedure in Chap. 22. If a quantity different from 15 g is used, *all* quantities of reagents must be adjusted accordingly (cf. Notes 2 and 3).

2. Potassium hydroxide pellets are about 85% potassium hydroxide and 15% water, so this must be taken into account in calculating moles of reagent.

3. Hydrazine is corrosive to the skin and toxic, so it should be handled with care and not boiled into the room. The reagent specified is 15% water and 85% $N_2H_4 \cdot H_2O$; the quantity specified contains 0.195 mole of hydrazine (N_2H_4).

4. If a ground-jointed flask is not used, it is recommended that a rubber stopper

be used, for considerable material is extracted from a cork by the hot diethylene glycol. Since a thermometer must be inserted into the liquid in the flask during distillation, the ground-jointed flask with side tubulatures (Appendix I) is quite convenient for this reaction; however, serious etching of the flask occurs. There is no difficulty with the joint freezing provided that the flask is not allowed to stand overnight with a joint attached. If the special flask is not used, a two-hole stopper is required during distillation. If a forced-draft hood is available, the hydrazine and water may be boiled off as a thermometer is inserted into the liquid in the open flask.

5. This heating period need not be continuous. If a thermometer is inserted in the liquid during the heating period, the temperature is usually recorded in the range 195–200°.

6. Removal of the dissolved and suspended benzene is important, otherwise it dissolves in the precipitated acid and may render it oily and unfiltrable. If a hood is not available, the solution must be distilled, *not* boiled into the laboratory. Benzene has a low order of toxicity; however, its destructive action on the liver is cumulative; *hence pollution of the air with benzene should be scrupulously avoided.*

Quinones

24

p-Benzoquinones may be obtained by oxidation of nearly any phenol or aniline derivative, as in the following equations:

$$\text{(phenol)} + 2[O] \rightarrow \text{(p-benzoquinone)} + H_2O \qquad (24\text{-}1)$$

$$\text{(aniline)} + 2[O] \rightarrow \text{(iminoquinone)} + H_2O \rightarrow \text{(p-benzoquinone)} + NH_3 \qquad (24\text{-}2)$$

The hydrolysis involved in the latter equation occurs so easily that the intermediate iminoquinone is ordinarily isolable only when the oxidation is carried out in anhydrous media. Such reactions are sometimes used to prepare quinones if the starting amine or phenol is cheap; however, the yield is always poor. Best yields are obtained if there is a second amino or hydroxy group in the *para* position. Such a preparation is illustrated in Chap. 39.

Any substituent in the *para* position to the hydroxy or amino group is eliminated in oxidation to a quinone, and this has sometimes been used for the determination of orientation in polysubstituted benzene derivatives. The group eliminated by oxidation is located as *para* to the hydroxy or amino group. If this *para* group is an alkyl or any of the *meta*-directing groups, the yield of quinone remains poor; however, if it is halogen, the yield of quinone is improved considerably. The quinone preparation described in this chapter is an illustration of this latter variety of oxidation.

The *main reactions* for the preparation of *6-bromotoluquinone* from *o*-cresol are the following:

$$\text{(o-cresol)} + 2Br_2 \xrightarrow[\text{solvent}]{\text{HOAc}} \text{(4,6-dibromo-o-cresol)} + 2HBr \qquad (24\text{-}3)$$

$$\text{(4,6-dibromo-o-cresol)} + [O] \xrightarrow[\substack{\text{aqueous} \\ \text{HOAc}}]{70\%} \text{(6-bromotoluquinone)} + HBr \qquad (24\text{-}4)$$
$$(CrO_3)$$

The 4,6-dibromo-*o*-cresol obtained as the product in Eq. 3 is a crystalline solid that precipitates when the acetic acid solution is poured into water. It is collected by filtration and used in the oxidation step without purification.

It is important that the oxidation step be carried out in 70% aqueous acetic acid rather than in glacial acetic acid; otherwise, the desired quinone is contaminated by quinones containing more than the expected number of bromine atoms in the ring. The student interested in a further discussion of this phenomenon may find it in *Organic Reactions*.[1]

Equation 4 might be written so as to yield 6-bromotoluquinone and HOBr, requiring two equivalents of oxygen; however, in practice, it is found that the hypobromous acid is also effective in the oxidation. One equivalent of atomic oxygen, required by Eq. 4 as it is written, does not give an optimum yield of quinone, but 1.6 equivalents do give as good yield as two equivalents. For determining the theoretical equivalency of oxidizing agent, it is convenient to balance the equation as above and consider the theoretical breakdown of chromic anhydride as in Eq. 5.

$$2CrO_3 \rightarrow Cr_2O_3 + 3[O] \qquad (24\text{-}5)$$

Side Reactions

The bromination of a phenol to yield the product containing bromine in all open *ortho* and *para* positions is a rapid and efficient reaction. At

[1] Roger Adams, *Organic Reactions*, Vol. IV (New York: John Wiley & Sons, Inc., 1948), Chap. 6, pp. 309, 310.

relatively low temperatures, there is very little tendency to oxidize the ring or substitute bromine in *meta* positions. The yield in the first step is nearly quantitative.

In the oxidation of a phenol to a quinone, it has been reasonably well established that the first step is the removal of hydrogen from the oxygen to give the free radical, A. Other forms of this resonance hybrid which

(A)   (B)   (C)   (D)

may be considered, as in B, C, and D, illustrate the several sites of reactivity. If oxidation occurs at the site of the free valence in form C, the desired quinone is obtained; however, if oxidation occurs at the site of the free valence in form B or form D, the *o*-quinone results. Attack at the latter points leads eventually to tarry materials, for *o*-quinones in aqueous media are polymerized or readily oxidized further. In addition, the free radicals may combine with each other to give assorted dimers, and these may become further oxidized to give dimeric quinonoid structures or higher polymers. The presence in the *para* position of an additional powerful electron-donating group, such as hydroxyl or amino, will naturally make this position more susceptible to oxidation (electron removal) and thus lead to a higher yield of the *para* quinone. Furthermore, if too weak an oxidizing agent or too low a concentration of oxidizing agent is used, the intermediate radicals will survive longer in the solution, hence have a better opportunity to get together and couple to give by-products. It follows that best results will be obtained with the strongest oxidizing agent that does not rapidly attack the quinone structure. Numerous oxidizing agents have been found effective, depending on the nature of the substituents in the quinone; however, for water-insoluble compounds, chromic anhydride or sodium dichromate in acetic acid has proved to be quite useful for a variety of structures.

Purification of the product is best effected by steam distillation, for all the by-products mentioned above are of too high molecular weight to steam-distill rapidly. The quinone obtained directly from the steam distillate is in good condition, and nearly pure material is obtained after one crystallization. It should be mentioned that the quinone is being fractionally steam-distilled from the tarry material, so the rate of quinone distillation slows down as the distillation progresses, and, finally, an appreciable amount of higher-boiling material begins to come over. The steam distillation should be stopped at this point, for the higher molecular weight material is very difficult to remove by crystallization. The last of the steam distillate may be collected separately, and the solid steam-distilled again, but this time-consuming process yields very little additional quinone. The procedure would be profitable only if the starting material were much more valuable than *o*-cresol. Since quinones are sensitive to light they should be dried and stored in a relatively dark place.

Quinones are nearly quantitatively reduced by various reagents to the hydroquinone, and the reaction is evidenced by a fading of the color of the quinone. This process, illustrated in Eq. 6, is useful for making *p*-dihy-

$$\text{(yellow)} + Na_2S_2O_4 + 2H_2O \rightarrow \text{(colorless)} + 2NaHSO_3$$

(24-6)

droxybenzene derivatives. Both hydroquinones and *p*-aminophenols are readily oxidized in air, so their solutions tend to darken rapidly. Such compounds may be conveniently purified by crystallization if a trace of sodium hydrosulfite is added to the solution to reduce any quinonoid compounds formed by air oxidation.

Oxidation of a benzene derivative not substituted with unstabilizing groups (electron-donating groups) will also yield a benzoquinone; however, such a strong oxidizing agent is required for attack on a benzene derivative of this type that the same oxidizing agent will attack and destroy the quinone as rapidly as formed. The final products of such oxidations are carbon dioxide, water, and maleic acid derivatives. In contrast to this situation, which applies in the benzene series, the higher condensed-ring hydrocarbons are more susceptible to attack by oxidizing agents. If a suitable oxidizing agent is used, there may be isolated a poor yield of quinone from oxidation of the hydrocarbon, naphthalene, while a very good yield of quinone may be obtained from anthracene, and a moderate yield may be obtained from phenanthrene. The sites most susceptible to attack are indicated by the formulas of the quinones that are isolated from these oxidations.

1,4-Naphthoquinone   9,10-Anthraquinone   9,10-Phenanthraquinone

The *main reaction* for preparation of *phenanthraquinone* is shown in Eq. 7. Since chromic anhydride is the oxidizing agent, Eq. 5 may be used

$$+ \; 3[O] \;\; \xrightarrow[\text{HOAc}]{\text{aqueous}} \;\; + \; H_2O \qquad (24\text{-}7)$$

as the other half reaction. As usual, a net reaction may be obtained, if desired, by addition of Eqs. 5 and 7.

Side reactions yield some polymeric tarry material, from coupling of intermediate radicals, as was the case in the benzene series; however, significant oxidation does not occur at sites other than the 9- and 10-positions. This results from the greater reactivity of the 9- and 10-positions, or it may be said that this illustrates the greater reactivity of the 9- and 10-positions. This follows from the fact that attack at the 9,10-double bond leaves intact two resonance stabilized benzene rings; hence, the 9,10-bond in phenanthrene behaves somewhat like an ethylenic double bond. For example, bromine may be added readily to the 9,10-positions in phenanthrene. Similar considerations are consistent with the attack at the median positions in anthracene.

It may be further noted that all three condensed-ring quinones whose formulas have been illustrated may be regarded as benzene derivatives substituted with *meta*-directing groups. It will be recalled that *meta*-directing (electron-withdrawing) groups stabilize benzene to oxidation. This makes the condensed-ring quinones more stable to oxidation than most benzoquinones; hence, they may be isolated as end-products after rather vigorous oxidations. The least stable, hence obtained in poorest yield, is 1,4-napthoquinone, which contains one nonbenzenoid double bond. Further oxidation of phenanthraquinone does not lead to attack on the aromatic rings, but cleavage between the carbonyl groups. A by-product in this preparation is 2,2'-diphenic acid, as shown in Eq. 8.

$$+ \; [O] \; + \; H_2O \; \rightarrow \qquad (24\text{-}8)$$

Anthraquinone is also a by-product in this preparation, although not the result of a side reaction involving phenanthrene, for it is formed by oxidation of the anthracene which is present in the technical phenanthrene used for starting material. Since higher condensed-ring hydrocarbons are isolated from the complex mixture present in coal tar, pure grades of these compounds are always relatively expensive. Technical grades are usually rather cheap, however, and they are useful in many reactions, including the present one. The only significant impurity in technical phenanthrene is anthracene.

Purification of phenanthraquinone consists, then, of separating it from tarry material, diphenic acid, and anthraquinone. Diphenic acid may be separated by extraction from aqueous alkali; however, the most important step in purifying the phenanthraquinone depends on the fact that it exhibits its ketonic character by forming a water-soluble addition compound with sodium bisulfite. As has been mentioned in Chap. 15, not all ketones form bisulfite addition compounds, but only the more reactive ones which are not sterically hindered. Anthraquinone proves not to form a bisulfite addition compound; hence, the water solution of the phenanthraquinone complex may be filtered to remove both tarry material and anthraquinone. Addition of sodium carbonate then destroys the bisulfite (cf. Eq. 15–10), and the purified phenanthraquinone precipitates. Any diphenic acid not removed by the alkali wash, and dissolving in the warm solution of the bisulfite complex, is retained in solution as the sodium salt in the alkaline solution from which the product is filtered. As usual, final purification for removal of traces of impurities by recrystallization is applied to the precipitated phenanthraquinone.

Other methods of preparation are not ordinarily used for phenanthraquinone, on account of the ease and effectiveness of the presently studied method. Furthermore, introduction of a powerful electron-donating group (hydroxyl or amino) into the 9-position in phenanthrene is laborious. The preparation may be accomplished, however, by oxidation of 9-phenanthrylamine. This amine may be secured via 9-bromophenanthrene, the Grignard reagent, the carboxylic acid, the amide, and the Hofmann hypobromite reaction. This sequence illustrates the preference for the presently studied method.

EXPERIMENTAL PROCEDURES

6-Bromotoluquinone

Bromination of o-cresol. A 250-ml round-bottomed flask (Note 1) is fitted with a two-hole stopper bearing a 125-ml separatory funnel (Note 2) and a glass tube for connection to a gas-absorption trap (see Fig. 8-1) containing 2N sodium hydroxide, or the trap in Fig. 8-5. The tube in the trap (Fig. 8-1) must not extend below the surface of the liquid, and the connection between the trap and the reaction flask should contain a short section of rubber tubing so that the reaction flask may be swirled. In the round-bottomed flask is placed a solution of 10.8 g (10.3 ml) of technical *o*-cresol in 30 ml of glacial acetic acid. To the funnel are added 30 ml of glacial acetic acid and 32 g (10.3 ml) of bromine (Note 2). A cork is placed loosely in the separatory funnel, and the gas-absorption trap is attached. The bromine solution is added dropwise, during 10–15 minutes, as the flask is cooled, with *gentle* swirling, in an ice bath. (*BE CAREFUL not to snap the stem of the separatory funnel during the swirling.*) At first, the bromine color is discharged rapidly; toward the end, the color persists. After addition is complete, the flask is allowed to stand for 15 minutes in a pan of water previously heated to about 60°. At the end of this period (bromine color usually remains), the contents of the flask are poured (in a hood) in a thin stream into a mixture of about 150 g of crushed ice and 100 ml of water contained in a 600-ml beaker, as the water and ice are stirred vigorously. Stirring is continued briefly to insure precipitation of the dibromocresol as fine particles rather than as lumps. The flask is rinsed into the beaker with a little water, then the mixture is allowed to stand a few minutes, with occasional stirring, until the solid settles to leave a clear supernatant liquid. The solid is collected by suction filtration and washed with two or three portions of water.

Oxidation. The moist 4,6-dibromo-*o*-cresol is placed in a 500–ml Erlenmeyer flask and dissolved in 120 ml of glacial acetic acid by heating to about 80°; then, with continued warming, 50 ml of water is added, with swirling. To this solution there is added during 5 minutes, with swirling, a solution of 11.0 g of chromic anhydride in 15 ml of water. By mild cooling, the temperature is maintained at 65–70°. After addition is complete, the mixture is allowed to stand on the desk for 15 minutes, with occasional swirling. The mixture is finally poured into 400 ml of water contained in a one-liter beaker; this is cooled with stirring in running water or allowed to stand until the next laboratory period.

The mixture of yellow crystals and a small amount of red tarry material is collected by suction filtration, washed with water, and placed in a 500-ml or one-liter flask arranged for indirect steam distillation. Steam is passed through rapidly, preferably as fast as permitted by the capacity of the condenser. Yellow crystals that fuse to a clear orange solid collect in the condenser and receiver. Care must be exercised to prevent clogging of the condenser, using the precautions previously described (cf. Chap. 6). After 400–500 ml of distillate has been collected, it will be noted that as the distillate flows from the condenser, crystals do not separate, but the mixture becomes cloudy. Also, material fused by steam does not solidify readily in the distillate. As soon as these effects are noted, distillation should be stopped at once. It is a wise precaution to collect distillate separately after the first 400 ml has passed over.

After the distillate has been cooled in running water, the solid is collected by suction filtration and dissolved in 50 ml of hot 95% ethanol (*NO
FLAMES!*). The solution is kept warm enough to prevent oil separation
as 25 ml of water is gradually added with swirling. The clear orange solution is allowed to cool, without agitation, and the side of the flask is
scratched occasionally until crystallization sets in. The flask is then corked
and allowed to stand undisturbed for about 15 minutes. The solution rapidly fills with beautiful fibrous yellow needles. The mixture is then placed
in an ice bath for about 25 minutes, at the end of which time the mass of
crystals is so dense that there appears to be no liquid in the flask. The
crystals are stirred up with a spatula and collected by suction filtration.
A part of the filtrate is used to rinse the last crystals onto the funnel; then
the crystal mass is pressed with a clean flat-headed glass stopper or a small
beaker. The crystals are washed with several portions (about 30 ml in all)
of 50% aqueous alcohol, and finally drained well on the funnel. The solid
is dried on a watch glass in the dark (inside the desk). The weight of brilliantly yellow crystals is 5–8 g, m.p. 90–93°. This material is pure enough
for most purposes. The purest 6-bromotoluquinone, obtained by repeated
recrystallization, melts at 93.6–93.9°.

Reduction.   About 0.1 g (estimated) of 6-bromotoluquinone and 20 ml
of water are placed in a small flask and heated to boiling. Most of the
quinone should dissolve to give a yellow solution. A small amount of sodium
hydrosulfite is added from a spatula, portionwise, with the mixture kept
hot, until the solution becomes homogeneous and colorless.

The equation for this reduction has been presented as Eq. 6. Write
the two half reactions whose addition will give Eq. 6.

NOTES

1. The flask with side tubulatures (Appendix I) is especially convenient for
this reaction. The side tubes are used for attachment of the funnel and the gas
trap. The center glass-jointed neck, not needed for this reaction, may be closed
with a glass stopper, or satisfactorily with a rubber stopper or cork.

2. For precautions in handling bromine, refer to the preparation of bromobenzene, Chap. 17.

In instances where a separatory funnel is used as a dropping funnel, as in
many reactions such as the present one, a cylindrical funnel is more convenient
for clamping or placing in a two-hole cork than is the pear-shaped funnel, which
is more conveniently supported in a padded ring. Whatever the shape of the
funnel, the *stem should not be too long*, and there should not be used a larger size
of funnel than specified. The stopcock of the funnel should be less than 3 inches
above the flask; otherwise, the large leverage increases the hazard of snapping the

stem of the funnel while swirling. It should be emphasized that only gentle swirling is required to effect the mixing that is needed.

9,10-Phenanthraquinone

In a 500-ml Erlenmeyer flask is placed 10 g of technical phenanthrene (Note 1), then 150 ml of glacial acetic acid is added. For later use a condenser is readied for attachment to the flask with a cork or ground joint. The phenanthrene is dissolved in the acetic acid by swirling as the mixture is heated to 60–80°. While this solution is allowed to cool somewhat, there is prepared a solution of chromic acid by dissolving 18 g of chromic anhydride (CrO_3) in 20 ml of water, then diluting with 50 ml of glacial acetic acid. The chromic acid solution is placed in a separatory funnel which is supported in a ring at a convenient height for allowing portionwise addition to the Erlenmeyer flask. The chromic acid is added to the phenanthrene solution at such a rate that the temperature of the swirled reaction mixture may be maintained at 60–65° by cooling in an ice bath. After addition of the oxidizing agent has been completed, swirling of the reaction mixture is continued for a few minutes until the temperature begins to drop without external cooling. Finally, a reflux condenser is attached (to keep acetic acid fumes out of the room), and the mixture is heated on a steam bath for about 30 minutes. The cooled reaction mixture is poured, with stirring, into about 700 ml of water containing a little ice, and the precipitated phenanthraquinone is collected by suction filtration on a Büchner funnel (filtration may be rather slow on a small Hirsch funnel). The product is washed on the funnel with several portions of water, then with 5% sodium carbonate solution (Note 2), and finally with water.

The crude, moist quinone is added to a 500-ml Erlenmeyer flask and digested at 55–65° for about 20 minutes with a *freshly prepared* solution of 70 g of sodium bisulfite (Note 3) in 140 ml of water. The mixture is swirled frequently during this digestion. The insoluble material is filtered from the warm solution by gravity, then returned to the Erlenmeyer flask and digested in similar manner with about 150 ml of water. The insoluble residue is again removed by filtration of the warm solution. The combined filtrates are placed in a one-liter beaker, cooled in an ice bath, and treated cautiously (frothing from carbon dioxide evolution) with a saturated solution of sodium carbonate. Addition of sodium carbonate is continued until the solution is alkaline and further addition causes no more precipitation of quinone. The product is collected by suction filtration on a Büchner funnel, washed well with water, and dried.

Final purification of the quinone is by crystallization from glacial acetic acid according to a usual procedure, with heating of the acetic acid under reflux or in a forced-draft hood. Cooling for crystallization is at room temperature or in water, for acetic acid will freeze in an ice bath. The yield of orange needles, m.p. 206–207°, is 4.0–4.5 g.

NOTES

1. Technical phenanthrene, with about 90% content of phenanthrene, is quoted by one supplier at $5.05 per kilogram, whereas pure phenanthrene is quoted at $48.50 per kilogram. Another supplier quotes the technical phenanthrene at $4 per kilogram, the pure grade at $19 per kilogram. The principal impurity in the technical product is anthracene, which does not interfere with the present preparation, as has been discussed.

2. The washing of the precipitated solid with sodium carbonate solution removes some of the diphenic acid, but is unlikely to remove all of it on account of its intimate mixture with the phenanthraquinone. This matter has been discussed in some detail in connection with the purification of capramide in Chap. 13. Since diphenic acid has some solubility in warm water, a little of it will also dissolve in the warm solution of the bisulfite addition product of the quinone. Since the bisulfite is decomposed with alkali, however, any diphenic acid is kept in solution as its sodium salt.

3. Sodium metabisulfite (the anhydride of sodium bisulfite) is actually the reagent used to prepare the bisulfite solution, for the metabisulfite is ordinarily the species which is crystallized from solution and marketed.

Reactions of Diazonium Compounds

25

Diazonium compounds are extremely useful in the synthesis of a great number of aromatic derivatives. This utility follows from the fact that the diazonium group can be replaced in good yield by halogen, hydroxyl, cyano, or hydrogen. Thus, many compounds that could not be made by direct substitution are easily available through replacement of the diazonium group. The process usually starts with a nitro compound, which often can be readily obtained pure. Further substitution can then be carried out under the *meta*-orienting influence of the nitro group or after reduction to the strongly *ortho, para*-orienting amino. The amino group is then diazotized and removed (replacement by hydrogen) or replaced by halogen, hydroxyl, or cyano. In the present chapter, examples are given of replacement by bromine and hydroxyl.

Another important use of diazonium compounds is in the preparation of dyes. The diazonium compound is coupled with another aromatic nucleus containing a strong *ortho,para*-orienting group (hydroxyl or amino) to give a colored azo compound. The preparation of methyl orange is an example of this type of reaction.

o-Bromochlorobenzene

The replacement of a diazonium group by bromine consists of three steps: (1) preparation of cuprous bromide, (2) diazotization of the amine, and (3) decomposition of the diazonium bromide-cuprous bromide complex, which is known as the Sandmeyer reaction. Cuprous bromide is first prepared by reducing copper sulfate with sulfite in the presence of sodium bromide (Eq. 1). The insoluble cuprous bromide is filtered and washed well

$$2Cu^{++} + 2Br^- + SO_3^= + H_2O \rightarrow \underline{2CuBr} + SO_4^= + 2H^+ \qquad (25\text{-}1)$$

with water. If cuprous bromide is not used soon after its preparation, it should be stored in a tightly stoppered bottle to prevent air oxidation. Slightly discolored samples are satisfactory for use in Sandmeyer reactions.

Diazotization is carried out according to Eq. 2. The *o*-chloroaniline is

$$+ \; 2HBr \; + \; NaNO_2 \xrightarrow{\;0\text{-}10^\circ\;} \qquad\qquad + \; NaBr \; + \; 2H_2O \quad (25\text{-}2)$$

dissolved in hydrobromic acid, then sodium nitrite is added while the temperature is controlled at 0–10° by external cooling. From two and one-half to three moles of acid per mole of amine are required. One mole serves to form the amine salt that is necessary for diazotization. The second mole liberates nitrous acid from the sodium nitrite. Since *o*-chloroaniline is a weak base, some dissociation of its salt occurs (Eq. 3); therefore excess acid

$$\rightleftarrows \qquad\qquad + \; HBr \qquad\qquad (25\text{-}3)$$

is used in order to reduce to a negligible amount the free amine present. This is important because any free amine that is present will engage in a *side reaction* with the diazonium salt to form a diazoamino compound (Eq. 4).

$$+ \qquad\qquad \rightarrow \qquad\qquad + \; HBr \qquad (25\text{-}4)$$

Temperature control at 0–10° during the diazotization is essential in order to prevent two other *side reactions*. Diazonium salts are unstable and, on continued standing or warming, decompose to form the phenol (Eq. 5). This phenol may then couple with the diazonium compound to give

$$+ \; H_2O \; \rightarrow \qquad\qquad + \; N_2 \; + \; HBr \qquad (25\text{-}5)$$

colored azo derivatives (Eq. 6). For this reason, it is imperative that the diazotization be carried out in the cold and that the diazonium solution be used directly after its preparation.

$$(25\text{-}6)$$

The last step in the process is the formation and decomposition of the diazonium bromide-cuprous bromide complex (Eq. 7). The cuprous bro-

$$(25\text{-}7)$$

mide, insoluble in water, is dissolved in hydrobromic acid, and the diazonium solution is slowly added to it with simultaneous steam distillation. As the *o*-bromochlorobenzene is formed, it is steam-distilled from the reaction mixture. Accompanying it will be any *o*-chlorophenol formed as a by-product (Eq. 5) and a small amount of azo compounds (Eqs. 4 and 6). The bulk of the azo compounds and other side products will remain behind because of their high molecular weight and consequent low volatility with steam.

Since the cuprous bromide complex is decomposed as rapidly as formed in the present preparation, it is unnecessary to use a full molar equivalent of cuprous bromide. In certain Sandmeyer reactions, better yields are obtained if the cuprous bromide complex is formed in the cold and then heated to effect decomposition. In such instances, use of a molar equivalent of cuprous bromide is necessary.

The organic portion of the steam distillate is washed with concentrated sulfuric acid in order to remove phenol and azo compound (both readily soluble in sulfuric acid), then the *o*-bromochlorobenzene is washed free of acid, dried over calcium chloride, and distilled. The yield is good and the product is relatively free of isomers, for technical *o*-chloroaniline contains only a small amount of *p*-chloroaniline. Commercial reagent grade *o*-chloroaniline is free of isomers, hence will yield pure *o*-bromochlorobenzene.

An appreciation for the advantages of the Sandmeyer reaction in this preparation will be gained by considering alternative syntheses. Direct bromination of chlorobenzene (Eq. 8) yields a mixture of *o*- and *p*-isomers,

$$(25\text{-}8)$$

in which the *p*-isomer predominates. As has been described in Chap. 17, separation of the more abundant, less soluble *p*-isomer is practical; however, the less abundant, liquid *o*-isomer cannot be obtained from this mixture (unless in small amount by gas chromatography). Of course the same difficulties apply in chlorination of bromobenzene. If chlorobenzene is first sulfonated, the isomeric chlorobenzenesulfonic acids can be separated, and the sequence outlined in Eq. 9 can be utilized to secure *o*-

$$(25\text{-}9)$$

bromochlorobenzene. Obviously, this method is inferior to the Sandmeyer reaction.

Guaiacol

For preparation of a phenol from an amine, the amine is first diazotized and then heated in the presence of sulfuric acid to replace the diazonium group by hydroxyl. As starting material for preparing guaiacol (*o*-methoxyphenol), *o*-anisidine is used. The diazotization is carried out as with *o*-chloroaniline (above), except that sulfuric acid is used instead of hydrobromic (Eq. 10). This is to keep the solution free of any anions that

$$(25\text{-}10)$$

might be substituted instead of the hydroxyl group.

The same considerations as to amount of acid, temperature control, and side reactions obtain in both cases, except that replacement of the diazonium group with hydroxyl (Eq. 11) becomes one of the *main reactions*

(the other is Eq. 10). Coupling of the diazonium salt with the phenol (analogous to Eq. 6) is a potentially serious side reaction; however, it is repressed by distilling the phenol from the solution as rapidly as formed and keeping the solution strongly acidic. Coupling occurs much more rapidly near neutrality (see methyl orange preparation, below). Removal of the phenol as rapidly as formed is accomplished by slowly dropping the diazonium solution into a distilling aqueous solution of sulfuric acid and sodium sulfate. The purpose of the sodium sulfate is to raise the temperature of the boiling solution so that decomposition is very rapid. This prevents any appreciable concentration of diazonium compound and therefore suppresses the coupling side reaction (Eq. 6). At the same time, the sodium sulfate decreases the solubility of guaiacol in the aqueous phase and thus aids its steam volatility.

In the presence of nitrous acid, decomposition of a diazonium salt to a phenol can be accompanied by two additional side reactions. A small amount of nitro compound may be formed (Eq. 12), and the phenol may

$$\text{[benzene ring with OCH}_3\text{ and N}_2^+\text{]} + HNO_2 \rightarrow \text{[benzene ring with OCH}_3\text{ and NO}_2\text{]} + H^+ + N_2 \qquad (25\text{-}12)$$

react with the nitrous acid to form a nitroso compound (Eq. 13). The

$$\text{[benzene ring with OCH}_3\text{ and OH]} + HNO_2 \rightarrow \text{[benzene ring with ON, OCH}_3\text{ and OH]} + H_2O \qquad (25\text{-}13)$$

resultant impurities in the final product are very difficult to remove. For this reason excess nitrous acid is destroyed, after diazotization is complete, by adding urea (Eq. 14). Other related compounds, such as ammonium

$$H_2N-\underset{\underset{O}{\|}}{C}-NH_2 + 2HNO_2 \rightarrow CO_2 + 3H_2O + 2N_2 \qquad (25\text{-}14)$$

sulfamate ($H_2N-SO_2ONH_4$), also react rapidly with nitrous acid.

Another side reaction can become of major importance if the decomposition is not carried out exactly as directed. If distillation is started before the addition of the diazonium solution or if distillation is more rapid than the addition, the sulfuric acid in the boiling solution becomes more concentrated and attacks the phenol to give tarry by-products.

Purification is effected almost completely in the steam distillation during the decomposition, for the guaiacol is the only organic material that distills to any extent. It is extracted with benzene and dried over magnesium sulfate (calcium chloride frequently forms complexes with oxygenated compounds) before its final distillation.

The alternative methods of preparation are again quite inferior. Partial etherification of catechol has been used to prepare guaiacol (Eq. 15), and

$$\text{(structure: benzene with OH, OH)} \xrightarrow{(CH_3)_2SO_4} \text{(benzene with OCH}_3\text{, OH)} + \text{(benzene with OCH}_3\text{, OCH}_3\text{)} \qquad (25\text{-}15)$$

it has also been obtained by the distillation of hard woods. In the latter case, it is accompanied by impurities that are exceedingly difficult to remove.

Methyl Orange

The use of diazonium compounds in the coupling reaction to prepare colored azo derivatives is illustrated by the preparation of methyl orange. The amine component to be diazotized is sulfanilic acid, which is only slightly soluble in water. It is therefore dissolved in sodium carbonate and the solution of the sodium salt diazotized by adding sodium nitrite followed by hydrochloric acid (Eq. 16). The *p*-diazobenzenesulfonate,

$$HO_3S\text{—}(\text{C}_6\text{H}_4)\text{—}NH_2 \xrightarrow{Na_2CO_3} \overset{+}{Na}\overset{-}{O_3}S\text{—}(\text{C}_6\text{H}_4)\text{—}NH_2 \xrightarrow[\substack{HCl \\ 0\text{–}5^\circ}]{NaNO_2} \overset{-}{O_3}S\text{—}(\text{C}_6\text{H}_4)\text{—}\overset{+}{N_2} \qquad (25\text{-}16)$$

which probably exists as an inner salt, is quite insoluble in water and is used as a suspension in the coupling step.

Diazonium compounds can be coupled with phenols and aromatic amines. In most cases, coupling takes place in the *para* position unless this is blocked, whereupon it goes *ortho*. With phenols, there is required an

$$\begin{bmatrix} \overset{+}{N_2}\text{—}(\text{C}_6\text{H}_4)\text{—}SO_3^- \end{bmatrix} + \begin{bmatrix} (\text{C}_6\text{H}_5)\text{—}N(CH_3)_2 \end{bmatrix} \rightarrow \left[HO_3S\text{—}(\text{C}_6\text{H}_4)\text{—}N{=}N\text{—}(\text{C}_6\text{H}_4)\text{—}N(CH_3)_2 \right]$$

$$\updownarrow$$

$$\overset{-}{O_3}S\text{—}(\text{C}_6\text{H}_4)\text{—}\overset{H}{N}{-}N{=}(\text{quinoid ring}){=}\overset{+}{N}(CH_3)_2$$

$$H^+ \updownarrow {}^-OH$$

$$\overset{-}{O_3}S\text{—}(\text{C}_6\text{H}_4)\text{—}N{=}N\text{—}(\text{C}_6\text{H}_4)\text{—}N(CH_3)_2 \qquad (25\text{-}17)$$

alkaline medium in which the phenol is soluble, whereas amines are coupled in a weakly acid solution. If the amine is primary or secondary, an intermediate diazoamino compound is formed (Eq. 4); however, tertiary amines couple directly in the *para* position. In this manner, methyl orange is prepared by coupling diazotized sulfanilic acid with dimethylaniline (Eq. 17). This dye is quite useful as an indicator, since it is yellow-orange in alkaline solution and violet-red in acid. The respective structures in acidic and alkaline solutions are depicted in Eq. 17. In the present preparation, the sodium salt is isolated by crystallization from alkaline solution.

No other practical preparations of methyl orange have been developed.

In addition to their wide use as dyes and indicators, azo compounds are also of importance synthetically as a means of introducing the amino group under exceedingly mild conditions. For example, if methyl orange is reduced with sodium hydrosulfite, *p*-aminodimethylaniline is formed and sulfanilic acid is regenerated (Eq. 18).

$$+ 2Na_2S_2O_4 + 4H_2O \rightarrow$$

$$+ 4NaHSO_3 \qquad (25\text{-}18)$$

EXPERIMENTAL PROCEDURES

In the preparation of both *o*-bromochlorobenzene and guaiacol, when the diazotization process is started, the procedure must be continued without interruption to the conclusion of steam distillation. For this reason, it is well to start promptly at the beginning of a laboratory period, after the apparatus (and cuprous bromide for *o*-bromochlorobenzene) has been prepared during a previous laboratory period.

o-Bromochlorobenzene

Cuprous bromide. A solution of 25 g of commercial crystalline copper sulfate and 14.5 g of sodium bromide in 85 ml of water is swirled while there is added, during about 10 minutes, 6.3 g of sodium sulfite. If necessary, a little more sodium sulfite is added in order to discharge the blue color. After the mixture has been cooled, the cuprous bromide is collected by suction filtration and washed with about 20 ml of water. The product is pressed as dry as possible on the funnel, with a clean glass stopper, and used directly in the Sandmeyer reaction. If this material is stored a day or more before use, it darkens from air oxidation, but this appears to be no disadvantage if the storage period is not too long.

Diazotization. In a 250-ml Erlenmeyer flask are placed 21.2 g (17.5 ml) of *o*-chloroaniline and 50 ml of 48% hydrobromic acid. The amine salt is partially dissolved by heating to boiling, and the mixture is cooled in an ice and salt bath until the temperature has dropped to about 0°. The hydrobromide separates as a slurry. As the mixture is swirled, there is added from a small flask a solution of 12 g of technical sodium nitrite dissolved in 22 ml of water. The addition is made portionwise as rapidly as is consistent with keeping the temperature of the reaction mixture below 10°. Any lumps of hydrobromide are crushed with a spatula or glass rod. The temperature should not be reduced below 0°, for in this case the diazotization is slowed down considerably. Cooling during nitrite addition may be augmented by dropping small pieces of ice directly into the reaction mixture. Too-slow addition of the nitrite is likely to lower the yield somewhat, by allowing more time for coupling to occur. The diazonium solution should be left in the cooling mixture until used, with proper precautions that the flask does not tip over when the ice melts.

Sandmeyer reaction. The 500-ml ground-jointed flask (Note 1) with side tubes (Appendix I) is fitted with the distillation head in the center neck. A 125-ml separatory funnel is inserted in the larger side tube so that the cold diazonium solution may be dropped directly into the hot cuprous bromide solution. The other side tube of the flask and the top of the distilling head are closed with corks, and the distilling head is attached to a condenser. The diazonium solution should not be added from the top of the distilling head, for warming of the solution occurs as it runs down the side of the distilling head. If only a single-necked ground-jointed flask is available, a long-stem separatory funnel may be inserted in the top of the distilling head so that the stem extends down to the top of the round-bottomed flask. This improves the situation, but is not as satisfactory as the side-tube flask.

In the round-bottomed flask are placed the cuprous bromide, 15 ml of 48% hydrobromic acid, and two boiling chips. The mixture in the flask is heated to boiling, and about one-fourth of the diazonium solution (containing much precipitate) is placed in the separatory funnel, after which the main portion is returned to the ice bath. The flame is turned sufficiently high to cause steam distillation during the addition of the diazonium solution over a period of 3–5 minutes (Note 2). A small copper wire should be available in the laboratory in case the bore of the stopcock becomes plugged with the solid. The *o*-bromochlorobenzene steam-distills as it is formed. An effort should be made to make the rate of distillation about equal to that at which liquid is added. As soon as the contents of the separatory funnel have been added, another fourth of the diazonium solution is put into the separatory funnel and added similarly. When all the diazonium solution has been added, the flask is rinsed with water, and this is added to the distilling mixture from the separatory funnel. The separatory funnel is then filled with water, and this is added at about the rate steam distillation is occurring. Distillation is continued until all the oil has passed over. About 165 ml of distillate is usually required.

The dense oil is separated in a separatory funnel and washed with 5-ml portions of concentrated sulfuric acid (which layer?) (*CAUTION! Do not get the acid on skin or clothing.*) until the acid becomes only slightly discolored. The oil is then washed with 20 ml of water, 20 ml of 0.5N sodium hydroxide, and 20 ml of water. The final separation from water should be very careful. Drying over calcium chloride (1–2 g sufficient) is greatly facilitated by frequent swirling, for the calcium chloride sinks to the bottom, while the water floats on top of the oil. The oil is filtered through a small filter paper into a 50-ml distilling flask and distilled. The colorless product, which is collected at 198–202°, amounts to 25–27 g.

If the product from bromination of chlorobenzene is available (Chap. 17), retention time of the present product should be compared with those of the two isomers from the previous bromination.

NOTES

1. If ground-jointed equipment is not available, the reaction may be carried out in a one-liter round-bottomed flask, fitted with a cork which has been bored to accommodate the 125-ml separatory funnel and an 8-mm bent tube attached to the condenser. The larger size flask is necessary in order to minimize splashing of the boiling solution into the delivery tube.

2. In order to minimize the side reactions that have been discussed, it is quite important that the chilled diazonium solution be added as rapidly as specified, but that a sufficiently large flame be used so that distillation continues during the addition. If there is a delay for any reason (e.g., to unplug the stopcock, or to add more diazonium solution) the flame should be turned down temporarily so that the hydrobromic acid is not lost by distillation.

Guaiacol (o-methoxyphenol)

Diazotization. (See first paragraph under "Experimental Procedures.") In 100 ml of 6N sulfuric acid contained in a 500-ml Erlenmeyer flask, there is dissolved 24 g of technical *o*-anisidine (*o*-methoxyaniline) by gentle warming. The mixture is cooled in an ice bath with vigorous swirling in order to obtain any amine salt that separates in a finely divided condition. As cooling is continued, there is added dropwise, from a separatory funnel supported above the flask, a cold solution of 14 g of sodium nitrite in 60 ml of water. The solution is kept well mixed during the addition, which is made over about 30 minutes, as the temperature is kept at 5–8°. After addition is complete, the mixture is swirled for about 5 minutes longer, and then tested for the presence of nitrous acid (Note 1). Any excess nitrous acid is then destroyed by the addition of urea in 1-g portions. (With technical o-anisidine as starting material, 2–3 g of urea will be required.) The solution is then left in the ice bath until the next step is carried out (Note 2).

Replacement by Hydroxyl

The 500-ml ground-jointed flask with side tubes is equipped with the 125-ml separatory funnel and distilling head, as described for preparation of o-bromochlorobenzene (also cf. Note 1 of that preparation). In the round-bottomed flask are placed, in the order named, 115 ml of water, 100 ml of concentrated sulfuric acid, 150 g of anhydrous sodium sulfate, and two boiling chips. The mixture in the flask is heated to boiling and about one-sixth of the diazonium solution is placed in the separatory funnel, after which the main portion is returned to the ice bath. The flame is turned sufficiently high to cause steam distillation during the addition of the diazonium solution over a period of 10 minutes (Note 3). An effort should be made to make the rate of distillation about equal to the rate at which liquid is added. As soon as the contents of the separatory funnel have been added, another portion of the diazonium solution is put into the separatory funnel and added similarly. Addition should be completed in about one hour and in no more than one and one-half hours. When all the diazonium solution has been added, the flask is rinsed with 35 ml of water, and this is added to the distilling mixture from the separatory funnel at the same rate. Two hundred ml of distillate should have been collected after this wash portion has been distilled. An additional 100 ml of water is added from the separatory funnel and distilled during one-half hour in the same manner, to give a total distillate of about 300 ml. The distillate is saturated with clean sodium chloride and extracted with two 50-ml portions of benzene. The benzene is separated very carefully from the water layer. If there is a large emulsion layer present, this is kept with the benzene, and the combined layers are dried over magnesium sulfate. The solution (after filtering) is distilled from a 250-ml distilling flask until most of the benzene has been removed. The flame is then extinguished and the residue is transferred to a 50-ml distilling flask with a small bulb pipette. The 250-ml flask is rinsed carefully with 1–2 ml of benzene, and this is added to the small flask. After the benzene and a small intermediate fraction have been collected, the guaiacol is collected at 195–210°. The yield is about 10–12 g. Pure guaiacol boils at 205° and melts at about 28°, but it crystallizes with difficulty. The purity may be checked by gas chromatography on silicone partitioning agent.

NOTES

1. At the end of the addition, a slight excess of nitrous acid should be present, as shown by a test with starch-potassium iodide paper; if this test is negative, add more sodium nitrite solution until it remains positive (an immediate blue color due to the starch-iodine complex) 5 minutes after the last addition. This test may also be used to follow the course of the diazotization by frequent checks of the nitrous acid consumption.

2. If the solution of the diazonium salt is cloudy or contains sediment, as is often the case with technical grades of anisidine, filtration will improve the color of the guaiacol obtained. Filtration on a Büchner funnel with suction is satisfactory. Both the flask containing the material to be filtered and the receiver are kept cooled in an ice bath.

3. It is critical that distillation not be started prior to the beginning of addition of the diazonium solution and that the rate of distillation not be faster than the rate of addition. If the concentration of sulfuric acid in the flask is increased considerably by concentration of the distilling solution, serious decomposition results. On the other hand, rate of distillation should not be too slow, for this leaves the guaiacol in the flask for an excessive length of time and also promotes decomposition. Use of a graduate to measure each portion of distillate may be helpful in maintaining a constant concentration.

Methyl Orange

All quantities in this preparation must be very carefully measured.

In 125 ml of water in a 600-ml beaker is dissolved 2 g of sodium carbonate; 5 g of sulfanilic acid monohydrate is then added. The mixture is stirred until all the acid has dissolved, and warmed if necessary; then 1.80 g of sodium nitrite is added. After the nitrite has dissolved, the solution is cooled in an ice bath to 0–5° and, with this temperature maintained, a cold solution of 5 ml of concentrated hydrochloric acid in 25 ml of water is added slowly with stirring.

To this suspension of diazotized sulfanilic acid is now added slowly, with stirring and cooling, an ice-cold solution of 3 g (3.1 ml) of dimethylaniline in 5 ml of concentrated hydrochloric acid and 20 ml of water. Dilute sodium hydroxide (about 60 ml of 1N) is now added slowly, with continued cooling, to permit coupling (Note 1) and to prepare the sodium salt of the dye. After coupling has been completed, 25 g of clean sodium chloride is added, and the mixture is boiled until all the sodium chloride has dissolved and the flocculent precipitate of methyl orange has become microcrystalline. After the mixture has been cooled in running water, the crystallizate is collected by suction filtration on a Büchner funnel, pressed well and drained on the funnel, then washed with about 25 ml of water. The product is pressed and drained well again, and then dried. The average yield is about 8 g. The melting point is not determined. (Why?)

NOTE

1. As alkali is added, coupling begins to occur as the pH approaches 7, and as more alkali is added the color changes to yellow. As the color begins to change, the alkali is added quite slowly and the mixture is stirred for 5 to 10 minutes as the remainder of the alkali is added. This allows adequate time for coupling to occur before the pH becomes too high. The total alkali added should be sufficient to convert the product entirely to the yellow sodium salt.

Pyrroles

26

The unsaturated cyclic compound containing four carbons and one nitrogen atom in the ring is known as pyrrole. As is generally true in heterocyclic systems, the ring atoms are numbered so that the hetero-atom has the smallest

$$\begin{array}{c} HC_4\text{———}_3CH \\ \| \qquad\quad \| \\ HC^5 \qquad\quad {}^2CH \\ \diagdown \;\; {}_1 \;\; \diagup \\ N \\ H \end{array}$$

Pyrrole

number. Compounds containing this pyrrole nucleus are very widely distributed in nature—for example, in the blood pigment, in chlorophyll, in proteins, and in some alkaloids.

Because of this frequent occurrence in compounds of physiological importance, there has been considerable interest in the synthesis of variously substituted pyrroles. Unfortunately, the methods of direct substitution into the parent nucleus, used so advantageously with benzene, are of limited use with pyrrole, because of its extreme sensitivity to acidic reagents. For this reason, most syntheses of substituted pyrroles proceed directly to the substituted compound by a ring-closure method. In the present chapter, we shall discuss the synthesis of *N*-methylpyrrole (or 1-methylpyrrole); however, a nearly identical procedure may be applied to synthesis of the parent compound, pyrrole.

The *main reaction* for the preparation of *N-methylpyrrole* consists in pyrolyzing the methylamine salt of mucic acid (Eq. 1). Although the mechanism of such a reaction may appear obscure at first, a closer examination

$$\begin{array}{c} CO_2H \\ | \\ H-C-OH \\ | \\ HO-C-H \\ | \\ HO-C-H \\ | \\ H-C-OH \\ | \\ CO_2H \end{array} + 2CH_3NH_2 \rightarrow \begin{array}{c} CO_2NH_3CH_3 \\ | \\ (HCOH)_4 \\ | \\ CO_2NH_3CH_3 \end{array} \xrightarrow{\Delta} \underset{\underset{CH_3}{|}}{\boxed{}_N} + 4H_2O + 2CO_2 \\ + CH_3NH_2$$

$$(26\text{-}1)$$

reveals a rational path for the formation of a pyrrole nucleus. If mucic acid is considered as a di-β-hydroxy acid, in analogy with other β-hydroxy acids, its first reaction upon heating would be to lose water and form the α,β-unsaturated acid at each end (Eq. 2). The resulting compound would be the dienol of a 1,4-diketone. Heating of the diketone with an amine, RNH_2, would form the pyrrole nucleus through elimination of two molecules of water. The formation of pyrroles from amines and 1,4-diketones is, in fact, a general method for preparing substituted pyrroles, and use of ammonia instead of the amine gives the nucleus without a substituent on nitrogen. The final step in the present process is the decarboxylation to *N*-methylpyrrole.

$$(26\text{-}2)$$

Owing to the reactive type of intermediates involved and the fairly drastic conditions used in the pyrolysis, there are a number of poorly defined side reactions. These lead to tarry, polymeric by-products, which, for the most part, fail to distill during the pyrolysis and are thus easily eliminated.

As carried out in the laboratory, mucic acid is mixed with excess aqueous methylamine, and glycerol is then added. Methylamine and mucic acid react to form methylammonium mucate, and the mixture is partially concentrated to remove most of the excess water. This allows the necessary high temperature to be reached during the subsequent pyrolysis. Glycerol is essentially inert as far as the reaction is concerned, but facilitates heat transfer during the pyrolysis since it is a high-boiling (290°) liquid. The distillate from this pyrolysis is redistilled, and the steam-volatile product is separated from the water layer (after saturation with sodium chloride since N-methylpyrrole is slightly water-soluble). Final recovery of the N-methylpyrrole is effected by distillation after it has been dried over sodium hydroxide.

The method described above becomes a general one for the synthesis of 1-substituted pyrroles merely by substituting the appropriate primary amine for methylamine. Furthermore, the parent compound, pyrrole, may be similarly prepared by use of ammonia instead of an amine.

An alternative path for preparing N-alkylated pyrroles is to first form pyrrole and then alkylate it on the nitrogen according to Eq. 3. The nitrogen

$$\text{(pyrrole-N-H)} + K \rightarrow \tfrac{1}{2}H_2 + \text{(pyrrole-N-K)} \xrightarrow{\ RI\ } \text{(pyrrole-N-R)} + KI \qquad (26\text{-}3)$$

of pyrrole is not basic; in fact, its hydrogen is very weakly acidic ($K_A = 10^{-16.5}$), and with potassium it forms the salt. Heating with an alkyl iodide then alkylates the nitrogen with elimination of potassium iodide.

Obviously, when R is simple and the amine, RNH_2, readily available, direct reaction with mucic acid is the most efficient path for preparing the N-substituted pyrrole. With relatively expensive groups, alkylation, as shown in Eq. 3, proceeds with high yields based on consumption of the group R.

EXPERIMENTAL PROCEDURE

N-Methylpyrrole (Note 1)

In a 500-ml round-bottomed flask is placed 106 g of mucic acid. To this is slowly added (under a hood or in a well-ventilated working space), with vigorous shaking, 130 ml of 10N aqueous methylamine. Next is added 60 ml of glycerol, and the mass is mixed well by shaking. The flask is next taken to your desk and equipped for distillation with a distillation head and a condenser fitted with a 125-ml distilling flask as receiver. The side arm of the distilling flask is connected to a gas trap (Fig. 8-1) containing 3N hydrochloric acid, or to the improved trap shown in Fig. 8-5, to remove the disagreeable fumes evolved during the distillation. The flask is carefully heated with a small flame, and 40–60 ml of water is distilled (until the first ready distillation of water ceases). This distillate is discarded, then the receiver is returned to the condenser and connected to the gas trap.

At this point, the flame is adjusted so that water and *N*-methylpyrrole distill as the pyrolysis proceeds according to Eq. 2. The flame should not be high enough so that glycerol distills, as is the case if the vapor temperature in the distilling head rises above 100°. The pyrolysis and slow distillation are continued until the drops of distillate are clear. This requires 2–3 hours, and may be interrupted at any point and resumed later.

The entire distillate is redistilled moderately rapidly from the flask in which it was collected until once again the drops of distillate are no longer cloudy. A gas trap on the receiver, while not essential during this second distillation, will probably be found desirable. The two-phase distillate is saturated with clean sodium chloride, and the water layer is separated. The light-yellow oily layer is run into a 50-ml Erlenmeyer flask and dried by shaking frequently for one-half hour with 5–6 g of sodium hydroxide pellets, then the oil is decanted into a 50-ml distilling flask and is distilled. The product is collected over a range of about four degrees, usually at about 108–112° (Note 2). *N*-Methylpyrrole darkens on standing and is extremely hygroscopic; so it should be kept in a tightly stoppered, preferably dark, container. The average yield is 8–10 g.

NOTES

1. Pyrrole may be prepared by essentially the same procedure, if the methylamine is replaced by 150 ml of concentrated aqueous ammonium hydroxide. There should not be used old bottles of ammonia that have been opened frequently, for the molarity decreases substantially. Since pyrrole is quite water-soluble, it is important that the final aqueous distillate be thoroughly saturated with salt. Pyrrole is collected over a range of about four degrees, usually at 127–131°. Like *N*-methylpyrrole, it is extremely hygroscopic and tends to darken rapidly on standing; so it should be stored in a tightly stoppered amber-colored bottle. The yield of pyrrole is usually somewhat lower than that of *N*-methylpyrrole.

2. Pure *N*-methylpyrrole is reported as boiling at 114–115°, but the product obtained by this procedure usually contains small amounts of water, hence distills over a broad range somewhat below the true boiling point. Water gives rather erratic results in gas chromatography, but on a silicone partitioning agent the water peak may be observable at a shorter retention time than N-methylpyrrole.

Thiazoles

27

The five-membered heterocyclic compound containing both nitrogen and sulfur in the ring is known as "thiazole." This system has become of interest because of its presence in vitamin B_1 and sulfathiazole (see Chap. 21), one

$$HC_4 \underset{}{\overset{}{-}} {}_3N$$
$$HC^5 \underset{S}{\overset{1}{\diagdown}} {}^2CH$$

of the more effective sulfa drugs; and a large number of thiazole derivatives have been synthesized. In most cases, the thiazole compound must be made by a ring-closure method, for the nucleus is very resistant to direct substitution. One of the general methods for preparing substituted thiazoles, the reaction of an α-halo carbonyl compound with a thioamide, will be discussed in this chapter.

The *main reaction* for the preparation of *2-aminothiazole* is shown in Eq. 1. Because of its extreme reactivity, chloroacetaldehyde cannot very

$$ClCH_2CHO + H_2N-\underset{\underset{S}{\|}}{C}-NH_2 \rightarrow \underset{S}{\overset{N}{\Longleftarrow}}\underset{NH_2}{} + HCl + H_2O \qquad (27\text{-}1)$$

well be stored as such, and it is usually used in the form of a stabilized 40% solution in water or as a derivative from which the aldehyde is generated *in situ*, that is, directly in the reaction mixture. In the present experiment either the aqueous solution or α,β-dichloroethyl ethyl ether is used as the source of chloroacetaldehyde. With water, the reactive α-chlorine atom of the halogenated ether is hydrolyzed to form the hemi-acetal, which then dissociates into chloroacetaldehyde and ethanol (Eq. 2).

$$\begin{array}{c}\underset{\underset{Cl}{|}}{CH_2}-\underset{\underset{Cl}{|}}{CHOCH_2CH_3}\end{array} + H_2O \rightarrow \left[\begin{array}{c}\underset{\underset{Cl}{|}}{CH_2}-\underset{\underset{OH}{|}}{CHOCH_2CH_3}\end{array}\right] + HCl \quad (27\text{-}2)$$

$$\downarrow\uparrow$$

$$ClCH_2CHO + CH_3CH_2OH$$

Another convenient source of nascent chloroacetaldehyde is diethyl chloroacetal, which in the presence of dilute aqueous acid is hydrolyzed according to Eq. 3.

$$ClCH_2CH\underset{\diagdown OCH_2CH_3}{\overset{\diagup OCH_2CH_3}{}} + H_2O \xrightarrow{\;H^+\;} ClCH_2CHO + 2CH_3CH_2OH \quad (27\text{-}3)$$

The chloroaldehyde condenses with the enol form of the thioamide to eliminate hydrogen chloride, and ring-closure is completed through addition to the carbonyl group and elimination of a molecule of water (Eq. 4).

$$H_2N-\underset{\underset{S}{\|}}{C}-NH_2 \rightleftarrows HN=\underset{\underset{SH}{|}}{C}-NH_2 \xrightarrow{ClCH_2CHO} \begin{array}{c}HC=O \quad HN\\ \underset{H_2C}{}\diagdown_S\diagup\overset{\|}{C}\diagdown_{NH_2}\end{array} + HCl$$

$$\downarrow\uparrow$$

$$H_2O + \begin{array}{c}HC\text{---}N\\ \underset{HC}{\|}\diagdown_S\diagup\underset{C}{}\diagdown_{NH_2}\end{array} \leftarrow \begin{array}{c}\overset{H}{|}\\ HO-\underset{\underset{H_2C}{|}}{C}\text{---}N\\ \diagdown_S\diagup\overset{\|}{C}\diagdown_{NH_2}\end{array} \quad (27\text{-}4)$$

The reaction is carried out by heating thiourea under reflux in water with either α,β-dichloroethyl ethyl ether or the equivalent amount of the stabilized solution of chloroacetaldehyde. It is important that the reflux be moderate and the condenser efficient so that the volatile chloroacetaldehyde will not be boiled from the solution before it has condensed with the thiourea. After heating under reflux, the solution is concentrated to remove any unreacted aldehyde and then basified to precipitate the 2-aminothiazole, which was dissolved in the water as the soluble hydrochloride salt. The precipitate is washed with sodium bisulfite solution to remove any residual aldehyde, and the solid is recrystallized from benzene to give pure 2-aminothiazole.

The only side reaction is the self-condensation of chloroacetaldehyde to form red polymeric substances, which are soluble in water and are removed at the filtration step. It is important that unreacted aldehyde be removed completely by the concentration and bisulfite-wash steps, since it will condense with the free amine to form by-products.

EXPERIMENTAL PROCEDURE

2-Aminothiazole

To a solution of 7.6 g of thiourea in 40 ml of water in a 200-ml round-bottomed flask fitted with an efficient reflux condenser is added 14.3 g of α,β-dichloroethyl ethyl ether. If the 40% aqueous chloroacetaldehyde is used, 17.8 ml of this solution is added to 7.6 g of thiourea dissolved in 22 ml of water. The mixture is heated under *gentle* reflux in a water bath for 2 hours. The flask is then fitted for distillation and, with a small flame, 30 ml of distillate is collected and discarded. The reaction mixture is now cooled in an ice bath and made distinctly basic to litmus by cautious addition of concentrated sodium hydroxide, but a large excess of alkali is avoided. After thorough cooling, the precipitated solid is collected by suction filtration, washed with two 10-ml portions of ice-cold half-saturated sodium bisulfite, and pressed dry (Note 1). For purification of this crude material, it is dissolved in benzene (10 ml per g), treated with decolorizing carbon, and filtered by gravity while hot (*CAUTION: EXTINGUISH FLAMES!*) into an Erlenmeyer flask. About half the solvent is distilled from the filtrate, *not* boiled into the room. When the remaining benzene solution is cooled, 2-aminothiazole crystallizes and is collected by suction filtration. The yield is about 6.5 g, m.p. 89–90°.

NOTE

1. If pressing is thorough, the small amount of water retained is easily removed by azeotropic distillation with benzene after filtration from carbon. Refer to Chap. 23, Note 6, concerning the *toxic nature of benzene*.

Pyridines

28

Pyridines are heterocyclic compounds in which the ring contains five carbon atoms and one nitrogen atom. They are very widely distributed in nature, and representative pyridines are found among the vitamins (B_6, pyridoxine), as part of enzymes (nicotinamide), and among the alkaloids (nicotine). Also, pyridine itself and many of its alkyl derivatives are found in the high-

Pyridoxine   Nicotinamide   Nicotine

boiling fractions of petroleum and coal tar. Until recently, the latter was the chief source of pyridine, which was a rather expensive chemical in comparison with benzene. A catalytic process for synthesizing pyridine from acetylene and ammonia has greatly reduced its cost and broadened its use.

Of at least equal importance with its wide occurrence is the fact that pyridine is the prototype for a large group of heterocyclic nitrogen ring-systems. These compounds are characterized by their high aromaticity, that is, by their high stability even though containing π electrons. Thus, a knowledge of the properties of pyridine can be profitably projected to a number of other heterocyclic systems.

Pyridine is highly resistant to electrophilic substitution. This behavior is reasonable when one considers the chief resonance forms of pyridine, resulting from the fact that nitrogen is more electronegative than carbon. In addition, since most electrophilic substitution reactions take place in strong

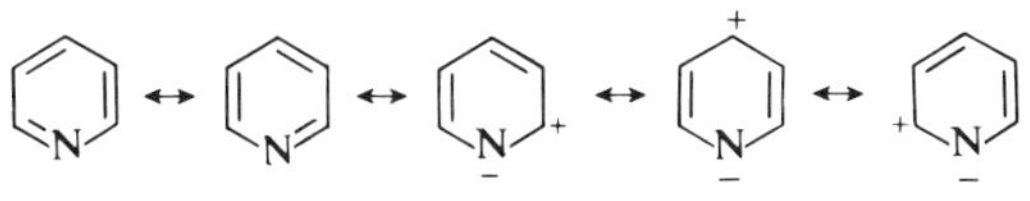

acid solution, the hetero-nitrogen is protonated, and the presence of a posi-tive pole in the ring makes electrophilic substitution even more difficult. For example, the following conditions are necessary to nitrate pyridine, and the yield is only 20%.

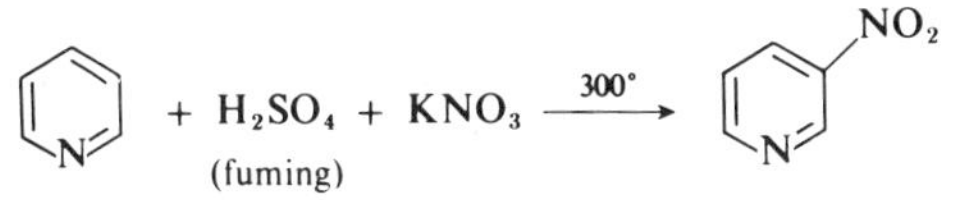

$$+ \ H_2SO_4 + KNO_3 \xrightarrow{300°} \qquad (28\text{-}1)$$

(fuming)

Nucleophilic substitution, on the other hand, occurs quite readily. When pyridine is heated with sodamide (Chichibabin reaction), 2-aminopyridine is formed in excellent yield (Eq. 2). Sodium hydride is the other product, and this reacts with the 2-aminopyridine to form the sodio-derivative which is then decomposed by water when the reaction is worked up.

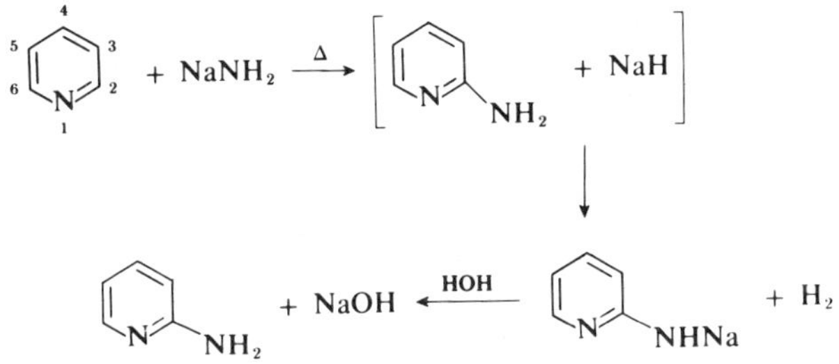

$$(28\text{-}2)$$

In addition to ease of preparation, another factor which makes 2-amino-pyridine (and various 2-aminoalkylpyridines) an attractive starting ma-terial for further reactions is the effect of the 2-amino group on electrophilic substitution. Since the amino group increases the electron-density in the ring, electrophilic substitution at the 3- and 5-positions now proceeds under less drastic conditions. This effect might be predicted by a consideration of the resonance forms:

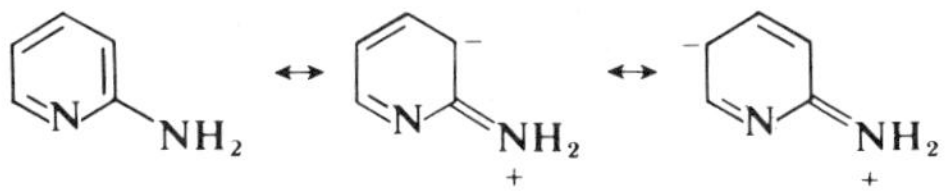

A third factor in the utility of 2-aminopyridines for further synthesis is the ease of replacement by hydroxyl, chlorine, and hydrogen, as shown in the following sequence:

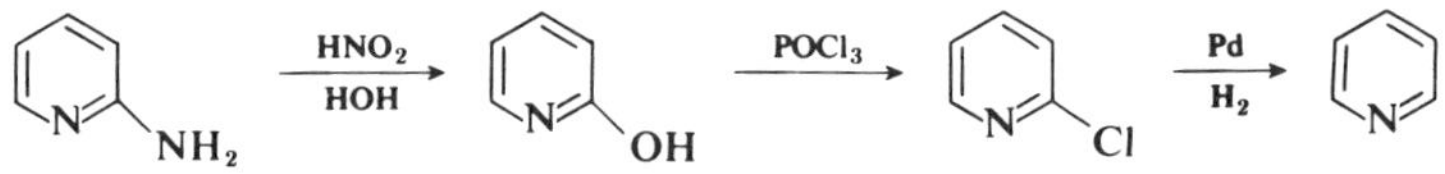

$$\text{(28-3)}$$

The *net reaction* for the *nitration of 2-aminopyridine* is given in Eq. 4; however, the process is more complicated than this equation reflects, and it

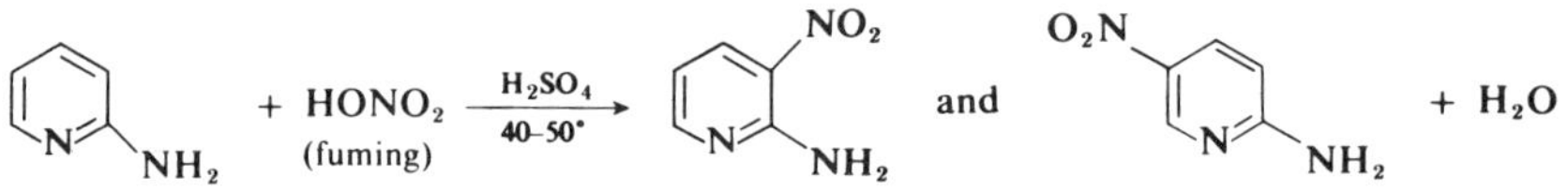

$$+ \text{ HONO}_2 \xrightarrow[\text{40-50°}]{\text{H}_2\text{SO}_4} \quad \text{and} \quad + \text{ H}_2\text{O}$$
(fuming)

$$\text{(28-4)}$$

will be instructive to consider the individual steps. First is the addition of sulfuric acid and the protonation of the 2-aminopyridine (Eq. 5). The ring-nitrogen is protonated since this leads to additional resonance stabilization (amidine type) and explains why 2-aminopyridine is a stronger base than pyridine. Addition of fuming nitric acid, with cooling, then forms the ni-

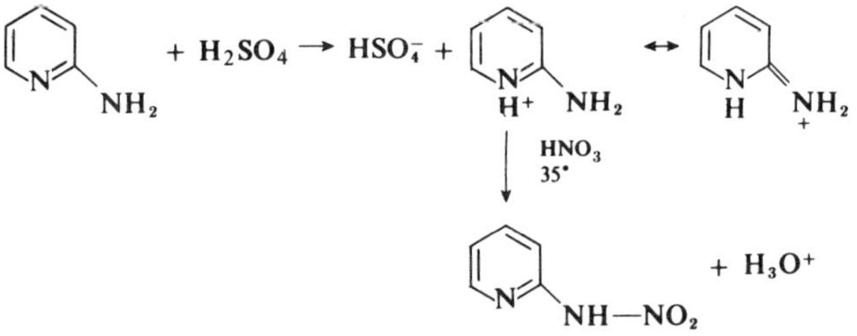

$$+ \text{ H}_2\text{SO}_4 \rightarrow \text{HSO}_4^- +$$

$$\xrightarrow[35°]{\text{HNO}_3}$$

$$+ \text{ H}_3\text{O}^+$$

$$\text{(28-5)}$$

tramine as shown in Eq. 5. If cooling is sufficiently extensive, the nitramine may be isolated as a discrete, well-characterized substance. As the preparation is carried out, no attempt is made to do this, and the reaction is allowed to proceed at a temperature such that rearrangement to the nitropyridine occurs concurrently (Eq. 6).

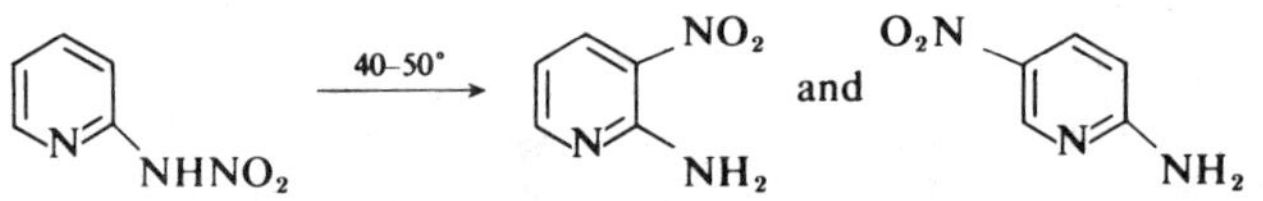

$$\xrightarrow{\text{40-50°}} \quad \text{and} \quad \text{(28-6)}$$

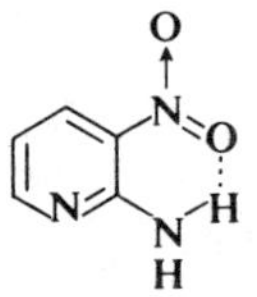

Both the 3-nitro and 5-nitro isomers are formed, but in the ratio of 1 to 10. Separation is easily effected by steam distillation after alkali has been added in order to liberate the pyridine from the pyridinium salt. The 3-isomer forms a chelate ring, as illustrated below, which leads to its low water-solubility and volatility with steam (see Chap. 18 for a discussion of chelation). Final purification for each isomer is obtained by crystallization from water.

There are no serious well-defined *side reactions*. Dinitration occurs to an extremely minor extent if at all, since the presence of the electron-withdrawing nitro group discourages further electrophilic substitution. Some hydrolysis of the 2-amino group may occur, but the resulting 2-pyridone is easily eliminated by its high water-solubility. This direct nitration procedure is the only practical method for synthesizing these compounds.

EXPERIMENTAL PROCEDURES

2-Amino-5-Nitropyridine

To 40 ml of cold concentrated sulfuric acid, contained in a 250-ml Erlenmeyer flask, there is added with efficient swirling 10 g of 2-aminopyridine. The rate of this addition is adjusted so that the temperature may be maintained at 40–50° by cooling in an ice bath, and *CARE IS TAKEN* that the sulfuric acid is not splashed out of the flask. After this addition has been completed and the temperature has been lowered to about 35°, 5 ml of *fuming* nitric acid (*CAUTION! Highly corrosive*) is added dropwise from a separatory funnel during about 5 minutes. The temperature is kept at 35–40° by continued cooling in the ice bath, and mixing by swirling is continued. After this second addition has been completed, the temperature is maintained at 40–50° for one hour by heating or cooling as necessary (Note 1). The reaction mixture is finally allowed to stand at room temperature overnight or longer (Note 2).

After the period of standing, the reaction mixture is transferred to a separatory funnel and added, very cautiously at first, to a stirred mixture of 125 ml of precooled ammonium hydroxide and about 100 g of ice contained in a one-liter beaker. The beaker is surrounded by an ice bath and its contents are stirred as the acid mixture is added dropwise from the separatory funnel. More ice is added to the beaker as necessary to keep the temperature from rising above about 10°; 200–400 g of ice are usually required. As neutralization proceeds, the reaction becomes less violent and the rate of addition may be increased. At the end of the addition, the mixture should be basic to litmus; if additional ammonia is required it should be added cautiously with stirring. The precipitated solid is collected by suction filtration, pressed well on the funnel, then washed with small portions of ice water. The wet solid is transferred to a 500-ml round-bottomed flask, which is fitted for indirect steam distillation, then 50 ml of water is added, and the mixture is rapidly steam-distilled until about 800 ml of distillate has been collected (Note 3). If more than about 100 ml of water collects in the steam-distillation flask, it is warmed with a small flame to keep the volume at about 100 ml during the distillation.

The residual solution from the steam distillation is heated to boiling and enough water (usually about 300 ml) is added to dissolve all of the 2-amino-5-nitropyridine at boiling. An additional 40 ml of water and about 1 g of charcoal are added, then the solution is reheated to boiling and filtered by gravity. The clear filtrate is concentrated to about 200 ml and allowed to cool without shaking; it may be placed in a pan of water after crystallization has set in. After the cooled mixture has stood at room temperature for a half-hour or longer (overnight is satisfactory), the crystals are collected by suction filtration, pressed well on the funnel with a small beaker, and washed with several small portions of cold water. A small sample (the amount held on the tip of a spatula) is placed on a small watch glass to dry, and the main portion is recrystallized from water, without charcoal treatment. The product from the second crystallization, which should be clear yellow crystals, is dried and weighed, and the yield is calculated. The average yield is in the range 4.5–6.5 g of material melting at about 184–186°. The melting point of the small once-crystallized sample, as well as the final product, should be determined and reported. What may be concluded concerning the purity of the material obtained after one crystallization?

NOTES

1. There sometimes occurs an exothermic reaction after an induction period; so the temperature should be watched very carefully during the period at 40–50°. If the temperature goes above about 60° the product is darkened considerably, and a "fume-off" (rapid decomposition blowing the contents out of the flask) may occur.

2. During this period the rearrangement from nitramine to nitroamine occurs. This rearrangement occurs rapidly above 60° but with the difficulties mentioned in Note 1.

3. This procedure removes the small amount of 2-amino-3-nitropyridine which is formed in this reaction. For isolation of this isomer, follow the procedure below.

2-Amino-3-Nitropyridine

This steam-volatile isomer is obtained by extraction of the steam distillate with three 25-ml portions of chloroform. The combined chloroform extracts are placed in an Erlenmeyer flask fitted for distillation, and *all* the chloroform is removed by distillation from a steam or boiling-water bath. (The distilled chloroform is returned to a bottle marked "Recovered Chloroform"; chloroform is a rather expensive solvent.) Crystallization of the residue is best effected from water, and a yield of 0.3–0.6 g of 2-amino-3-nitropyridine is obtained, m.p. 159–161°.

Quinolines

29

The heterocyclic ring system in which a benzene ring is fused to pyridine is known as quinoline. Because of their use in dyes and pharmaceuticals, especially antimalarials, there has been a wide interest in quinoline compounds, and many excellent syntheses have been developed that make possible the preparation of a large variety of derivatives. In the present chapter we shall describe the synthesis and some properties of 2-methyl-quinoline, known commonly as quinaldine.

The *main reaction* for the preparation of *quinaldine* is shown in Eq. 1.

$$(29-1)$$

The process, called the Döbner-Miller synthesis, consists of two steps, which take place concurrently. First, acetaldehyde in the presence of concentrated hydrochloric acid condenses with aniline to give 1,2-dihydro-quinaldine. The mechanism of the reaction has been well established and consists of several steps which will be considered in sequence.

Paraldehyde, the trimer of acetaldehyde that is actually used in the experiment, is de-polymerized by mineral acid to acetaldehyde (Eq. 2) which then self-condenses in the presence of strong acid to crotonaldehyde (Eq. 3). Crotonaldehyde, an α,β-unsaturated aldehyde, then reacts with

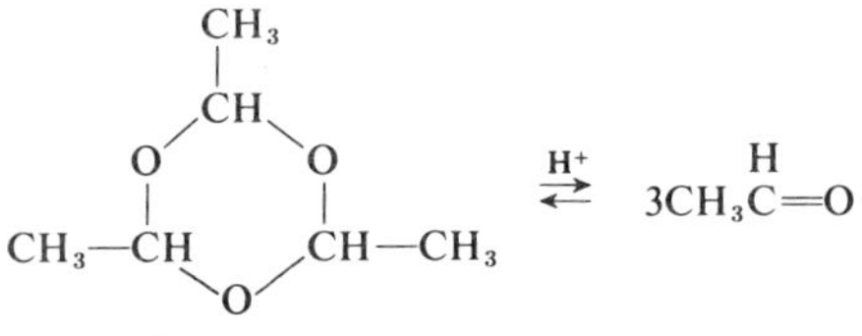

$$\text{Paraldehyde} \quad \overset{H^+}{\rightleftharpoons} \quad 3CH_3\overset{H}{C}{=}O \qquad (29\text{-}2)$$

Paraldehyde

$$2CH_3\overset{H}{-}C{=}O \quad \overset{\text{conc.}}{\underset{H^+}{\rightleftharpoons}} \quad \left[CH_3\overset{H}{\underset{OH}{-}C-}CH_2\overset{H}{-}C{=}O \right] \rightleftharpoons CH_3-CH{=}CH-\overset{H}{C}{=}O + H_2O$$

Crotonaldehyde

$$(29\text{-}3)$$

aniline by 1,4-addition, and the addition product, under the influence of strong acid, cyclizes to form the heterocyclic ring (Eq. 4).[1]

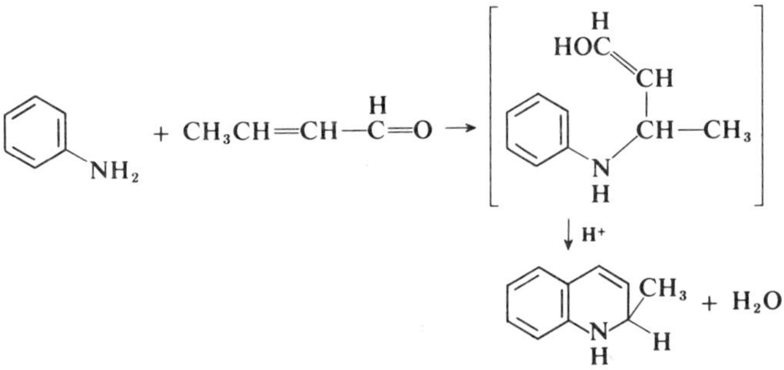

$$\text{(aniline)} \quad + \quad CH_3CH{=}CH\overset{H}{-}C{=}O \quad \rightarrow \quad \left[\text{(intermediate)} \right] \qquad (29\text{-}4)$$

$$\downarrow H^+$$

$$\text{(product)} + H_2O$$

Thus, the primary product is 1,2-dihydroquinaldine, and the second step, which begins as soon as a molecule of dihydro compound is formed, involves its dehydrogenation to the completely aromatic quinaldine. Since the product is stabilized by a much higher resonance energy, this dehydrogenation takes place rapidly in the presence of mild oxidizing agents already present in the reaction mixture. Although the oxidation is part of the main reaction, it will be discussed under side reactions because it leads to side products from which the main product must be separated.

The *side reactions* are, first, the condensation of aniline with the aldehydes present by 1,2-addition, that is, across the carbonyl, to form Schiff's bases (Eqs. 5 and 6). These anils then act as hydrogen-acceptors and oxidize

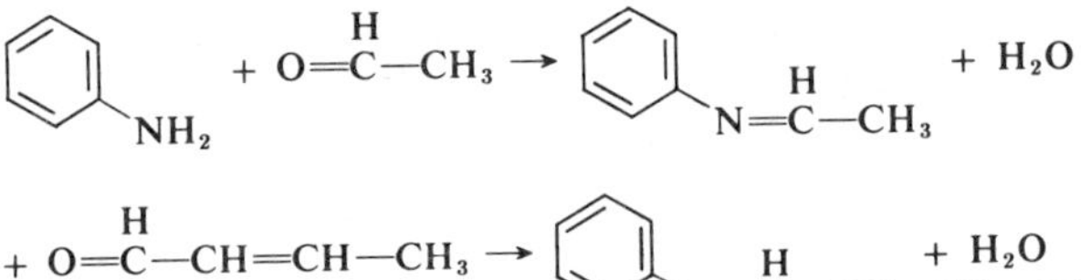

$$\text{(aniline)} \quad + \quad O{=}\overset{H}{C}{-}CH_3 \quad \rightarrow \quad \text{(anil)} \quad + H_2O \qquad (29\text{-}5)$$

$$\text{(aniline)} \quad + \quad O{=}\overset{H}{C}{-}CH{=}CH-CH_3 \quad \rightarrow \quad \text{(anil)} \quad + H_2O \qquad (29\text{-}6)$$

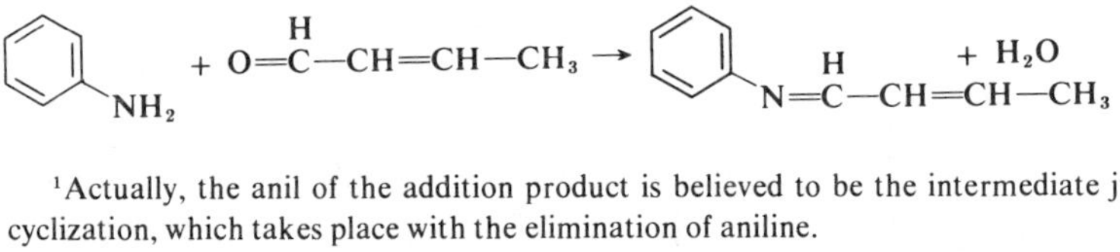

[1] Actually, the anil of the addition product is believed to be the intermediate just prior to cyclization, which takes place with the elimination of aniline.

the 1,2-dihydroquinaldine to quinaldine while being themselves reduced to *N*-alkylanilines (Eq. 7). In addition to *N-n*-butylaniline, *N*-ethylaniline is

$$2 \text{(quinaldine)} + \text{(aniline)} \longrightarrow$$

$$2 \text{(quinaldine)} + \text{(} N\text{-}n\text{-butylaniline)} \tag{29-7}$$

N-n-Butylaniline

also formed by the interaction with acetaldehyde anil. Since this oxidation step consumes aniline, it is not theoretically possible to obtain one mole of quinaldine from one mole of aniline. If the oxidant is the anil of crotonaldehyde (Eq. 7), the theoretical ratio of aniline to quinaldine is 1.5:1; however, if the anil of acetaldehyde is the oxidant, the theoretical ratio is 2:1. Although there is some oxidation by each of these anils, for purposes of calculating the theoretical yield it may be assumed (arbitrarily) that oxidation occurs according to Eq. 7. Another by-product, in addition to the alkylanilines, is a considerable amount of tarry polymer which results from polymerization of the anils.

Purification of the quinaldine must separate it from the two types of side products, namely, (1) alkylanilines and unreacted aniline and (2) polymeric material. Steam distillation would certainly remove the quinaldine from the high molecular weight polymers, but the alkylanilines and aniline would also be steam-volatile. Advantage is taken of the fact that the latter compounds are primary and secondary amines and thus can be acetylated, whereas the quinaldine is a tertiary amine and unaffected by acetic anhydride.

Benzene extraction, after basifying the reaction mixture, removes all the simple bases and some of the polymer. This extract is then acetylated with acetic anhydride, basified with sodium bicarbonate, and steam distilled. The acetylated amines are now much less volatile with steam and remain behind with the polymeric material while the benzene and quinaldine are steam-distilled. Direct distillation of the organic layer gives pure quinaldine.

The method used above for preparing quinaldine is the most direct and involves very easily available reactants. An alternative synthesis is the condensation of *o*-nitrobenzaldehyde with acetone followed by reduction (Eq. 8). Although not a competing method for the preparation of quinaldine, this general scheme of using an *o*-substituted aniline or nitrobenzene has proved useful in synthesis of more complicated derivatives.

2-(Tribromomethyl)-quinoline may be prepared readily, on account of the reactivity of the methyl hydrogens in quinaldine. The reaction is shown in Eq. 9. Merely on warming in glacial acetic acid, all three hydro-

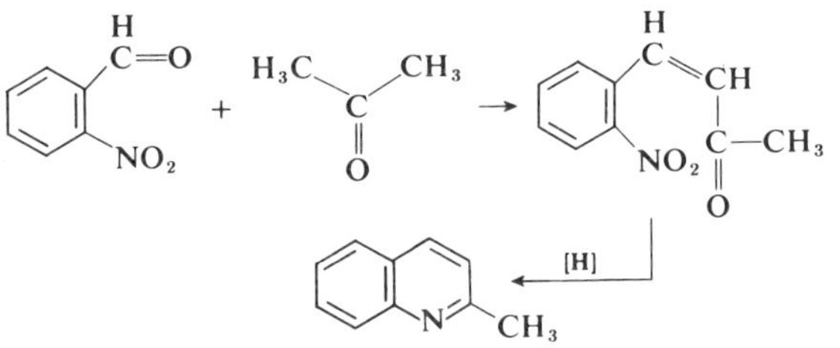

$$(29\text{-}8)$$

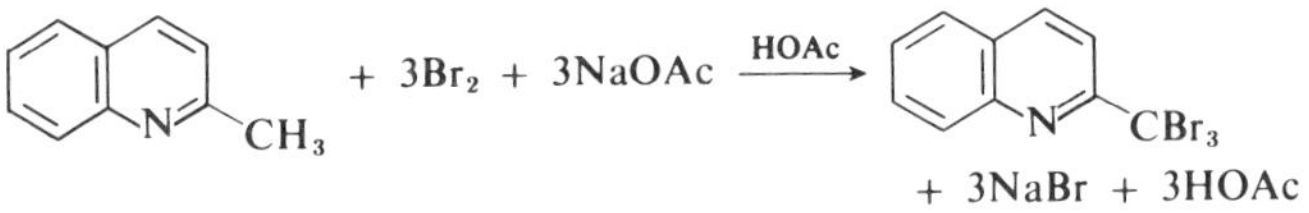

$$+ \; 3NaBr \; + \; 3HOAc \qquad (29\text{-}9)$$

gens of the methyl group are substituted by bromine. This type of reactivity is reminiscent of methyl ketones, and the analogy between the hydrogens of the 2- or 4-methyl group in quinoline and the α-hydrogens of a ketone is indeed close. Both show facile substitution by halogen and condensation with active carbonyl compounds.

The bromination (Eq. 9) is carried out in acetic acid containing excess sodium acetate to neutralize the hydrogen bromide. Dilution of the reaction mixture with water precipitates the tribromo compound. Substitution of the bromine atoms has resulted in a weaker, much less soluble base, and the sodium acetate-acetic acid mixture does not keep it in solution.

EXPERIMENTAL PROCEDURES

Quinaldine

A 500-ml round-bottomed flask is fitted with a condenser and trap as illustrated in Fig. 8-1 or 8-5, and 31 g (30 ml) of aniline is added to the flask (Note 1). To the aniline, with swirling and thorough cooling in an ice bath, is slowly added 60 ml of concentrated hydrochloric acid through the top of the condenser; this is followed by the addition of 45 g of paraldehyde. The solution is removed from the ice bath and shaken frequently at room temperature for 45 minutes, heated cautiously to a boil, and maintained under reflux for 1 hour. During the period of cautious heating to a boil, an ice bath is kept available in case the reaction should become violent and require moderating. The mixture is then cooled and basified slowly with about 50 ml of 12N sodium hydroxide. After 200 ml of additional water has been added, the solution is extracted (Note 1) with three 50-ml portions of benzene, as the separation of layers is performed carefully. The combined benzene extracts are concentrated by distilling about 25 ml (Notes 1, 2); then the residual solution is heated under reflux for about 15 minutes with 30 ml of acetic anhydride. The benzene solution is then cooled and basified by addition of 50 ml of 12N sodium hydroxide (Note 3) in 5-ml portions, with shaking and cooling to keep the temperature below 40°. Finally, 10 g of solid sodium bicarbonate is added (Note 3), and the mixture is indirectly steam-distilled. Benzene distills rapidly at first, then quinaldine comes over slowly. Distillation is continued until all the quinaldine has been distilled (Note 4). The benzene layer is separated, the aqueous phase is extracted with two 25-ml portions of benzene, and the combined benzene extracts are distilled from a 250-ml distilling flask until most of the benzene has been distilled. The flask is then cooled and the residual solution is poured (flames extinguished) into the 50-ml distilling flask, which has been fitted for distillation. A rinse of 2–3 ml of benzene is used. The remaining benzene is distilled from the small flask, the flame is turned up until the boiling ring of quinaldine reaches the thermometer, then receivers are changed, and quinaldine is collected in the range 240–250° (reported b.p. 246–247°). A yield of 12–15 g may be expected.

NOTES

1. After the reagents are mixed, it is advisable, although not imperative, to continue through the stage where the basified reaction mixture is extracted with benzene before the procedure is interrupted and the products are allowed to stand overnight. There may be aldehydes or anils in the reaction mixture which will polymerize on long standing and increase the difficulty of work-up.

As usual in extractions with benzene, the low-level but cumulative toxicity of this solvent should be respected. Unless the laboratory is well-ventilated, extraction should be carried out in a forced-draft hood. Even though steam heating may be used to avoid a fire, distillation of benzene into the laboratory cannot be tolerated.

2. Since excess acetic anhydride is used for acetylation of the secondary amines, it is not important that the benzene solution be rigidly dried; however, gross amounts of water should be avoided. If the layers are separated carefully, and water is removed azeotropically by distillation of a little benzene, sufficient dryness is assured.

3. It is important that the mixture not be acidic during the steam distillation, for this would convert quinaldine to its salt and thus prevent its steam distillation. On the other hand, if the mixture is strongly alkaline the amides will slowly hydrolyze and liberate amines which will distill with the quinaldine. Unless a rather inaccurate amount of sodium hydroxide is used, the addition of sodium bicarbonate insures a nearly neutral solution, for bicarbonate will neutralize either acid or alkali.

4. About one liter of steam distillate is usually required to distill the quinaldine. After about this quantity of distillate has been received, separate portions should be collected in a test tube in order to observe whether droplets of quinaldine are still appearing. When the cooled distillate is only somewhat cloudy, the steam distillation should be stopped.

2-(Tribromomethyl)-Quinoline

The 250-ml flask with side tubes (Note 1) is charged with 7 g of anhydrous, powdered sodium acetate, 15 g of glacial acetic acid, and 2 g of freshly distilled quinaldine. The flask is fitted with a reflux condenser in the center neck, a small separatory funnel in one side tube, and a thermometer extending into the liquid in the other side tube (Note 1). The separatory funnel is charged with a solution of 6.8 g of bromine (*CAUTION!* Note 2) in 16 ml of glacial acetic acid. After the flask has been heated to about 70°, the source of heat is removed, and the bromine solution is dropped in during the course of about 15 minutes. Finally, the flask is heated on a steam bath or boiling-water bath for about one-half hour, with frequent shaking. At the end of the reaction the mixture is cooled, then poured into 50 ml of ice water. The precipitate is collected by suction filtration and washed well with water, then drained well on the funnel. It is heated under reflux with 40 ml of 95% ethanol, and if solution does not occur after a few minutes, additional ethanol is added in 5-ml portions until solution does occur. On slow cooling, 2-(tribromomethyl)-quinoline crystallizes in a yield of about 4 g, m.p. 127–128°. It is collected, washed, dried, and bottled as a product in the usual manner.

NOTES

1. If the flask with ground joint and side tubes (Appendix I) is not available, an ordinary flask may be used, with the dropping funnel attached to the top of the condenser in such manner as not to close the system; however, addition of bromine from a funnel in this hazardous position is not recommended. It is better to use an extraction flask, with a two-hole cork to accommodate the dropping funnel and condenser. In either case, the thermometer is omitted and the flask is warmed on a steam bath for about 2 minutes before bromine addition is begun.

2. For proper precautions in handling the highly corrosive and poisonous bromine, refer to Chap. 17.

Separation and Identification of
Organic Compounds

30

An examination of the synthetic procedures which have been described in earlier chapters of this book will suggest that the actual preparation of an organic compound is frequently less laborious than separating the compound from the reaction mixture and obtaining it in a relatively pure condition. Of course this process becomes more difficult, although more intriguing perhaps, if the identities and properties of the compounds are not known. In chemical research involving unexplored syntheses, it is often necessary to separate the desired product from by-products of unknown identities and properties, even though the nature of the desired product may be reasonably well assessed or estimated from knowledge of the reaction used for the preparation, and from knowledge of the properties of similar compounds. In the separation of compounds from natural sources, it is nearly always necessary to accomplish the separation of many compounds, and some of these compounds may have very similar properties.

After a compound has been separated and obtained in what appears to be a pure condition, one may proceed with the identification of the compound. The first step in such an identification is determining whether the compound is one that is already known and characterized. This involves searching the literature for a compound whose physical properties are the same as the one in hand. Although the classical criteria of boiling point and melting point, especially the latter, remain of importance, spectral characteristics are the most important physical properties for characterization of a compound. The application of nuclear magnetic resonance for distinction between isomers has been discussed in Chap. 10, and absorption in the infrared has been discussed in several chapters. Perhaps the most powerful tool of all is mass spectrometry, wherein the vapor of a substance is bombarded with an electron beam of sufficiently high energy to give fragmentation of the molecule. Deflection of the resultant beam of positive ions in a magnetic and/or electric field allows determination of their masses. The "fragmentation pattern" is a very sensitive characteristic of a compound. In addition, knowledge has rapidly accumulated which allows deduction of structure from the fragmentation pattern of the molecule. Furthermore, the *molecular ion* may be recognized, so this furnishes at once the molecular weight of the compound, a very valuable datum. The high-resolution mass spectrum can also give the composition of the compound, i.e., the molecular formula.

If the compound under investigation proves not to be one that can be located in the literature, it is judged to be a new compound, and its structure must be determined by application of physical or chemical methods. At the present time, physical methods are most effective in structure elucidation on account of the large amount of spectral data that has become available on compounds whose structures had been previously proved by chemical methods. In determination of structure by chemical methods, it is necessary to convert the unknown compound to another compound (or compounds) whose identity will then be examined. This process must then be continued until known compounds are eventually encountered. The sequence of reactions eventually yielding the known compound or compounds may then be retraced and the pieces fitted together to give the structure of the original compound. Since this sequence is usually more profitable if the original unknown compound is converted to compounds of lower molecular weight, hence more easily identified, the process is often termed "degradation" of the unknown compound. On account of the increasing effectiveness of modern physical methods of examining molecules (absorption spectra, mass spectra, x-ray diffraction), it is no longer necessary in many instances to carry the degradative sequence all the way to previously known and characterized compounds. The structure of either the original compound, or of some degradative product obtained in relatively few steps, may often be fully established by application of physical methods.

Whatever methods may be required to establish the identity of a compound, it remains necessary to separate the compound in a pure state (with rare exceptions), and to characterize the compound by examination of its physical properties. In this chapter, we will illustrate the methods of attack that are used by application of simple methods of separation (extraction and distillation), and by manipulating small samples in order to supply solid derivatives which may be characterized by melting point. Similar manipulations of small samples are required to furnish the samples used to feed the spectrometers. In earlier chapters, we have actually applied in variety the most generally effective known methods for separation of compounds on a small scale—gas chromatography and thin sheet chromatography. As discussed in Chap. 4, collection of small samples from gas chromatography presents no problems. The application of spectroscopic methods for identification of very small samples of compounds, such as collected in glpc or eluted from a tlc spot, is not included in the scope of the present book.

Separation of Organic Compounds

Although chemical separations have been carried out in the course of purifying the compounds which have been synthesized during the study of earlier chapters, it is desirable to consider such separations at this time in a somewhat more detailed manner. It is usually most profitable to first accomplish a separation on the basis of the solubilities of the compounds, especially solubilities depending on the presence in the molecules of acidic or basic groups. Of course such a procedure also constitutes a beginning of the identification of the compounds, since the presence or absence of such functional groups becomes established.

In the gross separation of compounds based on functional groups, as studied in the present experiments, it will be assumed that the organic compounds will be soluble in a good organic solvent such as benzene and that suitable salts of acids or bases will be soluble in water. In the overwhelming majority of organic compounds, these assumptions prove to be true. In the relatively smaller, but not insignificant number of cases in which these solubilities do not hold true, this usually becomes apparent in the early stages of the examination, and suitable special solvents or other procedures must be used. For example, a sugar such as glucose is a neutral compound which is insoluble in benzene and soluble in water. A different problem arises in the case of a high molecular weight fatty acid, such as stearic acid, which is soluble in benzene, but its sodium salt is a soap which is very sparingly soluble in water.

In the usual type of separation, the mixture of organic compounds is shaken with a mixture of benzene and dilute hydrochloric acid (hydrochlorides of amines are usually rather water-soluble salts). The aqueous layer may then be separated and made alkaline to free the amine from its salt; then the amine is recovered either by filtration if it is a solid, or by extraction with a solvent if it is a liquid. The solid is then purified by crystallization, or the liquid is purified by distillation. The benzene layer is next shaken with a dilute solution of sodium hydroxide in order to separate acids as water-soluble salts. The acid is recovered from the aqueous solution by acidification, followed by either filtration or extraction. Neutral compounds are finally recovered from the benzene solution.

In case a mixture contains more than one basic, acidic, or neutral compound, further separation must be accomplished by physical methods. These methods will not be applied in the present experiments; however, the most effective methods have been discussed in earlier chapters (fractional crystallization, fractional distillation, liquid phase chromatography, and gas chromatography). Subsequent chapters extend the consideration of distillation to operation at reduced pressure (Chap. 31), and utilization of more effective fractional distillation equipment (Chap. 32).

Tests for Elements in Organic Compounds

After an organic compound has been obtained in a condition believed to be homogeneous (in other words, in a pure condition), one of the first tests normally carried out is qualitative analysis for certain elements. For new compounds, not previously identified, it is customary to secure quantitative analyses for elements found to be present; however, if the compound is a known one it is rarely an advantage to secure quantitative analyses. Identification may be secured by a study of properties in the manner described below, or by study of other physical properties such as absorption spectra. Qualitative tests for elements are useful, however, especially in neutral compounds. For example, a neutral nitrogen-containing compound may be a nitrile, amide, or nitro compound, but it will not be a ketone, ether, or ester (unless a polyfunctional compound).

Since all organic compounds contain carbon, and most of them contain hydrogen, qualitative analysis for these elements is rarely any advantage. If there is doubt about the organic nature of the compound, a sample may be tested for burning. Nearly all organic compounds burn more or less readily, and leave no ash unless they are metallic salts, while few inorganic compounds burn readily. Exceptions are sufficiently rare to cause little, if any, uncertainty.

The elements occurring most commonly in organic compounds, in addition to carbon and hydrogen, are oxygen, nitrogen, halogen, and sulfur. Qualitative tests for oxygen are very difficult and rarely performed; so the tests to be presently considered include those for nitrogen, halogen, and sulfur. Since elementary tests are usually based on detection of ions, the first step in qualitative analysis for elements in organic compounds is some drastic treatment which will rupture the covalently bonded molecules and convert nitrogen, sulfur, and halogen to suitable ions. One such procedure consists of heating the compound with molten sodium, and it will be used in the present tests.

Fusion of an organic compound with sodium converts sulfur to sulfide ion, which may be detected by precipitation of lead sulfide. Nitrogen is converted to cyanide ion, which is detected by addition of ferric and ferrous ions. Ferric ferrocyanide (Prussian blue) forms as a blue precipitate.

Halogen is converted to halide ion, and this is detected by the precipitation of silver halide. Tests to distinguish among the halogens are occasionally carried out, but this is rarely of value in identification of organic compounds. Another test for halogen, known as the Beilstein test, depends on combustion of the organic compound on a previously heated copper wire. If halogen is present, sufficient copper halide is usually formed to impart a green or blue-green color to the flame; however, this test is not as reliable as the test dependent on sodium fusion. Positive results may be obtained from compounds, such as organic acids, which do not contain halogen.

Identification of Organic Compounds

As has been studied in Chaps. 2 and 5, the melting point of a compound is far more useful than the boiling point as a criterion of identity and purity. A solid compound which is pure has a characteristic melting point, which may be accurately determined on a small sample, and the sample will melt completely over a rather narrow range of temperature. Addition of another compound, even in rather small amounts, will usually cause the melting to occur over a broad range, with the top of this range below the melting point of the pure compound. It follows from this behavior that even though two compounds have the same melting point, a mixture of the two will melt at a lower temperature and over a broad range. Thus, by the mixed melting-point behavior, it may be readily determined whether two samples of material are the same compound. If an authentic sample of a compound is available, the identity or lack of identity of an "unknown" is frequently established by observing the melting point of a mixture of the two samples of material. In case authentic samples are not available for comparison, a sample of unknown identity may still be limited to those compounds having nearly the same melting point as observed for the "unknown." If the "unknown" is then converted by a chemical reaction to another solid compound, the melting point of this derivative may also be determined and compared with the values reported in the literature for the same derivative of any compounds having melting points similar to the original "unknown." If necessary, still another derivative might be prepared, but the list of candidates is frequently narrowed to a single compound after one solid derivative has been prepared. This is especially likely to be the case when there are also used tests to distinguish between types of compounds. For example, the Hinsberg test (Procedure 2 in this chapter) may be used to determine whether an amine is primary, secondary, or tertiary; oxidation tests (Chap. 15) may be used to distinguish between aldehydes and ketones; and so forth.

In contrast to the situation prevailing in the case of a solid, the boiling

point of a liquid is of limited value. A reasonably good boiling point can
be determined only if at least a gram of material is available, and a larger
sample is desirable. An inaccurate boiling point will be observed unless
skillful precautions against superheating are observed (cf. Chap. 5). Furthermore, and worst of all, a mixture of two compounds of the same
boiling point exhibits the same boiling point as observed for the separate
compounds. For these reasons, it is common practice to seek a conversion
of a liquid compound to a solid derivative which may be readily characterized by its melting point.

For the reasons presented above, *a rather important operation in identification of organic compounds is the formation of solid derivatives*. In
order for a compound to qualify as a good derivative, the derived substance
must be obtainable by a relatively simple chemical reaction which may be
carried out on a small sample in a relatively short time. For example, a
nitrile or amide may be hydrolyzed to an acid, or an acid may be converted via the acid chloride to an amide. Both acids and amides are frequently solids. Ketones, which are often liquids, may be easily converted to
oximes (cf. Chap. 15) or semicarbazones, many of which are solids. Other
derivatives which are usually solids have been developed for the various
classes of compounds.

In Table I in this chapter (p. 266) are listed the compounds which will
be used to study methods of identification in the present experiments. For
each are listed boiling point or melting point and a solid derivative which
is regarded as satisfactory for identification purposes.

As a final comment on identification of organic compounds, it should
be mentioned that gas phase chromatography (Chap. 4) is remarkably
effective for the separation of compounds as well as their identification.
Indeed, a mixture may be analyzed both qualitatively and quantitatively
in a single operation. The only requirement is that the compound have a
vapor pressure of at least 2 mm at a temperature at which it is thermally
stable. For essentially nonvolatile compounds, thin sheet chromatography
(Chap. 7) is frequently as effective as is gas chromatography for the
volatile compounds. In the several types of chromatography, it is not important whether the compound be solid or liquid. This is also true in utilization of spectra for identification.

EXPERIMENTAL PROCEDURES

General Techniques

In many of the manipulations involved in identification of organic compounds, small volumes of liquid are transferred or a few drops of reagent

FIG. 1.   Bulb pipette for the transfer of small volumes.

are added in a test. For these purposes, a small dropping pipette is almost indispensable. A suitable pipette, as illustrated in Fig. 1, may be readily made from a 6-mm glass tube. The tube is rotated in a narrow flame (from a burner with a wing-tip or a blast lamp) as it is pressed lightly together until a ridge forms. After the glass has cooled, it is scratched near this ridge and broken, then fire-polished. This ridge holds the small rubber bulb (from a medicine dropper) firmly in place. By heating the tube at a suitable distance (about 15 cm) from the ridge and drawing it out carefully, a constriction is formed. The cooled tube is then broken at the center of the constriction, and the tip is fire-polished carefully so that it does not become sealed.

When a small volume of solution is *filtered hot* to remove insoluble impurities, as is common in preparing derivatives (cf. later procedures), this is done by gravity in a relatively small, short-stem funnel with a small filter paper. If only larger filter paper is available, it may be easily trimmed down with scissors after it has been folded in quarters. The warm solution is then transferred portionwise to the filter, by use of the bulb pipette, after the heated solution has first been drawn into the pipette a few times and forced out in order to heat the pipette. A portion of about 1 ml of warm solvent is finally used to wash the vessel, the pipette, and the

Table I

Derivatives and Properties of Selected Compounds

Compounds are arranged in groups according to functional group, as follows: amines, acids, phenols, aldehydes, ketones, esters, nitriles, amides, alcohols, alkylbenzenes, sulfonic acids, or salts. The numbered procedures for making derivatives are on pp. 277–292.

Compound	M.P.	B.P.	Derivative, M.P. (Procedure No.)
Aniline		183°	Benzenesulfonamide, 112° (2)
N,N-Dimethylaniline		193°	Methiodide salt, 225° (dec.) (1)
N-Methylaniline		195°	Benzenesulfonamide, 79° (2)
o-Toluidine		200°	Benzenesulfonamide, 124° (2)
N-Ethyl-N-methylaniline		201°	Methiodide salt, 136° (1)
m-Toluidine		203°	Benzenesulfonamide, 95° (2)
o-Chloroaniline		207°	Benzenesulfonamide, 129° (2)
Heptanoic acid		223°	Heptanamide, 96° (3)
Caprylic acid		237°	Caprylamide, 106° (3)
Azelaic acid	106°		Azelaic diamide, 172° (3)
m-Methylbenzoic acid	111°		m-Methylbenzamide, 97° (3)
Benzoic acid	121°		Benzamide, 130° (3)
o-Chlorobenzoic acid	142°		o-Chlorobenzamide, 139° (3)
m-Nitrobenzoic acid	140°		m-Nitrobenzamide, 143° (3)
o-Bromophenol		195°	Aryloxyacetic acid, 143° (4)
m-Cresol		203°	Aryloxyacetic acid, 103° (4)
Guaiacol		205°	Aryloxyacetic acid, 121° (4)
m-Ethylphenol		217°	Aryloxyacetic acid, 77° (4)
n-Heptaldehyde		155°	Semicarbazone, 109° (5)
Cyclohexanone		155°	Semicarbazone, 166° (5)
2-Ethylhexanal		163°	Semicarbazone, 75° (5)
Diisobutyl ketone		168°	2,4-Dinitrophenylhydrazone, 92° (6)
3-Methylcyclohexanone		169°	Semicarbazone, 180° (5)
Benzaldehyde		179°	Semicarbazone, 222° (5)
o-Chlorobenzaldehyde		214°	Semicarbazone,* 146° (5)
2-Octanone		173°	Semicarbazone, 123° (5)
5-Nonanone		190°	Semicarbazone, 90° (5)
Methyl phenyl ketone		202°	Semicarbazone, 199° (5)
Methyl caprylate		193°	Caprylamide, 106° (7, 3)
Methyl benzoate		199°	Benzoic acid, 121° (7)
Methyl o-chlorobenzoate		235°	o-Chlorobenzoic acid, 142° (7)
Methyl m-nitrobenzoate	77°		m-nitrobenzoic acid, 140° (7)
Benzonitrile		191°	Benzoic acid, 121° (7)
Caprylonitrile		200°	Caprylamide, 106° (9)
o-Chlorobenzonitrile	46°		o-Chlorobenzoic acid, 142° (7)
p-Nitrophenylacetonitrile	116°		p-Nitrophenylacetic acid, 152° (7)
m-Nitrobenzonitrile	117°		m-Nitrobenzoic acid, 140° (7)
Benzamide	130°		Benzoic acid, 121° (7)
p-Methylbenzamide	160°		p-Methylbenzoic acid, 180° (7)

Table 1 *(continued)*

Compound	M.P.	B.P.	Derivative, M.P. (Procedure No.)
1-Hexanol		158°	3,5-Dinitrobenzoate, 58° (10)
Cyclohexanol		161°	3,5-Dinitrobenzoate, 112° (10)
2-Octanol		180°	3,5-Dinitrobenzoate, 46° (10)
1-Octanol		195°	3,5-Dinitrobenzoate, 61° (10)
1,3-Propanediol		215°	3,5-Dinitrobenzoate, 178° (10)
o-Chlorotoluene		159°	o-Chlorobenzoic acid, 142° (11)
m-Chlorotoluene		162°	m-Chlorobenzoic acid, 155° (11)
p-Chlorotoluene		162°	p-Chlorobenzoic acid, 243° (11)
Sodium p-toluenesulfonate	. . .		p-Toluidine salt, 198° (12)
β-Naphthalenesulfonic acid†	125°		p-Toluidine salt, 221° (12)

*This derivative is polymorphic (two crystal forms with different m.p.); it may crystallize in the form melting at about 230° or higher.
†There is given the m.p. of the monohydrate, which is very hygroscopic; m.p. of trihydrate, 83°.

funnel, in sequence. With small quantities, where yield is less important than purity, a more dilute solution is frequently used for crystallization, so that heating the funnel, as described in Chap. 3, may be unnecessary.

Filtration of small quantities of crystals and extractions of small volumes are carried out in a usual manner, except that suitable small equipment must be used. The crystals are collected by suction filtration on the small funnel with sloping sides and small filter plate, known as a Hirsch funnel. Most extractions are conveniently carried out in a 125-ml separatory funnel; however, very small volumes may be conveniently separated in a test tube by using the small bulb pipette to remove one layer. If the lower layer is being removed, the bulb is squeezed to empty the pipette after the tip has been passed through the upper layer, so that only the lower layer is drawn in when the bulb is released. If a tiny upper layer is desired (as for withdrawing a tertiary amine for the solubility test in the Hinsberg procedure), it is skimmed off with the bulb pipette, along with some lower layer, then the lower layer is forced out of the pipette until only the upper layer remains. A very few drops may be collected off the surface in this manner.

Nickel spatulas are quite convenient for transferring small amounts of solids, pressing crystals on a suction funnel, and the like. Nickel is attacked by aqueous acidic solutions, however, so a *nickel spatula should never be used to stir an acidic solution*, for this will cause one's products to come out green.

A *drying tube* charged with calcium chloride is used in several of the procedures. After such a tube has been prepared and used, it should be corked and saved in case it is needed again.

Tests for the Elements

Ordinarily, it is not necessary to carry out qualitative tests for the elements on known compounds prior to testing the unknown. In case inconsistencies are encountered in the course of identifying an unknown, it may become desirable to repeat the tests for elements after a known has been tested. A suitable mixture containing the three elements of interest is *p*-dibromobenzene and diphenylthiourea. It should be mentioned that the nitrogen test is most likely to be missed, while trace impurities (such as may be in distilled water) may give a faint cloudiness in the halogen test, even though halogen is absent.

The Sodium Fusion

The oil is removed with a piece of filter paper from a piece of freshly cut sodium (*CAUTION!* Note 1) about 4 mm in diameter, and the sodium is placed in a 5-inch Pyrex test tube that is supported vertically by a clamp lined with a piece of asbestos cloth. The tube is heated with a hot flame until the vapors of sodium rise about one-half inch, then a small amount (about 0.2 g) of the compound to be analyzed is dropped directly into the sodium vapor, as particular care is taken that the material does not touch the inside of the tube. There may be a slight explosion when the organic material strikes the sodium vapor; consequently, the eyes should be protected with glasses or goggles. After the sample has been added, the tube is heated to redness for about 1 minute. The tube is allowed to cool, 3 ml of methyl alcohol is added, the walls of the tube are rubbed with a stirring rod until any unreacted sodium has been decomposed, then the tube is filled to half its volume with distilled water and boiled gently for 1 minute. The clear, colorless filtrate obtained by filtering the aqueous solution is used in the following tests. The Pyrex test tube should be saved for regular use in sodium fusions.

The Sulfur Test

After 1 ml of the filtrate has been acidified with acetic acid, a few drops of a solution of lead acetate are added by use of the bulb pipette shown in Fig. 1. A black precipitate of lead sulfide is indicative of sulfur.

The Test for Nitrogen

To 3 ml of the filtrate are added five drops of a 5% solution of ferrous sulfate and five drops of a 10% solution of potassium fluoride. After the resulting mixture has been boiled gently for a few seconds, the suspension of iron hydroxides is cooled and treated with two drops of a 5% ferric chloride solution. Sufficient dilute sulfuric acid (25%) is then added to dissolve the insoluble iron hydroxides and to make the solution distinctly acid to litmus.

If cyanide ions are in the filtrate from the sodium fusion, a brilliant blue precipitate or suspension of Prussian blue appears at this point. A small amount of precipitate is easily seen against the white background of a filter paper; if in doubt, the solution should be filtered.

General Test for Halogen

A 2-ml portion of the filtrate from the sodium fusion is acidified with dilute nitric acid and, if sulfur or nitrogen was shown to be present by the preceding tests, the solution is boiled to expel all the hydrogen sulfide or hydrocyanic acid present. After the solution has cooled, a few drops of a silver nitrate solution are added. A white or pale-yellow precipitate that darkens rapidly on exposure to light shows the presence of halogen. Standard methods may be used to determine which halogen is present, but this is rarely desirable in organic work.

NOTE

1. *Sodium metal constitutes a serious hazard* if allowed to come into contact with water. The reaction with water evolves hydrogen, and is so exothermic that the hydrogen usually explodes as it combines with oxygen in the air. For this reason, sodium is stored under a heavy oil in order to prevent contact with moist air. Since the hands are somewhat moist, *sodium should never be picked up with the hands*. No larger piece of sodium than specified should be used, and any scraps resulting from cutting a larger piece should be returned to the bottle of oil.

Separation of a Mixture; The Basic Component

The mixture issued to you will not contain more than one acid, base, or neutral compound. About 12 g of this mixture, which may be partly liquid and partly solid, is placed in a 250-ml separatory funnel containing 50 ml of benzene and 75 ml of 1N hydrochloric acid. The mixture is shaken gently for about a half minute, then the layers are allowed to separate (Note 1), and the water layer is drawn off. The benzene is extracted with two 10-ml portions of water, which are combined and extracted with a fresh 15-ml portion of benzene (a simple countercurrent extraction). Finally, the water extracts are combined with the original acidic solution, and the second benzene extract (15 ml) is reserved, but kept separate from the main benzene solution (50 ml).

For recovery of any amine extracted as its salt in the aqueous layer, this layer is made distinctly alkaline to litmus paper (Note 2). If a solid separates, the mixture is cooled in ice, and the solid is collected by suction filtration, then washed on the funnel with cold water. After the solid has been dried, its melting point is determined. If the melting range indicates a rather impure compound, it is crystallized from a suitable solvent (cf. Chap. 3) before the procedure for identification is applied.

If a liquid separates from the basified solution (Note 3), the aqueous phase is extracted with two portions of benzene (25 ml, 10 ml). These extracts are kept separate and washed in sequence with two 10-ml portions of water, as the final separation is made very carefully. These water washes are discarded. The total benzene extract is finally distilled from a 50-ml distilling flask, as the distillate is condensed with a condenser in the usual way (Note 4). Since *benzene vapor has sufficient toxicity to render highly inadvisable the inhaling of large amounts of it, under no circumstances should it be boiled into the room*, even if fire hazard be avoided by heating with steam. After distillation of benzene, if the liquid is rather high-boiling, as are those in Table I, there will be very little intermediate in the distillation. As the heat input is increased, the boiling ring of the liquid may be seen to rise in the neck of the distilling flask. At this point, the condenser may be removed, and the compound may be received directly in a test tube. The test tube is clamped in position with the side arm of the distilling flask extending into it and to a point about 3 cm from the bottom. For small amounts of high-boiling materials, cooling of the test tube with a damp cloth is usually unnecessary; however, distillation should not be so rapid that vapor escapes the test tube and catches fire. The distilled product, which should be collected over not more than a 5° range, is used for the identification procedure.

There are not included in Table I liquid compounds of too high a boiling point to be distilled at atmospheric pressure. In case such compounds are encountered, they may be purified in most instances by distillation at reduced pressure (cf. Chap. 31).

If the residue for distillation is less than about 4 ml, it should be transferred for distillation to a 25-ml distilling flask. This transfer may be accomplished with the small bulb pipette (Fig. 1) with essentially no loss.

NOTES

1. There may appear a solid at this stage, which is not entirely dissolved in the two-phase solution. A larger amount of solvent could be used to dissolve the solid,

but if a considerable amount of solid is present, it is more convenient to filter it from the two-phase solution by suction, then carry out tests to learn its identity. If this is done properly, the solid causes no difficulty.

The solid may be: (1) an amine hydrochloride which did not entirely dissolve in the aqueous phase, (2) an acid or a neutral compound sparingly soluble in benzene. If the solid is the amine salt, it will dissolve in water. If this proves to be the case, the solid may be simply reserved and added to the aqueous acid solution of the remainder of the amine salt, before the salt solution is made basic for precipitation of the amine.

If the solid is insoluble in water, hence in category (2) above, its solubility in 1N sodium hydroxide is tested, as described later for examination of a pure compound. If the compound dissolves in aqueous sodium hydroxide solution, it is an acid, hence is reserved for addition to the acid recovered from the alkaline extract, as described in the next section. If the compound proves to be neutral, it is dried and reserved for addition to the neutral compound isolated in the procedure described below.

If the solid is a *mixture* of an acid and a neutral compound (partly soluble in sodium hydroxide solution), the neutral compound is filtered by suction from a solution of the salt of the acid in 75 ml of 1N sodium hydroxide. The neutral compound so recovered is washed well on the funnel with water, dried, and added to any neutral compound recovered as described below. The alkaline solution of the salt is used as the alkali for extraction of the benzene solution in the section entitled "The Acidic Component."

2. If the acid extract is colored, but no precipitate separates on basifying, the color may be due to water-soluble impurities in a phenol which will be separated later in the extraction with base.

3. There may have been present in the aqueous acidic extract the salt of an amine which is sufficiently soluble in water to remain dissolved as the free base after the solution has been basified. Furthermore, there could be present a neutral or acidic compound which is in the water layer not because of salt formation but because the substance itself is more soluble in water than in benzene. In either case, if nothing separates from the basified solution, it is most economical of time to simply reserve this solution until the work-up procedure has been completed. Since there will be only two compounds in the unknown mixture, if an acid and a neutral substance are separated in the later part of the procedure, there is no object in searching for a base by further examining the above-mentioned aqueous solution. If only one compound is found, then this aqueous solution must be extracted for recovery of the soluble amine, or worked up for the sulfonic acid or salt (cf. below).

There are only two compounds in Table I which would preferentially dissolve in water rather than benzene. These are the sulfonic acid and the sulfonic acid salt. These may be "salted out" of the water solution (cf. Chap. 19). Compounds such as sugars are relatively difficult to recover from the aqueous solution. It is often necessary to remove ions by use of such a device as ion exchange resins, then evaporate the water.

4. Since benzene forms a minimum-boiling azeotrope with water, it is unnecessary to dry the extract before distillation. The first distillate will be cloudy and will distill at a temperature below the boiling point of benzene.

The Acidic Component

The benzene solutions (50 ml and 15 ml) remaining after extraction with acid are next extracted with about 75 ml of 1N sodium hydroxide solution. First the 50-ml portion of benzene is extracted, then the 15-ml portion is extracted with the same alkali. Since basic solutions are prone to encourage formation of emulsions, especially if salts of higher fatty acids are present, the extraction is accomplished by gently rocking the separatory funnel back and forth for about a minute. If a salt should precipitate, sufficient water (not sodium hydroxide solution) is added to dissolve the precipitate. After the alkaline extract has been separated from the second (15-ml) portion of benzene, the two portions of benzene are washed in sequence with two 10-ml portions of water. As in separation of the basic component, appropriate extracts are combined before isolation of the components. The combined aqueous phases are acidified to Congo red paper with 6N sulfuric acid, and the organic acid is recovered according to the procedure described for recovery of bases. In this case, however, any material recovered from the aqueous extract must be an acid, for any material going into the aqueous phase because of high water-solubility would have already been removed by the previous extraction of bases with dilute acid.

The Neutral Component

The combined benzene extracts remaining after extraction of bases and acids will contain any neutral compounds. The neutral component is recovered by distillation of the benzene from a 125-ml distilling flask. Care should be taken not to overheat any residue remaining after solvent distillation has become quite slow. If there is a residue it is cooled in an ice bath, and if it becomes crystalline (Note 1) a sample is scraped out of the flask and dried to remove residual benzene. It must be borne in mind at this point, and whenever a sample is recovered from a solvent, that *drying is essential before the melting point is determined*—solvent will lower the melting point just as will any other impurity. If the melting point indicates a reasonably pure compound, the identification procedure is applied directly; if the compound is impure, the entire sample is recrystallized before the identification procedure is applied. In case recrystallization is unnecessary, the material in the distilling flask which cannot be scraped out readily may be dissolved later in a suitable solvent for use in a test or for preparation of a derivative. Weight of this residue may be determined by difference after the flask has been cleaned and dried.

If the residue does not crystallize on cooling, or remelts at room temperature, it is transferred with the bulb pipette to a 25-ml distilling flask and purified by distillation.

NOTE

1. If the crystals remelt on warming to room temperature, recrystallization is likely to be very troublesome, and it is usually best to proceed with distillation of the material.

Identification of a Pure Compound

If the compound has been separated from a mixture, as described above, the melting point or boiling point will have already been determined. If such a separation has not been necessary, the melting point or boiling point is determined as an initial step in the identification. It is convenient to distill a liquid compound in the course of determining the boiling point and thus accomplish purification, if necessary, by collecting the distillate over a boiling range of not more than five degrees. If a solid compound has a melting point which exhibits a broad range (more than about three degrees), the compound is purified by crystallization before further examination is carried out. If the compound does not melt below 275° or simply decomposes on heating, it may prove to be a salt; so a sample should be ignited on a metal spatula, and any residue from the burning noted.

After a pure compound is assured, and its melting point or boiling point has been determined, it is subjected to *elementary analysis*. Next, unless a separation procedure has already yielded the information, the *solubility* of the substance is determined by testing a sample of about 0.2 g or 0.2 ml for solubility in about 3 ml of water, in 1N hydrochloric acid, and in 1N sodium hydroxide. It is best to follow the solubility by adding the solvent in 1-ml portions. If the quantities are grossly in error, misleading observations are likely to occur. If the substance does not dissolve completely in a given volume of water, then its acidic or basic character may be determined by its solubility in that volume of acidic or basic solution. In case the substance is very soluble in water, the acidic or basic character may be determined with indicators, but weak acids and bases will be detected only by use of pH paper, which gives the pH with an accuracy of about 1 unit. The acidic or basic character may also be determined by extraction of an alkaline and an acidic test solution with 2-ml portions of benzene. Determination of whether material was extracted is by evaporation of the extract in a tared 25-ml Erlenmeyer flask on a steam bath in the hood (*no flames, and no boiling of benzene into the room!*). An acid, for example, will be extracted from the acidic solution but not from the basic solution. Such test extractions are carried out in a test tube, with use of the bulb pipette as previously described. Of course such test extractions are unnecessary, and of no value, if the melting point, ignition test, and elementary analysis have already shown presence of a salt or of a sulfonic acid.

After the above procedures have been carried out, the *following information is in hand:*

1. The melting point or boiling point is known.
2. The presence of halogen, nitrogen, or sulfur is known.
3. The neutral, acidic, or basic character of the substance is known.

The next step in the identification is reference to Table I (p. 266) and noting which compounds are candidates for identity with the unknown substance. A longer list[1] than included in Table I may be used by following the same procedure. In fact, if additional compounds having the same functional groups are added to the table, it may prove unnecessary to use any additional procedures for making derivatives. In order to allow for experimental inaccuracies, *any compound melting within five degrees of the unknown or boiling within ten degrees of it* should be regarded as a possibility, if its other properties are in agreement with those of the unknown. At this stage it may appear reasonable to proceed with confirmation of identity by preparing a derivative; however, it is often desirable to apply certain additional tests. The additional tests may be necessary before it can be known which derivative to prepare, and they will always add evidence for or against a given candidate. Selection of additional tests will depend on the type of compound, as discussed in the following paragraphs.

If the substance is an *amine*, it is nearly always desirable to eliminate possibilities by applying the Hinsberg test (Procedure 2). Since the derivative used for primary and secondary amines is different from that used for tertiary amines, it is imperative that this test be correctly interpreted. If there is any doubt about the results, the test should be repeated—the test is very reliable if carried out properly.

If the substance is an *acid*, and the possibilities include both carboxylic acids and phenols, these may usually be distinguished by testing solubility in sodium bicarbonate solution (5% aqueous solution). Most phenols are too weakly acidic to dissolve in this solution by forming salts, and most carboxylic acids give water-soluble sodium salts. If a solid is being tested,

[1]A convenient source of properties of compounds is *Tables for Identification of Organic Compounds* (Cleveland: Chemical Rubber Publishing Co., 1960).

it is important to warm the solution slightly and stir well with a stirring rod, otherwise, insolubility of the acid may prevent salt formation. There should also be raised a caution against phenols substituted with halogen or nitro groups, especially the latter. Such groups increase acid strength, and may cause solubility in sodium bicarbonate solution.

If the substance is *neutral*, presence of halogen or nitrogen is often important in determining identity. For this reason, a word of caution is in order if the neutral component was separated from a base or an acid containing halogen or nitrogen. Incomplete separation will naturally cause a test for the element in the neutral component, and may lead to very serious false leads.

A specific sequence of tests on neutral compounds is usually most convenient, as described below.

1. If the compound contains nitrogen, a saponification test (Procedure 7) should be carried out, with test for evolution of ammonia. This confirms the elementary analysis for nitrogen, and definitely establishes presence of a nitrile or amide.

2. If the compound did not test for nitrogen, or failed to evolve ammonia in saponification, the carbonyl group should be tested with 2,4-dinitrophenylhydrazine (Procedure 6).

3. If the test for carbonyl was negative, the saponification test should be applied (would have been tried first if nitrogen present). Since nitrogen is easily missed in the analysis for elements, evolution of ammonia should always be tested during saponification.

4. If the above tests are negative, presence of a primary or secondary alcohol should be tested by oxidation (Procedure 8). Tertiary alcohols (of relatively little importance) do not give a positive oxidation test. If a tertiary alcohol is suspected, it may be recognized by its very easy dehydration with acid.

5. If the test for carbonyl was positive, distinction between aldehyde and ketone should be made by use of the oxidation test (Procedure 8). Also note that a distinction may usually be made between aliphatic and aromatic aldehydes.

6. If the above tests indicate a ketone, test should be made for a methyl ketone (Chap. 15). In this test, *positive results may be missed* with compounds that are very sparingly soluble in water, *especially if more than a drop of unknown is used.* The unreacted insoluble unknown will dissolve any iodoform generated and thus mask its presence.

After any desirable tests have been applied, final characterization is accomplished by preparing a derivative and determining its melting point. Many solid derivatives are available for most classes of compounds, but convenient ones are listed in Table I (p. 266). In some instances, especially if larger lists than that in Table I are considered or if all known compounds are considered, as in research work, it may be necessary to prepare additional derivatives.

It should be mentioned that a few classes of compounds are relatively troublesome to convert to solid derivatives. The most important class of compounds for which derivatives are prepared with difficulty is that of the organic halides. It will be noted that the three aryl halides occurring in Table I are converted to derivatives by applying the procedure for making derivatives of alkylbenzenes. The best derivative for halides (not used in the present work) is probably the anilide prepared according to the relatively lengthy procedure involving the Grignard reagent, which is outlined in the following equations.

$$\text{R—Br + Mg} \xrightarrow[\text{ether}]{\text{dry}} \text{R—MgBr} \qquad (30\text{-}1)$$

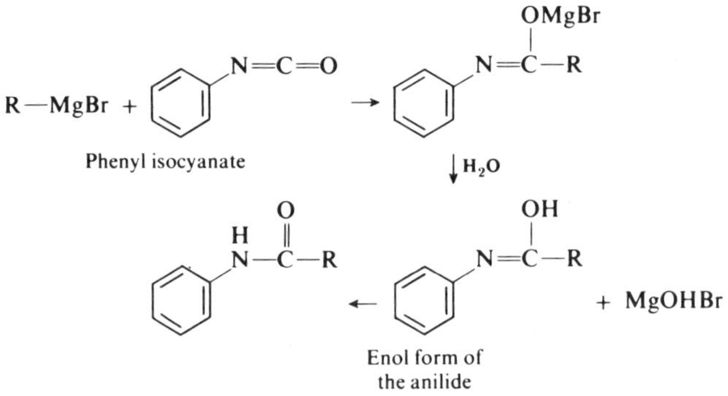

Phenyl isocyanate

Enol form of
the anilide

$$+ \text{ MgOHBr} \qquad (30\text{-}2)$$

Notebook Reports on Identification of Unknowns

If the *unknown is a single compound*, there are recorded in the notebook in tabular form the physical and chemical properties itemized on page 274. Next there are recorded the results of any tests such as those mentioned on page 275. After any test results are recorded, there are listed all candidates (from Table I or some longer list that may be used) for the identity of the unknown. Finally is reported the derivative that was prepared, and its melting point. *This derivative is turned in*, contained in a properly labeled vial, when the completed notebook is presented to the instructor as the unknown is reported.

If the *unknown is a mixture*, the report begins with a flow-sheet outlining the separation of the mixture. This is followed by reports for each component of the mixture, according to the scheme outlined above.

PROCEDURES

1. Methiodides of Tertiary Amines

$$R\overset{\displaystyle R'}{\underset{\displaystyle R''}{|}}R'' + CH_3I \rightarrow R\overset{\displaystyle R'}{\underset{\displaystyle R''}{|}}\overset{+}{N}{-}CH_3\ I^- \tag{30-3}$$

A 50-ml Erlenmeyer flask is equipped for distillation, and a 15-ml portion of thiophene-free benzene is distilled from it until 5 ml of distillate has been collected. The residue of dry benzene is cooled after the flask has been attached to a drying tube filled with anhydrous calcium chloride. To the cooled solution is added 0.5 ml of the amine and 0.5 ml of methyl iodide (volatile, b.p. 43°), then the flask is corked tightly and the solution is allowed to stand overnight or longer inside your locker. The precipitated salt, which is collected by suction filtration and washed with a little benzene, is usually pure enough for identification purposes. Since these salts usually melt with decomposition, the observed melting point may vary with rate of heating somewhat more than usual. If the melting point indicates that this product is not pure, it may be recrystallized from absolute ethanol. Methiodides are sometimes hygroscopic and tend to become oily if recrystallization from 95% ethanol is attempted, or dry solvent is not used for the preparation.

2. Benzenesulfonamides of Amines

(a) *Hinsberg test.* Although the Hinsberg test is simple and rapid, and probably the best of several possible methods for distinguishing between the classes of amines, a thorough understanding of it is necessary in order to avoid misinterpretation of the results. The reagent used for the test is benzenesulfonyl chloride in the presence of aqueous alkali. Since a tertiary amine has no hydrogens on nitrogen, it fails to react to form a sulfonamide and is thus distinguished from the primary and secondary amines. In this case, the benzenesulfonyl chloride reacts slowly with the alkali to give the water-soluble sodium benzenesulfonate, and time must be allowed for removal of the sulfonyl chloride in this manner.

A primary amine gives a sulfonamide of the structure shown in

$$\underset{\text{I}}{C_6H_5{-}SO_2\overset{\displaystyle H}{\underset{}{|}}N{-}R} \qquad \underset{\text{II}}{C_6H_5{-}SO_2\overset{\displaystyle R}{\underset{}{|}}N{-}R} \qquad \underset{\text{III}}{C_6H_5{-}SO_2\overset{\displaystyle R}{\underset{}{|}}N{-}SO_2{-}C_6H_5}$$

formula I, while a secondary amine gives a sulfonamide of the structure shown in formula II. Note that formula I still has a hydrogen attached to nitrogen, while formula II has no hydrogen attached to nitrogen. Since sulfonamides having one or two hydrogens on the nitrogen are weakly acidic, they give sodium salts which usually dissolve in water. It follows that the amide from a primary amine (formula I) will dissolve in the reaction medium for the Hinsberg test, whereas the neutral product from a secondary amine (formula II) is insoluble. Occasionally, a complication arises as a result of the monosubstituted sulfonamide (I) reacting further to give the disulfonyl derivative (formula III), which is alkali-insoluble. This is especially likely if the reaction mixture is heated, or an excessive amount of benzenesulfonyl chloride is used. Interpretation of the results is described below.

Procedure.   As all quantities are measured with care, there are placed in a test tube, in the order mentioned, 10 ml of 1N sodium hydroxide, 0.3 ml of the amine to be tested, and 0.5 ml of benzenesulfonyl chloride. The tube is corked and shaken vigorously (*CAUTION! Heat evolution may cause some pressure, which should be vented cautiously and sufficiently frequently.*). Shaking is continued until the odor of benzenesulfonyl chloride is no longer apparent (usually 5–10 minutes). It is advisable not to warm the solution since this promotes formation of a disulfonyl derivative (III) of a primary amine, and also may cause formation of a dye with tertiary amines.

Interpretation of results.   If the solution becomes homogeneous, the amine was primary. As a confirmatory test, the solution is acidified to precipitate the sulfonamide. Frequently, this gives the sulfonamide in a solid state, and it may be crystallized from 95% ethanol to give a satisfactory derivative. In case an oil separates, which refuses to crystallize, the derivative may be obtained more satisfactorily by the procedure outlined below under (b).

If there is a second phase at the completion of the reaction, it should be noted whether it is liquid or solid and whether it has a different density (in relation to water) from the starting amine. Although the sulfonamides are usually solids, they may crystallize with difficulty. If a solid is obtained, it may be the derivative of a secondary amine, but failure to obtain a solid is not sufficient evidence that the amine was tertiary and did not react. The insoluble material may be one of the following:

1. The starting amine, in which case it was tertiary.
2. The disubstituted sulfonamide, II, in which case the amine was secondary.
3. A small amount of the disulfonyl derivative, III, in which case the amine was primary.

4. An insoluble salt of the monosubstituted sulfonamide, I, in which case the amine was primary. Ordinarily, this happens only when the salt is "salted out" by an excessively high concentration of sodium hydroxide.

In order to distinguish between the possibilities cited above, the insoluble material is removed by filtration if it is a solid and by use of the bulb pipette if it is a liquid.

If the substance is soluble in water, possibility (4) is the case.

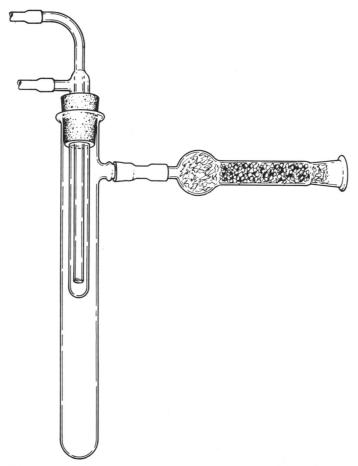

FIG. 2. Apparatus for heating small volumes under reflux with protection from atmospheric moisture. If protection from moisture is unnecessary, the cold finger is simply inserted in the neck of a test tube or small flask, without attachment by a cork. Of course the system would be closed, and blow apart on heating, if the cold finger were attached by a cork to a vessel without the side arm.

If the substance is insoluble in water, but soluble in 1N hydrochloric acid, possibility (1) is the case.

If the substance is insoluble in both water and 1N hydrochloric acid, possibility (3) may be tested by acidification of the solution from which the material was removed. If a precipitate forms (sulfonamide I), then possibility (3) is the case, and if the precipitate is a solid it may be used as the derivative.

Possibility (2) remains if the others have been eliminated as described above, and if the material can be obtained crystalline, it may be recrystallized from 95% ethanol as the derivative.

The Hinsberg test, as described above, fails with very weakly basic or highly hindered amines on account of the acid chloride's reacting more rapidly with alkali than with the amine. Testing of such amines is discussed in texts on qualitative organic analysis.[2]

(b) *Derivative formation.* If difficulty is encountered in obtaining a solid sulfonamide by the procedure under (a), the following procedure may prove more satisfactory. A mixture of 0.3 ml of the amine, 0.5 ml of benzenesulfonyl chloride, and 3 ml of pyridine is heated in a steam bath or boiling-water bath for about 20 minutes. A convenient vessel for this procedure is a test tube attached with a cork to a 7 mm × 20 cm glass tube, which acts as an air-cooled condenser. The top of the condenser tube is attached to a calcium chloride tube. If a cold finger is available, there may be used the apparatus shown in Fig. 2. The cooled reaction mixture is poured into about 10 ml of cold water, with stirring, and the precipitated material is worked with a stirring rod until it sets to a crystalline mass. This product is collected by suction filtration, washed well with water, then crystallized from 95% ethanol.

3. Simple Amides of Carboxylic Acids

The most convenient and general procedure for forming amides is by way of the acid chloride (cf. Chap. 13). The easiest method for making the acid chloride is by use of phosphorus trichloride, and the procedure described below is adapted to the small scale appropriate for making a derivative. Some acids, notably cyclohexanecarboxylic acids and benzoic acids substituted with negative groups, fail to give a satisfactory yield of acid chloride with phosphorus trichloride. In such instances, success is usually attained by using thionyl chloride (cf. Procedure 10); however, this more laborious method is recommended only if the procedure described below fails.

[2]See Samuel M. McElvain's *Characterization of Organic Compounds* (New York: Macmillan, 1953), p. 115. More modern books seem to have a far less adequate discussion of this topic.

Procedure. A dry test tube is arranged for heating under reflux, using a well-fitted cork and a condenser protected by a calcium chloride drying tube (Note 1). To the test tube are added 5 ml of hexane (Note 2), 0.5 ml of phosphorus trichloride (*Corrosive! Handle under a hood and transfer with use of a bulb pipette*), one drop of pyridine, and 1 g of the acid. The mixture is heated under reflux (*boiling chip!*) for 30–45 minutes. Use of a very small flame (*hexane is inflammable!*) placed somewhat to one side will avoid too violent reflux, or a steam bath may be used for heating. The reaction mixture is cooled without shaking, as the condenser and drying tube are left attached, so that any suspended phosphonic acid will settle out of the hexane. The cooled hexane solution is poured off the syrupy layer of phosphonic acid into 10 ml of ice-cold concentrated aqueous ammonium hydroxide contained in a 50-ml Erlenmeyer flask. If hexane was omitted, the acid chloride will be in solution in the excess phosphorus trichloride, and a gummy solid will line the tube. In this case, the gummy solid is left undisturbed as the solution of acid chloride is drawn carefully into the bulb pipette and added dropwise to the swirled and cooled ammonium hydroxide solution (*sputtering and smoking!*).

The mixture containing the precipitated amide is shaken and stirred with a stirring rod for 2–3 minutes as it is cooled in an ice bath. The precipitate, which may be rather frothy, is collected by suction filtration, pressed well on the funnel, then placed in a small beaker and stirred well with about 5 ml of water. The precipitate is again collected, pressed on the funnel, and washed with water. It is unnecessary to dry the amide prior to recrystallization.

Methanol is usually the best solvent for recrystallization of the amide, and it is often necessary to filter the warm solution for removal of a little ammonium chloride which was occluded by the precipitating amide. In some instances, it may also be desirable to add a little water to the filtered warm solution to decrease the solubility of the amide. As usual, addition of too much water will cause the amide to oil out, rather than crystallize, and this will defeat the purification.

NOTES

1. When a small volume is being heated under reflux in a test tube or a small Erlenmeyer flask, it is usually most convenient to insert a cold finger condenser (Fig. 2), without a cork unless protection from atmospheric moisture is desired. If protection from moisture is desired, as in the present instance, the cold finger is attached with a cork to a side-arm test tube, and a drying tube is attached to the side arm (Fig. 2). In this case, it is approximately as convenient to attach a micro condenser to the test tube in conventional fashion, and attach the drying tube to the top of the condenser.

2. *If the acid is a solid*, it is likely to be so insoluble in hexane that reaction with phosphorus trichloride will be extremely slow. For solid acids, therefore, the hexane should be omitted, and there should be used 1.0 ml of phosphorus trichloride (excess for solvent purposes).

4. Aryloxyacetic Acids as Phenol Derivatives

$$+ Cl^- \qquad (30\text{-}4)$$

In a 50-ml Erlenmeyer flask are placed 1 g or 1 ml of the phenol, 3.0 g of chloroacetic acid (Note 1), 3 ml of water, and 4 ml of concentrated (14N) sodium hydroxide solution. The flask is corked *loosely* and heated on a steam bath, or in a boiling-water bath, as the mixture is swirled until the solutes are dissolved. If solution does not occur on heating and swirling, an additional 5 ml of water should be added. Heating of the mixture is continued for about 1 hr. The cooled solution is diluted with about 10 ml of water, then acidified to Congo red paper with concentrated (12N) hydrochloric acid (a precipitate may separate). The resultant mixture is transferred to a separatory funnel and extracted with two 25-ml portions of benzene (Note 2). The two extracts are kept separate and washed in sequence with one 10-ml portion of cold water. After the water wash, the two extracts are combined, and the aryloxyacetic acid is extracted with 25 ml of a 5% aqueous sodium carbonate solution. The carbonate solution is run into a 250-ml beaker and acidified cautiously (*foaming!*) to Congo red with concentrated hydrochloric acid. The acidified mixture is cooled in water, then the precipitated aryloxyacetic acid is collected by suction filtration on the Hirsch funnel and washed with cold water. If the derivative does not crystallize immediately from the acidified solution, it is cooled in ice and allowed to stand for 15–30 minutes, as the wall of the beaker is scratched occasionally with a glass rod at the surface of the liquid.

If the melting point of the derivative indicates an impure specimen, it is recrystallized from water.

NOTES

1. A side reaction in this preparation is displacement of the halogen in chloroacetic acid by the hydroxide ion, rather than by the phenoxide ion as desired.

There is used, therefore, a large excess of chloroacetic acid. Separation of the by-product, hydroxyacetic acid, presents no problem, on account of its great water-solubility. It is important, however, that the quantities of reagents be measured carefully.

2. The aryloxyacetic acids are more soluble in ether, but benzene presents a lesser fire hazard. Two extractions with benzene usually remove a sufficient amount of the derivative from the water phase.

5. Semicarbazones

$$R-\underset{\underset{O}{\|}}{C}-R' + H_2N-\underset{\underset{H}{|}}{N}-\underset{\underset{O}{\|}}{C}-NH_2 \rightarrow R-\underset{\underset{R'}{|}}{C}=N-\underset{\underset{H}{|}}{N}-\underset{\underset{O}{\|}}{C}-NH_2 + H_2O \qquad (30\text{-}5)$$

In one test tube is prepared a solution of 0.5 g of the aldehyde or ketone in 3 ml of 95% ethanol, and in another test tube is prepared a solution (Note 1) of 0.5 g of semicarbazide hydrochloride and 0.75 g of crystalline sodium acetate in 5 ml of water. The two tubes are heated on a steam bath or in boiling water for 2–3 minutes, then the water solution is added in one portion to the alcohol solution in such manner that the two are mixed well on addition. After the tube has been shaken or swirled to promote further mixing, it is heated on the steam bath for 4–5 minutes, with occasional shaking. The contents of the tube are added to about 5 ml of water contained in a 50-ml Erlenmeyer flask, and the mixture is cooled in water. If the semicarbazone does not crystallize readily, the mixture is cooled in ice and the oil is rubbed against the flask with a glass rod. 2-Ethylhexanal semicarbazone is usually the most reluctant to crystallize. The solidified semicarbazone is collected by suction filtration, washed with water, and recrystallized from methanol. If the substance is inconveniently soluble in methanol, 20–30% of water may be added to the warm solution. Addition of too much water will create a tendency for the crystals to oil out of the solution.

NOTE

1. It is important that the ratio of semicarbazide hydrochloride to sodium acetate be reasonably accurate, for the sodium acetate functions as a base which frees the semicarbazide from its salt. Semicarbazide is shipped and stored as its salt on account of instability of the free base. In order to avoid weighing small amounts, it may be desirable to prepare five times the amount of solution required for one experiment and use 5 ml of this solution; however, such a solution should not be allowed to stand for more than one or two days before use.

6. 2,4-Dinitrophenylhydrazones

$$R-\underset{\underset{O}{\|}}{C}-R' + \quad \text{[2,4-dinitrophenylhydrazine]} \quad \rightarrow \quad \text{[2,4-dinitrophenylhydrazone]} \quad + \text{ } H_2O \quad (30\text{-}6)$$

(a) *Qualitative test.* To 5 ml of the test reagent (Note 1) contained in a test tube are added 3–4 drops of a liquid sample (if a solid is being tested, about 25–50 mg is dissolved in a minimum quantity of 95% ethanol). The mixture is corked and shaken vigorously for a few minutes. If the test is positive, the insoluble 2,4-dinitrophenylhydrazone usually separates rapidly, frequently as an orange oil which solidifies. When a liquid is being tested, it is desirable to obtain a solid, if possible, in order to be sure that the material separating is not the sample that was added; however, many 2,4-dinitrophenylhydrazones are quite reluctant to crystallize. In case a solid is being tested, and a solid precipitates from the test mixture, it may be desirable to filter the precipitate, dry it, and determine its melting point, in order to make sure that it is not unaltered starting material. On long standing, 2,4-dinitrophenylhydrazine may separate.

In case a cloudiness appears relatively slowly, this may result from oxidation of a secondary alcohol by the reagent, followed by formation of the derivative of the ketone. As in most qualitative tests, the results must be examined carefully in order to avoid errors. Tests on knowns are highly desirable, before the unknown is tested. Cyclohexanol is an alcohol prone to give a slow positive test for carbonyl compounds.

(b) *Preparation of derivatives.* The procedure is the same as described for a qualitative test, except that the scale is increased three-fold. If there is difficulty in securing the derivative in a crystalline state, the oil should be rubbed against the side of the test tube with a glass rod as the mixture is cooled in ice. Sometimes, success is achieved by withdrawing some oil on a glass rod, and rubbing it in the bottom of a test tube containing a few drops of ice-cold ethanol. If all efforts fail, allowing the mixture to stand overnight or longer may result in crystallization. After crystallization is secured, a tiny bit of the crystalline solid ("seed") is reserved when the remainder of the derivative is dissolved in a very small amount of 95% ethanol. The solution is cooled to induce crystallization, as a trace of the seed crystals are added to prevent oiling out. The crystallized derivative is collected and washed in the usual manner.

NOTE

1. The reagent is prepared by dissolving 1 g of 2,4-dinitrophenylhydrazine in 8 ml of concentrated sulfuric acid, then adding this solution to a mixture of

75 ml of 95% ethanol and 250 ml of water. The reagent is mixed by swirling, and any precipitate is removed by filtration. Additional reagent precipitates from solution on standing, so the supernatant liquid should be used for tests. On long standing, most of the reagent precipitates and the solution becomes of no value for tests. 2,4-Dinitrophenylhydrazine is such a weak base that its salt is sufficiently dissociated in solution to free the base for reaction. This is in contrast to semicarbazide (cf. Procedure 5).

7. Saponification of Esters, Amides, and Nitriles
(Cf. Eqs. 12-7 and 13-4.)

In order to perform the test quickly, there is used a high-boiling solvent, ethylene glycol ($HOCH_2CH_2OH$), so that heating to 150° may be easily accomplished.

(a) *Qualitative test.* A suitable reagent is prepared by dissolving about 1.5 g of potassium hydroxide pellets (85% KOH, 15% H_2O) in 10 ml of ethylene glycol contained in a 50-ml Erlenmeyer flask. Dissolution, which is highly exothermic, is accomplished by *cautious* heating with a small flame, as the face is kept well back.

In a test tube is placed about 0.2 g or 0.2 ml of the substance to be tested, and there is added from the bulb pipette about 2 ml of the test reagent. A thermometer is placed in the liquid, then the tube is warmed carefully with a small flame to about 150° (± 10°). A piece of moist red litmus paper held over the tube is used to test for evolution of ammonia. If this test is positive (litmus paper becomes blue soon after 150° is reached), it is usually desirable to carry out a complete saponification on a larger scale as described in part (b) below.

If the test for ammonia evolution is negative, the test solution is cooled below 100° after only brief heating at 150°, and poured into 5 ml of water contained in another test tube. If the mixture becomes homogeneous (slightly opalescent if the salt of a higher molecular weight aliphatic acid is present), the test is positive (Note 1) for saponification of an ester to give the water-soluble sodium salt of the acid. As a confirmatory test, the alkaline solution may be acidified to precipitate the acid. If the acid is a solid, this test may give sufficient product for a derivative, unless purification by recrystallization is required. If the acid is a liquid, which must be characterized as the amide, a larger sample is saponified as described in part (b) below.

NOTE

1. There are no esters of water-insoluble alcohols in Table I; however, if such an ester were saponified, the alcohol would naturally appear as a water-in-

soluble liquid or solid. In such a circumstance, it would become necessary to determine whether the water-insoluble component were the starting material or a saponification product.

If the ester of a very high molecular weight fatty acid, such as stearic acid ($C_{17}H_{35}CO_2H$), were saponified, the alkaline solution would have a characteristic soapy appearance, and some of the soap might precipitate.

(b) *Preparation of derivatives.* To the saponification reagent, prepared in a 50-ml Erlenmeyer flask from 1.5 g of potassium hydroxide pellets as described in part (a) above, is added 1.5 g of the substance to be saponified. A thermometer is placed in the liquid in the flask (conveniently held in a cork which is channeled to avoid closing the heated vessel), and the solution is heated at 150° (± 10°) over a small flame. It is usually necessary to place the flame slightly to one side, for it is important not to heat the glycol sufficiently to boil it out of the flask. An ester will be completely saponified in 5 minutes (unhindered esters are saponified before the solution reaches 100°), but a nitrile or amide should be heated for about 45 minutes. For the longer heating period, it is convenient to ensure no escape of solvent vapor by inserting a cold finger (Fig. 2) in the neck of the flask, *without* attachment by a cork.

The reaction mixture is cooled below 100°, and poured while still warm into about 40 ml of water. If the solution is not clear, it is filtered after addition of about 1 g of Super Cel. The clear solution is acidified to Congo red with concentrated hydrochloric acid, then cooled in an ice bath. If the acid is a solid, it is collected by suction filtration and recrystallized from acetone or aqueous acetone. Most acids are conveniently handled in acetone containing 10–30% water.

If the acid is a liquid (never the case for aromatic acids, frequently the case for aliphatic acids), it is extracted with 6–7 ml of hexane so that it may be converted to the amide as described in Procedure 3. Before the procedure for making the acid chloride is applied, the hexane extract should be dried for about 20 minutes, with occasional swirling, over about 0.5 g of anhydrous sodium sulfate or magnesium sulfate (calcium chloride is not suitable, for it usually contains some calcium oxide, which will form a salt with the acid).

8. Oxidation Test[3]

Oxidation under mild conditions may be used for distinction between an aldehyde and a ketone in cases where the test with dinitrophenylhydrazine has demonstrated the presence of a carbonyl compound. Further-

---

[3]This procedure was first published as an alcohol test by F. G. Bordwell and K. M. Kellman, *J. Chem. Educ.*, **39**, 318 (1962); the same reagent was developed as an aldehyde test by J. D. Morrison, *J. Chem. Educ.*, **42**, 554 (1965).

more, in the oxidation with chromic acid described below, it is usually possible to distinguish between an aliphatic and an aromatic aldehyde: aliphatic aldehydes give a green color (positive test) within about 15 seconds after the reagents are mixed; an aromatic aldehyde requires about one minute. Since this test is carried out in acetone solution, in which nearly all aldehydes and ketones are soluble, it is quite superior to the Fehling's test and Tollens' test, which are conducted in water solution (Chap. 15). The latter tests have been most useful with carbohydrates (quite water-soluble).

The chromic acid oxidation is also useful for detecting a primary or secondary alcohol in instances where the test for the carbonyl group (Procedure 6) is negative. Primary and secondary alcohols give a positive test almost immediately, whereas alkenes, alkynes, and ethers do not. This test for alcohols (except tertiary alcohols, of relatively minor importance), combines with the tests in Procedures 6 and 7 to give a definitive test for each class of oxygen-containing neutral compounds.

Procedure. One drop (or about 10 mg if solid) of the test compound is dissolved in one ml of reagent grade acetone, then one drop of the chromic acid test reagent (Note 1) is added and the mixture is shaken. Formation of a green to blue-green precipitate constitutes a positive test. Interpretation of the test is discussed above.

In case of any doubt about the purity of the acetone used as solvent, a blank run is easily made by omitting addition of a test compound. A "positive blank" may also be run by testing a known sample of an alcohol (ethanol or propanol is convenient).

NOTE

1. The chromic acid reagent is prepared by dissolving 25 g of chromic anhydride (CrO_3) in 25 ml of concentrated sulfuric acid, then pouring this solution carefully into 70 ml of water. An additional 5 ml of water is used as a rinse for adding the last of the acid solution. Of course the reagent should be cooled to room temperature before use.

9. Conversion of Nitriles to Amides

Since an amide is hydrolyzed at about the same rate as a nitrile, it is usually difficult to accumulate a satisfactory yield of amide by saponification. A nearly quantitative yield of amide may be obtained, however, by first adding anhydrous sulfuric acid to the multiple bond, then hydrolyzing this adduct (cf. Eq. 13-5). This conversion is useful in instances where the acid is a liquid and the amide is a solid.

An 0.5-g sample of the nitrile is added to 2 ml of concentrated sulfuric acid (Note 1) in a test tube, the test tube is attached to a calcium chloride drying tube, and the mixture is warmed on a steam bath or a boiling-water bath for 6–8 minutes, with frequent agitation. During the agitation, the sulfuric acid should not be splashed on the cork. The *cooled* solution is poured *carefully* with stirring into 10 ml of cold water, and the precipitated amide is collected by suction filtration and washed thoroughly with water. The amide is purified by crystallization, as described in Procedure 3.

NOTE

1. The success of this procedure depends on the occurrence of the reaction shown in Eq. 13-5 in preference to hydrolysis. If the sulfuric acid has absorbed considerable water, from standing in a bottle which is opened frequently, the reaction is likely to fail on account of formation of a mixture of amide and acid. There should be used a fresh bottle of sulfuric acid, which is opened only for use in making this derivative. Acid should be removed with a clean bulb pipette, then the bottle should be closed promptly.

10. 3,5-Dinitrobenzoates

There are many derivatives of alcohols which have been investigated, but some give liquid products with many alcohols, others are formed with difficulty, and still others give derivatives of nearly the same melting point from many alcohols. Although some of the 3,5-dinitrobenzoates (Eq. 7) are

$$(30\text{-}7)$$

low-melting, they are probably as satisfactory as any derivative for alcohols.

3,5-Dinitrobenzoyl chloride may be purchased, but it reacts with moisture so readily that it can be used satisfactorily for making derivatives only if it is stored in 1-g sealed vials so that only the material used is opened and exposed to moist air. Acid formed by reaction of the acid chloride with moisture will react with additional acid chloride to give the anhydride. The latter is unsatisfactory for preparation of derivatives of alcohols; so old samples of the acid chloride should always be checked for melting point, and those which melt higher than about 75° should not be used. It is usually more practical to prepare the acid chloride, as described below, then use it at once for preparation of the derivative. This acid chloride cannot be prepared in satisfactory yield with phosphorus trichloride.

(a) *Acid chloride preparation.* A mixture of 1 g of 3,5-dinitrobenzoic acid, 3 ml of thionyl chloride (handle in hood), and *one* drop of pyridine is placed in a 50-ml Erlenmeyer flask, which is attached to a reflux condenser protected by a *soda lime* tube (also cf. Procedure 3, Note 1). The soda lime tube will absorb the sulfur dioxide and hydrogen chloride so that the heating may be in the laboratory. The mixture is heated under reflux for 10 minutes after the acid has dissolved. The total time of heating is usually about 30 minutes. As heating is interrupted, a fresh boiling chip is added to the solution, and the condenser is replaced by the cold trap shown in Fig. 3. A *rubber stopper* is used for connection of the flask to the trap, so that

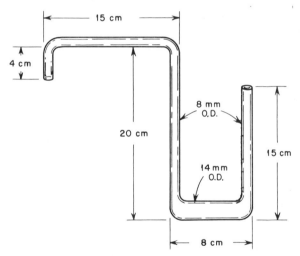

FIG. 3.   Cold trap for thionyl chloride. When the lower bulb is cooled in an ice and salt bath, thionyl chloride will be condensed at pressures as low as 15 mm, which pressure is attainable with a good water pump.

the connection will be vacuum tight, then the lower loop of the trap is cooled in an ice-salt bath, and the outlet of the trap (right side in the diagram) is connected to the aspirator via the usual trap by a section of suction tubing. The flask is evacuated (*Caution!* Although a 50-ml Erlenmeyer flask may be safely evacuated, *larger sizes will collapse.*) by use of the aspirator, as it is heated on a steam bath or hot-water bath. This rapidly removes the excess thionyl chloride, which is condensed in the cooled section of the trap and thus prevented from passing through the rubber tubing to the aspirator (thionyl chloride immediately ruins all rubber that it touches; the effect on the rubber stopper may be noted). As soon as the thionyl chloride has been removed, heating of the flask is discontinued, *air is let into the system cautiously at the trap*, as cooling of the cold trap is continued, then the flask is disconnected. The residue in the flask is kept dry and used immediately for the preparation of the derivative. The thionyl chloride in the trap is poured directly into a drain, *with caution*.

(b) *Ester preparation.* To the residual acid chloride obtained in the above preparation (or 1 g of satisfactory acid chloride from some other source) are added 1.5 g of the alcohol (only 0.7 g of a diol) and 2 ml of dry pyridine (dried by standing over solid sodium hydroxide). The flask is attached to a calcium chloride tube, and the mixture is heated on a steam bath or boiling-water bath for about 30 minutes (15 minutes is sufficient for primary alcohols). After the mixture has been cooled, there is added about 15 ml of 5% aqueous sodium bicarbonate solution, then the mixture is stirred vigorously for a minute or two (this dissolves most of the dinitrobenzoic acid that may have been in the acid chloride or formed by hydrolysis of unreacted acid chloride). The mixture is finally stirred in an ice bath, and the oily derivative is worked with a stirring rod until it crystallizes. In some instances, it is an advantage to decant the aqueous layer, wash the oil once with 10 ml of water, and then work the oil under a few ml of 1N sulfuric acid (this extracts pyridine from the oil). For the lower-melting derivatives, cooling in an ice-salt bath may prove necessary.

After the material has been obtained as a crystalline solid, it is washed well on the suction funnel with cold water and crystallized from 95% alcohol. It is well to save a few crystals as "seed," in case there is difficulty with "oiling out" on recrystallization. More dilute alcohol is sometimes satisfactory, but for a low-melting derivative, oiling out will occur unless sufficient solvent is used to keep the material in solution well below the temperature of its melting point. For the lower-melting derivatives, final cooling for crystallization in an ice-salt bath is recommended. Of course well-cooled solvent, handled with the bulb pipette, should be used for washing the crystals on the suction filter, when they are collected.

11. Oxidation of Alkylbenzenes

$$\text{R}\!\!-\!\!C_6H_4\text{CH}_3 + 3[O] \xrightarrow[\text{(KMnO}_4)]{-OH} \text{R}\!\!-\!\!C_6H_4\text{CO}_2\text{H} + H_2O \qquad (30\text{-}8)$$

The half reaction for breakdown of potassium permanganate in alkaline solution to supply oxidizing power may be obtained by reference to Eq. 14-3.

In a 100-ml round-bottomed flask, preferably equipped with ground joint for attachment of a condenser, are placed 1.5 g of potassium permanganate, 2.5 ml of 10% aqueous sodium hydroxide, 40 ml of water, and 0.5 ml of the hydrocarbon to be oxidized. A boiling chip is added, and the mixture is heated under reflux with a small flame, but with sufficient heat to give vigorous boiling, for about 3 hours. The heating period may be intermittent provided that a new boiling chip is added whenever heating is resumed. The manganese dioxide which separates sometimes causes severe bumping, so the flask should be clamped securely. With a hydrocarbon as insoluble as the chlorotoluenes, traces of it may be left at the end of the heating period, but this impurity in the product is readily removed when the solution is filtered. Any excess permanganate, denoted by its purple color, is consumed by addition to the boiling solution of a few drops of ethanol or propanol.

Since the manganese dioxide separated slowly from a hot solution, it is usually not excessively finely divided; however, it is best practice to filter the reaction mixture through a mat of filter aid (cf. Chap. 14, Notes 2 and 3). Filtration of the reaction mixture, preferably while still warm, is by suction on a small Büchner funnel containing the mat of filter aid. About 10 ml of water is used to wash the mass on the funnel, and this wash is collected with the initial filtrate. The total alkaline filtrate, which should be clear and colorless, is acidified to Congo red with 6N hydrochloric acid. This precipitates the substituted benzoic acid as fine white crystals. The mixture is cooled in water for 10–15 minutes in order to insure complete crystallization, then the derivative is collected by suction filtration on the small Hirsch funnel and washed with cold water. The yield is usually in the range of 50–100 mg of a white product with a sharp melting point.

In case purification of the derivative is indicated by a broad melting point, crystallization from dilute solution in water is usually satisfactory. For a very insoluble benzoic acid, addition of a few per cent of acetone to the water is convenient.

12. *p*-Toluidine Salts of Sulfonic Acids

$$R\text{—}SO_2OH \;+\; H_3C\text{—}NH_2 \;\rightarrow\; R\text{—}SO_2O^-\;H_3N^+\text{—}CH_3 \tag{30-9}$$

In a test tube there is prepared a solution of 1 g of the sulfonic acid or its salt in a minimum amount of hot water. In a 50-ml Erlenmeyer flask is prepared a solution of 0.5 g of *p*-toluidine in 1.5 ml of concentrated hydrochloric acid and the minimum amount of water required for complete solution at boiling. The hot solution of the sulfonic acid is added to the solution of *p*-toluidine hydrochloride, and the mixture is heated if necessary to effect complete solution of any precipitate. Addition of a little more water may be required. As soon as a clear solution is obtained it is cooled in an ice bath with stirring. If crystallization of the *p*-toluidine salt does not promptly ensue, the walls of the flask should be scratched with a stirring rod at the surface of the solution. After crystallization has been induced, the mixture is left in the ice bath without stirring for about 10 minutes, then the crystals are collected by suction filtration and washed with a little cold water. In such salts as *p*-toluidine sulfonates, the ionic bond is such a small per cent of the bonding in the molecule that relatively low (below 300°) melting points with narrow ranges are usually obtained. If the salt is discolored or the melting point is rather broad, the salt is recrystallized from water. The hot solution is clarified with charcoal if indicated. It is well to save a few crystals as "seed," rather than to recrystallize the entire yield. If induction of crystallization proves troublesome, addition of a few "seed" crystals will always start crystallization.

Distillation at Reduced Pressure

31

Since a great majority of organic compounds have boiling points too high to permit distillation, without decomposition, at atmospheric pressure, distillation at reduced pressure is widely practiced. Even in instances when a compound may be distilled without decomposition at temperatures of 200° or higher, it is often more convenient to distill at reduced pressure. The distillations encountered in Chaps. 34–38 are carried out at reduced pressure ("vacuum distillation").

The rate at which the boiling point is reduced by a reduction of pressure is a function of the molar heat of vaporization of the compound, as shown by the Clausius-Clapeyron equation (remembering that the boiling point at a given pressure is the temperature at which the vapor pressure of the compound equals the pressure in the system). It is convenient, however, to remember certain generalities based on assumption of an average value for heat of vaporization. Reduction of the pressure from atmospheric to 25 mm usually reduces the boiling point between 100° and 125°. Below 25 mm, reduction of the pressure by one-half lowers the boiling point by about 10°. Thus, the advantages of very low pressure for the distillation of slightly volatile materials are obvious. Below about 0.2 mm, however, the vapor density becomes so low that distillation in the ordinary sense becomes impractical, and *molecular distillation* becomes necessary. In molecular distillation, the pressure is reduced to a very low value and a large condensing surface is placed relatively close to the surface of the heated liquid, so that the mean free path of the vapor molecules exceeds the distance from liquid surface to condenser. Thus, this process really amounts to evaporation. It is very useful for the distillation of materials of very low vapor pressure or materials that decompose at a relatively low temperature, but very little fractionation is possible. A large variety of molecular stills are commercially available.

A simple apparatus for vacuum distillation is shown in Fig. 1. Some modifications of this apparatus will be mentioned, but the device illustrated is quite effective and useful. Several features illustrated in the figure, as well as the handling of the equipment, should be discussed.

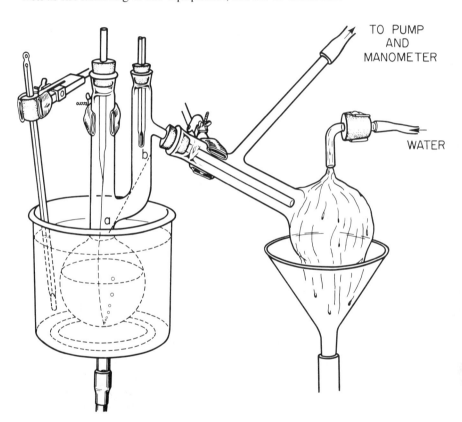

TO PUMP
AND
MANOMETER

WATER

FIG. 1.   Simple apparatus for distillation at reduced pressure.

For assembly of the apparatus shown in Fig. 1, all connections are made with heavy-walled suction tubing and rubber stoppers. Before material is put into the flask for distillation, the entire vacuum system should be checked for leaks. This is best done by evacuation of the system, isolating the pump by means of a screw clamp and noting the rate at which the pressure rises. The pressure will always rise gradually in a system containing rubber connections, but if there is a rapid rise in pressure the leak should be located. In case of a leak, it should first be determined if all stoppers are tight (cf. "Precautions," below), if all glass tubes fit tightly in the holes in the stoppers, and if all pieces of suction tubing fit tightly over the glass tubing. It may be necessary to test various parts of the system separately. Sometimes, there are "pinholes" around side arms on account of faulty glass-blowing. These are often nearly impossible to locate by visual inspection, but may be located with a "spark tester" at pressures below 20 mm. If a spark tester is not available, another flask may be substituted. *Only after the tightness of the system has been established is it wise to proceed with the distillation.*

The distilling flask used as a receiver is a rather effective condenser if there is a film of water flowing over the entire surface. This cooling surface is as large as in a long Liebig condenser. If the water tends to run over the flask in rivulets, rather than in a film, this can be corrected by washing the outside of the flask with soap. The side arm of the Claisen flask should extend to, but not into, the bulb of the distilling flask, as shown. If it extends into the bulb, the tip will become immersed when the receiving flask is less than half full. Under no circumstances should the side arm of the Claisen flask fail to extend well beyond the side arm of the distilling flask.

The vapor density in vacuum distillation is much lower than at atmospheric pressure; therefore, when a high-boiling substance is being distilled at low pressure, there is often trouble with the vapors condensing in the side neck before reaching the side arm. This difficulty is increased if part of the bulb of the Claisen flask is exposed to the air, so *the bulb should always be completely immersed in the oil bath*, as shown. Further, the vapors may just reach the side arm and pass over without rising appreciably above the side arm. For this reason, the thermometer bulb should be placed as shown. This insures against vapor sneaking beneath the bulb in such a way that thermal equilibrium is not maintained at the thermometer bulb.

Direct heating with a flame is nearly always very undesirable in vacuum distillation, not only because it promotes bumping (see below), but also because it makes accurate control of heat input difficult. The importance of controlled heat input will be developed shortly. A liquid bath is highly recommended for vacuum distillation, for it is cheap and one bath may be used for various sizes of flask. Also, the temperature of the bath may be determined with a thermometer placed in the heat-transfer medium near the flask. *Heaters of the mantle type are not recommended for several reasons.* They are expensive, a different mantle is required for each size of flask, the heat transfer through air and glass is so inefficient that a relatively high mantle temperature is required, and the heat is focussed in the flask so that the vapor is overheated when the flask is less than half full. The chief function of the mantle-type heater in this laboratory has been in sizes larger than two liters, in which instances an oil bath is so large and heavy as to be dangerous. Heat-transfer media will be discussed below.

It should be realized that in distillation at atmospheric pressure (760 mm) the vapor density is one hundred times as great as it is at 7.6 mm. It follows that one drop of liquid distillate collected at 7.6 mm requires one hundred times greater volume of vapor to pass the side arm than would be the case at 760 mm. This means a very high vapor velocity in the side neck and especially in the side arm of the flask. For this reason, the side arm should not be too small; 8 mm is recommended. The practice in commercial flasks of using a smaller side arm on smaller-volume flasks seems inadvisable. Further, rate of distillation should not be too high, for this will cause back pressure in the side arm, thus giving a higher pressure in the flask than read at the pressure gauge, which is beyond the receiver. This gives a false boiling point. The boiling point is further raised, in rapid distillation, by overheating of the vapors, so that all liquid is evaporated from the bulb of the thermometer. The high vapor velocity naturally promotes this effect. For these reasons, bath temperature is very important, and really should be reported in connection with the boiling point. One can convince himself of the importance of these considerations by raising the bath temperature during a distillation and noting the considerable increase in the boiling point. The ratio of bath temperature to boiling point depends on the temperature of the boiling point, but, as a general working basis, a bath temperature of 10–25° above the boiling point is often satisfactory. For very high boiling points, a greater differential is necessary (and the boiling point is correspondingly more inaccurate). If there is a nonvolatile residue, the bath temperature must be raised considerably, near the end of the distillation, to remove most of the desired product, for its partial pressure is reduced according to Raoult's law.

The difficulties mentioned above become increasingly more troublesome at lower pressures and higher temperatures—hence the limitation of pressure mentioned at the beginning of the chapter. At pressures below 0.5 mm, vapor velocities for any appreciable rate of distillation are so enormous that the pressure in the flask is only remotely a function of that read at the pressure gauge. The serious discrepancies in low-pressure boiling points reported in the literature are a result of this situation; in fact, one should not expect too accurate a check on literature boiling points at pressures below 50 mm.

For boiling points above about 160° at pressures below 5 mm, it becomes very difficult to force vapor to the side arm without gross overheating of the bath. Asbestos insulation of the side neck helps some, but often the best solution is judicious and *very cautious* warming of the side neck with a small, soft flame. Frequent gentle heating is superior to occasional stronger heating. Intelligent heating, so that the refluxing liquid just rises to the side arm, gives fairly accurate boiling points and frequently improves yields by decreasing the bath temperature necessary to accomplish distillation.

Precautions in Vacuum Distillation

When a vacuum distillation is being started, the system should always be evacuated and the pressure regulated before the heating bath is applied to the flask. If the flask is heated first, the sudden drop in pressure may cause such violent boiling that much of the contents of the Claisen flask will surge into the receiver. This is especially likely to happen if the mixture in the Claisen flask contains residual solvent not removable by heating at atmospheric pressure.

When a vacuum distillation is interrupted or ended, air should always be let into the system before the pump is stopped. If an aspirator is stopped with the system evacuated, water is very likely to be sucked into the system, for check valves on water aspirators fail frequently. Oil pumps usually have a valve to prevent oil from being sucked into the system, but this device sometimes fails. When a distillation is interrupted, it is advisable to lower the heating bath and allow boiling to stop before air is let into the system. It is better to lower the bath rather than to raise the flask, for an evacuated system should never be adjusted, as mentioned below; however, due caution against spilling the hot bath medium must be exercised. It is advisable to wear a pair of canvas gloves.

Glass vessels, such as beakers, should never be used as heating baths, for breakage may lead to serious burns. Stainless-steel beakers are excellent, but expensive; ordinary enamelware saucepans are quite satisfactory. A saucepan with a relatively large ratio of depth to diameter should be chosen, since it is desirable to immerse the bulb of the Claisen flask in the heat-transfer medium.

It should be remembered that a system evacuated to 25-mm pressure has nearly the same pressure on it as a system evacuated to 0.1-mm pressure. In each case, the pressure is approximately atmospheric pressure, 15 pounds per square inch; so a surface of six square inches is supporting a weight of 90 pounds. Thus, *large, flat-bottomed flasks should never be evacuated unless the flask is a heavy-walled suction flask. This applies specifically to Erlenmeyer flasks, whose bottoms are flat and thin.* Such flasks of 50-ml or less capacity may be evacuated with safety, but flasks of 125-ml capacity sometimes collapse, and larger ones are almost certain to collapse. Such a collapse of the evacuated system amounts to an explosion and may result in serious injury, especially to the eyes. Evacuation of a round-bottomed flask is entirely safe, for this shape can withstand far more pressure than that of the atmosphere.

The pressure on the system should also be remembered in connection with any adjustment of the evacuated system. This refers to such matters as the tightening or moving of a clamp. Adjustments should be completed before the system is evacuated. The pushing in of stoppers more tightly should be especially avoided, for when the system is evacuated the pressure applied by the operator is being supplemented by an additional 15 pounds per square inch.

Movement of any hard objects, such as ironware or burners (as in heating the side neck), around an evacuated system should be attended with caution, for breakage may result in an explosion as air rushes into the system. A particular hazard of such an accident is the scattering about of the hot contents of the heating bath.

Protection of the Oil Pump

In buildings where water pressure is adequate, the pressure may be reduced to 15–30 mm by a water pump (aspirator). This device is very useful for vacuum distillation, especially since solvents and acid vapors do not seriously damage the pump. A trap of at least 500-ml capacity should be included between the water pump and the system, as a precaution against water being sucked into the system.

For lower pressures, or where water pressure is inadequate, an oil pump must be used. Since the pump contains precision machine parts, it must be protected from corrosive agents. Also, solvent must be kept out of the pump, for a pressure lower than the vapor pressure of the oil cannot be obtained. When the pump will not give a low pressure, or if corrosive materials are known to have escaped into the pump, the oil should be changed. The pump should always be protected by a tower of flake sodium hydroxide placed between the pump and the system. This will prevent any reasonable amount of acid vapors from reaching the pump; this is the type of material most likely to cause the pump permanent damage.

The most common error in the use of an oil pump is that of allowing solvent vapors to reach the pump, as a result of overlooking the effect of Raoult's law in reducing the partial pressure of a solvent from solution in some higher-boiling material. When the mole fraction of solvent is reduced to a value such as 0.01, the vapor pressure of the solvent in the mixture is only one-hundredth its value when alone. Thus, when ether has been removed from a mixture by heating as high as 150°, there is still appreciable solvent in the mixture. Before an oil pump is connected to a system containing a mixture in which solvent is present, the pressure should first be reduced as low as possible with a water pump, as the bath temperature is raised at least as high as will be later used for distillation with the oil pump. These conditions are maintained until the pressure in the system ceases to drop and is as low as the water pump will produce.

Only then may one be assured that all solvent has been removed from the system.

An alternative to the removal of solvent as described above is the removal of solvent with an oil pump that is protected by an adequate cold trap cooled in an acetone-Dry Ice mixture. In fact, the most positive protection of the oil pump from solvent is routine operation with a cold trap in the system; however, this is always an inconvenience and sometimes not feasible. The removal of solvent as described above usually permits long operation without changing oil, and the alkali tower assures protection of the moving parts of the pump.

Control of Bumping

There is a great tendency toward bumping in vacuum distillation; hence, the Claisen flask with delivery tube on the side neck is always used rather than a simple distilling flask. The geometry of the side neck and the position of the delivery tube should be such that material cannot readily bump directly into the delivery tube. In other words, a line, such as *ab* in Fig. 1, should intersect the outside wall of the side neck somewhat below the delivery tube, as shown.

Simple devices, such as boiling chips, are almost without value in con-

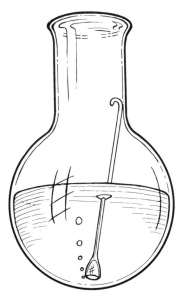

FIG. 2.   Ebullition tube as it appears in operation. The top part is made of a suitable length to hold the tube upright in the size of flask being used. The rod is made thin so the tube will be light enough not to crack a flask if dropped, and the hook on top is for lifting the tube out of the flask.

trolling the vigorous bumping often encountered in vacuum distillation. Various special devices include packing the distilling bulb with glass wool, inserting an ebullition tube (Fig. 2), and inserting in an upright position an applicator stick of soft wood (such as used in medical practice for swabbing the throat with cotton). These devices are quite effective against bumping at atmospheric pressure, especially the ebullition tube. At reduced pressure, they are often satisfactory, but may cease to work after a period; all are almost sure to fail if the solution stops boiling momentarily. Some chemists report success by using a combination of two boiling chips, two applicator sticks, and one ebullition tube—one may continue to function throughout the distillation. Another device, which is shown in the illustration (Fig. 1), is a fine capillary. This very rarely fails to continue functioning indefinitely, and the fine stream of bubbles is very effective in controlling bumping. It is usually the case that one who has acquired skill at making proper capillaries rarely uses any other device.

Drawing of Capillaries for Distillation

The capillary is drawn in two stages from soft-glass tubing. A 6–mm tube fits snugly in the size of hole usually found in commercial one-hole rubber stoppers. Pyrex glass gives brittle capillaries, which are more easily broken than those made from soft glass. A piece of tubing about 30 cm in length is softened near the center by heating, with rotation, in a hot gas flame without a wing-tip on the burner. During the heating the tubing is held together, rather than pulled slightly apart, so that a thick-walled section of soft glass is collected. It is then withdrawn from the flame and pulled *slowly*, with slight rotation to keep it even, into a heavy-walled capillary, 4–6 cm in length [Fig. 3 (a)]. The hole in this heavy-walled capillary should be less than 0.5 mm in diameter, and the wall should be thicker than the hole. Next, this heavy-walled capillary is heated in the center, crosswise over a burner with wing-tip [Fig. 3 (b)], until it *almost* melts together; then, it is rapidly pulled out to a thread. A little experience will acquaint the operator with the amount of pressure to be used without breaking the thread. The thread is then pinched off to a length of 10–15 cm [Fig. 3 (c)], and the capillary is tested by blowing through the tube while the capillary thread is immersed in a test tube containing a little acetone [Fig. 3 (d)]. A proper capillary should emit a barely perceptible stream of bubbles; the smaller the bubbles the better. Such a capillary admits so little air that its presence in the system has no perceptible effect on the pressure read with a mercury manometer. It may also be used with safety in distilling compounds sensitive to air or moisture, such as aldehydes, acid chlorides, or isocyanates. In exceedingly careful work, nitrogen may be admitted to the capillary instead of air.

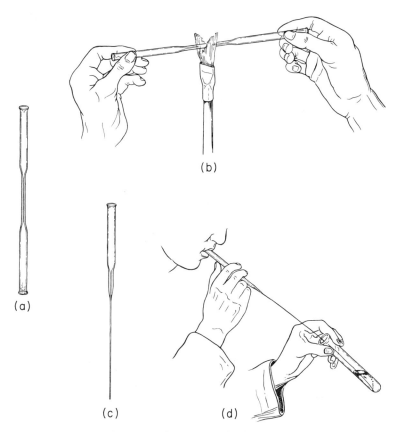

FIG. 3. Construction of a capillary for use in distillation at reduced pressure. (a) Heavy walled capillary resulting from the "first pull"; (b) heating heavy walled capillary for the "second pull"; (c) finished capillary; (d) testing the capillary—note very fine bubbles.

If there is no hole at all in the capillary thread, it should be pinched off about 2 cm, and tested again. This process is continued until a point is reached where there is a fine hole, or the capillary has become too short for use. If the latter occurs, another thread should be pulled by heating the heavy capillary again, just above the first pull, and heating a little less strongly. If the bubbles are large enough to ruffle the surface of the acetone, the capillary is too large, and another should be pulled with more heating for the second pull.

Since the heavy capillary on each side after the thread is pulled out may be used for pulling two or three additional threads, one heavy capillary may be used to make several threads. It should be mentioned that the most common source of difficulty is the failure to make the first thick-walled capillary sufficiently heavy. After a capillary has been used for distillation and air is let into the system, some of the viscous residue remaining from most distillations is sucked into the thread. It is usually not possible to blow or suck this out to clear the capillary; hence, a new one must be pulled for the next distillation. The capillary should be saved, however, until all the heavy section has been used in additional pulls.

Heat-Transfer Media

Cottonseed oil is useful as a heat-transfer medium in the bath, but hydrogenated cottonseed oil is better, for it smokes less at high temperatures and carbonizes more slowly. Hydrogenated soybean oil appears to be even better than hydrogenated cottonseed oil, and compares favorably with the "bath wax" sold at a much higher price by supply houses. The hydrogenated oils melt between 50° and 60°, which is an advantage, for the solid at room temperature does not creep out and get on the outside of the container. The oils are useful for temperatures up to about 240°. At higher temperatures, they smoke badly; and above about 260°, they are likely to take fire.

The polyethylene glycol polymer known as Ucon lubricant (Carbide and Carbon, No. 50-HB-280-X) has about the same useful temperature range as the oils, and has the considerable advantage that it is sufficiently soluble in water to allow easy cleaning from a flask.

For higher temperatures, Wood's metal is often used, but has the disadvantages of being quite dense, rather expensive, and rapidly oxidized at 300° or above. A Wood's-metal bath of more than about 500-ml capacity should always be supported on an automobile jack of the hydraulic or worm-gear type (laboratory supply houses sell a "lab-jack"). A more satisfactory medium for temperatures up to 500° is an equimolar mixture of sodium nitrite and potassium nitrate. This mixture fuses at about 150°. Cheap commercial mixtures of these salts are sold under the names of "heat-transfer salt" or "heat-treating salt." A flask or thermometer should never be left in a salt bath when it solidifies, for the solidifying salt will crush such objects. Salt baths are clean, give no smoke, and are easily cleaned from flasks, but it should be emphasized that they are *EXCEEDINGLY DANGEROUS, and should never be handled without the following precautions:* The salt should be contained in a steel beaker with a flanged top, or the equivalent, so that the bath may be suspended from the top in a strong iron ring, and the shank of the ring should be supported in a large clamp holder. The ring stand holding the bath should be bolted to the desk or be a part of a permanent lattice of rods. These precautions make it nearly impossible to turn the bath over, but splashing is still possible, so the operator should wear heavy gloves and goggles, and a canvas laboratory coat with long sleeves. These precautions are necessary because of the severe and dangerous burns received if the molten salt strikes the skin. It solidifies at 150°, and the heat of fusion keeps the temperature at this point for a considerable period; furthermore, the mixture is chemically oxidizing. The results can well be visualized.

For ordinary distillations, baths heated by a burner or a hot plate are quite satisfactory. However, the construction of a bath with an internal electric heating element is described in connection with fractional distillation, Chap. 32. Such baths are useful for all heating purposes in running reactions.

Fraction cutters are also described in Chap. 32. Such devices may be used in Claisen-flask distillations, but in this type of distillation it is usually no great disadvantage to let air into the system in order to change receivers.

Pressure Gages

It is obvious that a boiling point at reduced pressure is of significance only if the pressure is known accurately. The pressure is always reported together with the boiling temperature. Pressures above 5 mm may be measured with sufficient accuracy by the use of a mercury manometer. An open manometer is inconvenient, for it must be at least 760 mm long, and the pressure on the open arm must be determined by reading a barometer. A closed manometer is nearly always used by organic chemists. A conventional type is shown in Fig. 4, with a stopcock for closing off the manometer when solvent vapor is in the system. Since the closed arm is completely filled with mercury, the pressure on this arm is zero (except for the negligible vapor pressure of mercury). When the other arm is attached to the system, the difference in level between the two columns of mercury is the pressure in the system. If vapors are allowed to get into the manometer, they will usually dissolve in the mercury to some extent and exert a vapor pressure in the closed arm. When this happens, the pressure in the closed arm is not zero; hence, an erroneous pressure reading is obtained. This, in turn, causes an error in boiling point. For this reason, the manometer should be equipped with a stopcock, which may be closed when there is solvent vapor in the system.

The manometer shown in Fig. 4 has the disadvantage that the detection of the presence of a small amount of gas in the closed arm is often difficult. Also, the manometer is troublesome to clean and to fill with mercury in such a manner that all gas is removed from the closed arm. These difficulties are avoided by the type of manometer known as a Zimmerli gage, illustrated in Fig. 5. Use of the Zimmerli gage is highly recommended, especially since it is only slightly more expensive than a conventional

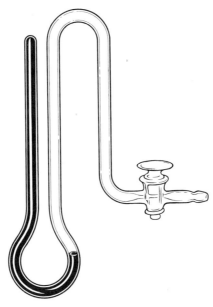

FIG. 4. Conventional closed manometer. This type of manometer is rarely used any more, but illustrates the principle of the closed manometer.

manometer. When a suitable amount of mercury is placed in the right side of this gage, and the gage is tipped, the mercury flows through the capillary in a continuous column; in an upright position, the mercury assumes the position shown in Fig. 5 (a). When the gage is evacuated, the capillary column of mercury breaks at the top bend, and the pressure reading is the difference in level of the mercury in the two right arms, Fig. 5 (b). When air is let into the gage, the capillary column again rejoins. Thus, unless a gas bubble is visible in the capillary column, one may rest assured that the pressure on the center column of mercury is zero. In

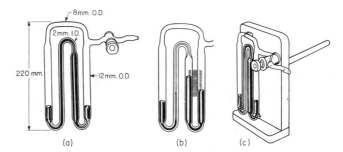

FIG. 5. Zimmerli gage: (a) unevacuated, (b) evacuated to about 20 mm pressure, (c) mounted for convenient attachment to ring stand.

addition, this gage is very easy to clean and fill. The Zimmerli gage may be bought from supply houses, but is more cheaply assembled and mounted as shown in Fig. 5 (c). A sheet of millimeter paper is glued to the board behind the mercury columns where pressure is read, and a rod for insertion in a clamp holder is attached to the back of the board.

The error in reading pressure on a Zimmerli gage is of the order of magnitude of 0.5 mm. Below 5 mm, this error is sufficient to cause appreciable error in boiling point, and is especially serious near 1 mm. For many purposes, such errors are not of significance, but accurate readings of pressure in this region may be obtained by the use of the McLeod gage. There is commercially available a "tilting" McLeod gage that is compact, easily attached to the system, and subject to rapid pressure reading. The model with a range of 0.01–5 mm is especially useful for organic distillations, and a lower-pressure range is available.

Pressure Regulation

Various devices for the control of pressure have been described, many of them depending on an electronic relay operated by a mercury switch either to open and close a capillary leak or to connect and disconnect the pump from the system. The objective is to maintain a constant pressure in the system that is higher than the minimum pressure that the pump will give. The devices mentioned above require a slight variation in pressure for the operation of the mercury switch; also, the construction and maintenance of such devices are relatively expensive and time-consuming. For this reason, organic chemists frequently control pressure by the use of a manually adjustable leak in the system. A stopcock is the crudest such device; a needle valve such as used on high-pressure gas cylinders is more easily adjusted. There has been described,[1] however, a very simple and inexpensive device that maintains a constant pressure in the system so long as the minimum pressure delivered by the pump remains constant. Since an oil pump in good condition delivers a constant minimum pressure, after an initial warming-up period of a few minutes, this device is very useful and actually maintains a more nearly constant pressure than do the more expensive and elaborate devices. The Newman regulator is illustrated in Fig. 6.

In using this regulator, the system is evacuated, with the stopcock open, to about the pressure desired; then the stopcock is closed. The system must now be evacuated through the tube, so that the pressure in the system is higher than that delivered by the pump by the amount of the hydrostatic head of the liquid in the regulator. If it is recalled that pressure must be

[1]M. S. Newman, *Ind. Eng. Chem., Anal. Ed.*, **12**, 274 (1940).

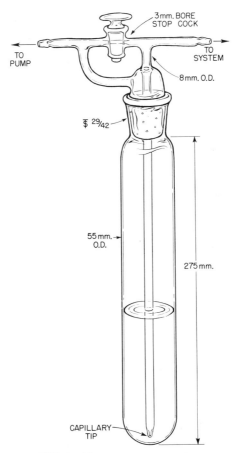

FIG. 6.   Newman pressure regulator.

applied to a gas to force it through a wash bottle, the principle of this regulator becomes evident. It is a device for maintaining a constant pressure differential between the system on the side of the pump and the system on the other side of the regulator. The difference in pressure is equal to the head of liquid in the regulator, and, since mercury has a density some 13 times greater than that of dibutyl phthalate, the liquid commonly used in the regulator, the pressure may be very accurately adjusted by the variation of the amount of liquid in the regulator. Small changes in pressure in the system may be accomplished, even while the system is evacuated, by tilting the regulator. For larger changes in pressure, air must be let into the system so that the amount of liquid in the regulator may be changed. Obvious complications may be introduced into the device so that the amount of liquid may be changed without letting air into the system; however, this seems hardly worthwhile. When air is let into the system at the end of a distillation, the stopcock is opened so that there will not be excessive splashing of the liquid. The device illustrated is useful for obtaining pressures up to about 15 mm, if the minimum pressure delivered by the pump is less than 1 mm. If higher pressures are desired, it is more convenient to use two or more of these devices in series than to use a longer one. It is also possible to secure higher pressures by using mercury in the regulator.

It should be mentioned that although the stopcock and glass joint are convenient, they are by no means essential. A rubber stopper may replace the ground joint, and a rubber tube and screw clamp may replace the stopcock. Thus, the regulator may be constructed from a large test tube and two T tubes. Similar types of regulators are commercially available.

Modifications of the Simple Claisen Flask

Certain features of the simple Claisen flask, such as shown in Fig. 1, are subject to improvement or modification for special purposes. A difficulty with the simple flask, which is frequently encountered, is attack of the hot vapors on the rubber stopper used to hold the thermometer. This may cause dark material to run down the side neck into the side arm and thus contaminate the distillate. This may be prevented by the modification shown in Fig. 7. Instead of holding the thermometer in a stopper, the upper part of the neck is constricted so that the thermometer just passes through the tube. The thermometer is held in place by a short section of suction tubing, as shown. Since a liquid seal is formed in the narrow annular space between the thermometer and the tube holding it, hot vapors are prevented almost entirely from reaching the rubber connection. As a matter of fact, it is easier to make an airtight attachment of the thermometer in this manner than with a stopper. The center neck of the Claisen flask should not be constricted in this manner, for this makes the introduction of material into the flask rather troublesome.

As an additional precaution, the side arm may be inset, as shown in Fig. 7, so that any material that might flow back will not get into the side arm. This is almost an unnecessary precaution, with the illustrated type of thermometer attachment, but the inset side arm has an additional advantage. Because of the high vapor velocities encountered in vacuum distillation, a liquid film on the wall of the side neck may actually be swept up along the wall and into the side arm. This is probably a more common cause of contamination of distillate than is actual entrainment (sweeping of tiny liquid droplets along with the vapor). It is true that entrainment is a factor in the contamination of distillate with nonvolatile material; however, the sweeping of a film along the wall seems more significant, and

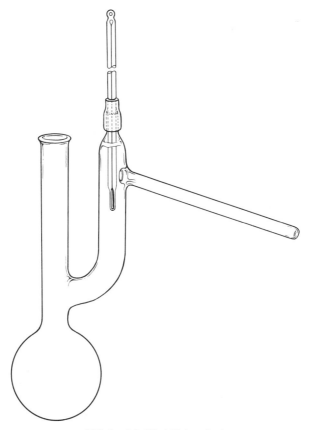

FIG. 7.   Modified Claisen flask.

this mode of contamination may be prevented by the use of the inset side
arm. In the construction of such a flask, the side arm should not be inset
far enough to interfere with placing the thermometer in the position
shown in Fig. 7; hence, the ring seal should project a bit beyond the wall of
the side neck.

It has been recommended by some that a thermometer well be sealed
into the side neck so as to occupy the position shown for the thermometer
in Fig. 7. The thermometer may then be placed in the well, and thermal
contact established with a high-boiling liquid such as dibutyl phthalate
(mercury has been used, but is a health hazard). The authors have found
this device very unreliable for the accurate recording of boiling point in a
vacuum distillation, for the thermometer is insulated by a piece of glass,
a very poor thermal conductor. This results in quite a lag in the thermometer reaching equilibrium with the vapor temperature, and at low
pressure the thermometer usually fails to reach the boiling point.

Sometimes a fractionating zone is introduced into a Claisen flask by extending the side neck below the side arm and indenting this portion in the manner of a Vigreux column (cf. Chap. 32). This permits a certain improvement in fractionation if the substances being distilled are sufficiently low-boiling to pass such an extended side neck and reach the side arm; however, the fractionating efficiency of such an arrangement is very low. The bath must always be overheated to force vapor through the elongated neck, and much of the reflux is in the lower part of the neck. Insulation of the side neck with asbestos helps some. In general, any distillation requiring more fractionating efficiency than realized in the usual Claisen flask is best carried out in a column such as described in Chap. 32, but the Claisen flask with Vigreux column attached is occasionally useful.

For the construction of large Claisen flasks (greater than 250-ml capacity), it is convenient to construct a Claisen head with a ground joint just below the attachment of the side neck. The assemblage is similar to that shown in Fig. 5–5, but the side-tube flask should be avoided, for these tubes are additional openings which must be sealed against leakage under vacuum. Also, a joint on the delivery tube is usually inconvenient for vacuum distillation (cf. discussion below of von Braun flask). Of course any size of round-bottomed flask may be attached to the Claisen head, and this combination is especially recommended for sizes larger than a liter. For this type of Claisen flask assembly, the round-bottomed flask must be supported by a clamp on the joint; and, since this joint becomes heated by the vapors passing through it, the clamp should have jaws covered with asbestos. The separate head and flask may be used for the construction of small Claisen flasks, but distillation of high-boiling materials from such an assemblage is unsatisfactory. The joint has considerable heat capacity, and cannot be immersed in the bath because of the necessity for clamping it. The large volume of vapor renders these difficulties less pronounced in the larger flasks. If a reaction is to be carried out by heating under reflux and the reaction mixture is to be directly distilled in a vacuum, it is especially advantageous to use the round-bottomed flask and Claisen head. For distillation, the reflux condenser is simply replaced by the Claisen head. When the Claisen head is used, the center neck may also be constricted in the manner shown for the side neck in Fig. 7, and the capillary may be inserted in the manner shown for the thermometer. Since the material may be placed in the round-bottomed flask before the head is attached, inserting material through the constricted neck of the head becomes unnecessary.

When materials that melt above about 50° and crystallize readily are being distilled, there is difficulty with preventing them from solidifying in the side arm and plugging it. The neck of the receiving flask may be warmed cautiously below the point at which solidification is taking place, and the whole may be heated with an infrared lamp, but particular diffi-culty is sometimes encountered in preventing plugging inside the stopper. If plugging of the side arm cannot be prevented with the usual setup (Fig. 1), the receiver may be sealed to the side arm. Such a flask, shown in Fig. 8, is sometimes called a von Braun flask. Since the whole side arm may be

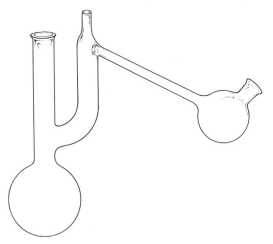

FIG. 8.   Von Braun flask, useful for distillation of solids at reduced pres-sure.

heated directly with a flame, materials melting as high as 265° (for example, 1,2,5,6-dibenzanthracene) may be distilled with ease. The weight of the distillate may be determined by weighing the entire flask and contents, removing the distillate, and weighing again. A liquid forerun may be removed with a bulb pipette. A solid forerun may be melted and so removed. The receiver may then be rinsed with a little solvent. In case it is desirable to leave the distillate in the receiver, the side arm may be cut a few centimeters from the receiving flask and a new receiver sealed on the side arm. This procedure is recommended as most satisfactory, although a small ground joint may be used to attach the receiver to the side arm. The ground joint materially increases the cost of the assemblage, and there is difficulty in keeping grease in the joint when it is heated with a burner. Without grease, the joint may freeze after strong heating under a vacuum.

Removal of Solvent at Reduced Pressure

Reduced pressure may be used either to increase the speed of sol-vent removal or to avoid prolonged heating of the solute as solvent is removed. In many instances, distillation of solvent at reduced pressure is carried out with such equipment as already discussed, especially the Claisen head attached to a round-bottomed flask. Since complete condensation of volatile solvent being rapidly distilled at reduced pressure is quite difficult, normal practice is to evacuate the system with a water pump (aspirator) and allow the solvent vapor to pass through the pump and into the water stream. With the usual volatile solvents (b.p. < 100° at atmospheric pressure), pressure in the system cannot be reduced below 100 mm unless a cold trap is included in the system. Immersing a receiver such as that shown in Fig. 1 in an ice-salt bath is moderately effective. When the last traces of solvent have been distilled at reduced pressure, this is signaled by a drop in pressure in the system to the minimum obtainable with the water pump.

In some situations, very rapid removal of small amounts of solvent (100 ml or less) becomes desirable. This may occur, for example, when a reaction is being followed by work-up of aliquots at frequent time intervals, or when solvent is removed from fractions of eluant in adsorption chromatography. For this purpose, there is utilized a pan of water heated to 70–80° (conveniently on a hot plate) and a Kjeldahl trap attached by a rubber hose to a system evacuated with an aspirator. As depicted in Fig. 9, the entry tube of the trap is passed into a one-hole rubber or neoprene stopper but not quite through it. That side of the stopper which is entirely flat (no trademark or size mark) is placed down. When a round-bottomed flask (whose top must be flat) is placed against the stopper as the system is evacuated, the flask is held to the stopper by the external pressure. The flask and stopper are held together in the hand as the flask is swirled and shaken (no boiling chip required) to allow rapid evaporation of the solvent from a very large surface. The flask is heated in the water bath in order to maintain a rapid rate of evaporation. If evaporation becomes too rapid to control, the vacuum may be broken *instantly* by merely pulling the flask to one side and thus breaking the contact with the stopper. On account of this instant control, solvent may be removed quite rapidly if the flask is less than half full. When most of the solvent has been removed, the flask is held in the water bath for 2–3 minutes, with evacuation, at which time essentially all solvent is removed, so that the approximate weight of the residue may be determined.

In instances where there is no premium on very rapid removal of solvent, the evaporation may be accomplished without close attention from the experimenter by use of commercially available *rotary evaporators*. These devices utilize a low-speed motor, further geared down, to turn a standard taper joint to which flasks may be attached and evacuated. If the flask is placed at about a 45° angle, liquid is spread over the surface of the rotating flask so that rapid evaporation occurs without actual boiling of

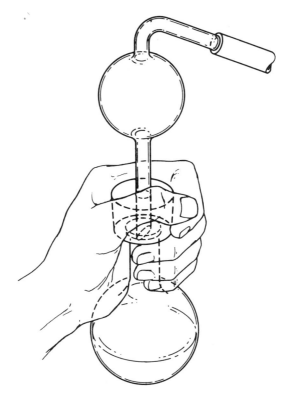

FIG. 9.   Evaporation of solvent from a chromatography fraction.

the liquid. Heating in a water bath prevents excessive cooling and consequent slowing of the evaporation. Sealing of the rotating spindle in rotary
evaporators, necessary to allow evacuation, has usually been accomplished
in commercially available models with a neoprene or Kel-F O-ring. This
ring is attacked by solvents, and must be replaced periodically. A rotary
evaporator constructed for use in our laboratories, but now commercially
available, is designed so that a Teflon ball joint on the rotating spindle turns
against a glass ball joint. The lubricating properties of Teflon allow an
adequately tight fit, without excessive friction to turning. This type of
seal is not attacked by solvent, hence operates indefinitely without repair.

The principal advantage of the rotary evaporator is that solvent may
be removed at low temperature, without attention from the operator. Other
methods are faster, and frequently more convenient.

Attention should be directed to the fact that *relatively high-boiling
solutes will be partly distilled during removal of large quantities of solvent*
if no fractionating equipment is used for distillation of the solvent, as in

the methods that have been discussed above. Significant amounts of a compound boiling as high as 200° will be lost during distillation of ether solvent. In such instances, the solvent must be distilled through a simple fractionating column, but it may be distilled quite rapidly. The Vigreux column described in Chap. 32 is quite useful for this purpose, and no provision for forcing reflux in the head is required.

Fractional Distillation

32

The development of efficient laboratory fractionating columns has made possible the separation of mixtures boiling only a few degrees apart. Fractional distillation must always remain far less effective than gas phase chromatography (cf. Chap. 4); however, quantities greater than about 100 mg are handled more easily by distillation. Indeed, there is essentially no upper limit on quantities that may be handled in fractional distillation; throughput from industrial stills is frequently described in terms of gallons per minute.

The best commercially available laboratory fractionating equipment[1] is occasionally required for a difficult separation; however, most needs are met by relatively simple equipment that may be constructed in laboratories having modest glassblowing and machine shop facilities. Indeed, the equipment described in this chapter may be constructed by a moderately skillful amateur. The authors do not wish to imply that the equipment here described is the best that can be constructed, but it is simple and economical to construct, adaptable for use with a wide variety of compounds, and capable of the performance described if it is properly operated. The importance of proper manipulation cannot be overemphasized. Mastery of this technique comes only with experience, and the beginner should not be discouraged or lose confidence in his equipment because

[1]The Nester Faust Auto Annular Still is capable of effective separation of components boiling only 2° apart at pressures below 10 mm. In a single distillation, more than two-thirds of the components may be obtained in fractions of about 99% purity (glpc analysis). This equipment has a maximum boiling point limit of about 150°, however, and there must be used a better pressure regulator than that which has been supplied with the still.

initial results fall short of expectations. Although there is no substitute for experience and personal instruction by one skilled in the field, this chapter introduces briefly some of the more important principles involved in the operation of fractionating equipment.

Two types of columns will be described: the Podbielniak column with simple wire spiral, and the indented Vigreux column. The latter is somewhat less efficient, but adaptable to larger quantities, also more versatile, more rugged, and more easily assembled. The Vigreux column is commonly used for advanced synthetic work in undergraduate courses, while the Podbielniak column is usually used in research. A two-foot Vigreux column, properly operated, gives satisfactory separation of components boiling 25° or more apart, and is about equal in efficiency to a 15-inch Podbielniak column. A four-foot Podbielniak column gives satisfactory separation of components boiling as little as 10° apart. These figures refer to a single distillation at reduced pressure. Distillation at atmospheric pressure, on account of the higher vapor density, allows separation of components boiling closer together. Also, redistillation of intermediate fractions naturally improves separation. Nevertheless, separation of components differing no more than five degrees in boiling point requires the more elaborate types of fractionating equipment.

The diversity of still heads is almost as great as that of types of columns, but the present descriptions will be confined to three types of relatively simple construction that are quite satisfactory. Two of these are of the partial-condensation total takeoff type, whereas the third is a total-condensation, partial takeoff head. The practice of inserting a ground joint to attach head to column has been found very inconvenient, and columns without such a joint are preferred. This inconvenience arises partly from the difficulty of supporting the head and column independently, especially during attachment or removal of the flask from the bottom of the column. There are other drawbacks, especially when high-boiling materials are being distilled. Since the construction of the column is usually simple and cheap, and the head is the more troublesome component to construct, it has been found more convenient to attach a column permanently to each head and have these units interchangeable in the heated jacket. Since the jacket is always the same, it is shown in only one diagram and is discussed separately. A jacket for each column is highly recommended, for exchanging columns in a jacket is time-consuming and always carries some extra liability of breakage.

The Heated Jacket

Since the fractionating zone in a column should be as nearly adiabatic as possible, the column must be either heated or insulated, or both. One type of insulation is an evacuated and silvered jacket. This rather expensive construction is the only type that is effective for distillation at temperatures below that of the room. However, at higher temperatures the efficiency of an evacuated jacket falls off very rapidly, and it is rather ineffective above 100°. At the higher temperatures, columns are frequently insulated with several inches of steam-pipe covering or similar material. This has a great disadvantage for laboratory columns in that a long heating-up period is necessary before the column reaches equilibrium. The heat capacity of the system is large, and the only source of heat input is the boiling liquid. The heated jacket is very convenient in that equilibrium may be reached very quickly and the temperature of the jacket may be varied rapidly. Furthermore, glass construction is feasible; this allows easy observation of the contents of the column, a very desirable feature.

The jacket is constructed from two pieces of Pyrex glass tubing of such a length as to extend from the bottom of the head to just above the ground joint on the bottom of the column. The relative length of the jacket is indicated in Fig. 2. The column should not extend below the bottom of the jacket, for this will permit a cold zone where flooding will occur unless the pot is grossly overheated. On the other hand, it is recommended that the jacket not extend over the joint, for this interferes with direct heating of a frozen joint with a hot flame. If direct heating is possible, a frozen joint is nearly always loosened easily and without damage. For columns of the size described here, the inner tube of the jacket is 30 mm outer diameter, and the outer tube is 48 mm outer diameter. This allows room for the column with attached thermometer inside the inner tube. Three strips of asbestos paper, 6–8 mm wide, are painted with water glass and placed lengthwise on the inner tube, equally spaced from each other [Fig. 1 (a)]. The strips are pressed firmly on the glass. There is used only as much water glass as is soaked up by the asbestos paper, for if the amount of water glass is too generous it may combine with the Pyrex glass sufficiently to cause cracking on heating. After the asbestos strips have dried in place, the Nichrome or Chromel A heating wire is wound on this tube [Fig. 1 (b)], as described below.

For a 24-inch jacket, a winding consisting of 20 feet of No. 24 Nichrome wire (about 33-ohms resistance) is satisfactory for operation up to 250° if a 0–130-volt variable transformer is used for control. For longer columns, there should be used larger wire of lower resistance. Since the theory of the fractionation process requires a higher temperature at the bottom of the column than at the top, the windings should become very slightly closer together, proceeding from the top of the column to the bottom; the tendency, however, is to make this differential too great. The temperature of the contents of the column tends to make this adjustment, to some extent. As an example, if the average distance between the wind-

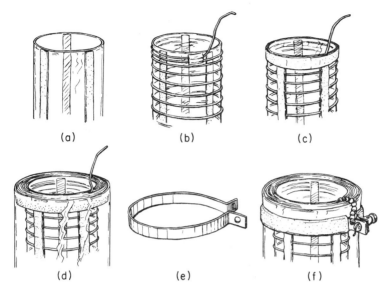

FIG. 1.   Steps in construction of heated jacket for fractionating column.

ings is 10 mm, the variation between top and bottom should be from about 11 mm to about 9 mm. In addition, the last three or four windings at each end of the jacket should become progressively closer together, with the last two only 2–3 mm apart and very near the end. This prevents a cold zone at each end. A given section in the middle of the column is heated not only by the wire in that section, but to some extent by the sections on each side of it; whereas, at the end, there is no heated section on one side. Since Nichrome wire is stiff and troublesome to handle, the winding should first be made and properly spaced with a piece of string; then the wire is wound beside the string as a guide. Sufficient wire is left at each end to serve as leads. Each end of the wire is conveniently held in place by rubber bands, which are removed when asbestos is placed over the windings. After the winding is in place and the string is removed, three strips of asbestos paper are painted with water glass and placed over the first three strips, with the wire between the two strips [Fig. 1 (c)]. This layer of asbestos paper is pressed down firmly over the wires. Additional pieces of asbestos paper, painted with water glass, are placed at the ends to secure the wire [Fig. 1 (c)]. Three or four layers are used at the ends. A heater constructed in this way will not loosen and shift out of position as a result of heating and cooling during operation.

After the asbestos holding the winding in place has dried, the leads are brought out the ends. One lead may be brought out each end and attached to a terminal near that end, or one lead may be passed back down the jacket so that both leads come out the same end, as in Fig. 2. If a lead is brought back in this manner, insulation may be assured by passing it through a small piece of glass tubing. Each end of the inner tube is now built up with strips of asbestos about 10 mm wide, using water glass as adhesive, until the asbestos collar will just slip inside the outer tube. The Nichrome wire leads pass through this asbestos collar. The inner tube is then slipped into the outer, and the ends are tightly packed with shredded wet asbestos paper until both ends are packed smoothly with asbestos flush with the ends of the tubes [Fig. 1 (d)]. After drying, the unit holds together well and does not slip apart on handling. For terminals, copper, monel or stainless-steel strips, 10 × 210 mm, are cut from a thin sheet of the metal. A hole of a size to take the screw in an ordinary brass terminal is drilled 5 mm from each end, and the strip is bent as shown in Fig. 1 (e). A strip of asbestos is wetted and wound around the jacket, and the metal strip is placed on top of it and drawn tight by attaching the terminal. The Nichrome lead is insulated with glass beads or ceramic rings, and the end is wound around the screw holding the terminal. A wider strip of asbestos is placed over the metal strap, using water glass, to prevent the operator from touching the metal and receiving a shock. The terminal in place is shown in Fig. 1 (f). After the insulated copper lead wire is attached, it is advisable also to cover the terminal with asbestos paper. The jacket is now complete. The time required for the assemblage is 2–4 hours, and the materials cost about five dollars.

The Podbielniak Column[2] with Partial Reflux Head

The column described in this section is suitable for distillation of samples weighing 2–100 g and boiling in the range from 90° at 20-mm pressure to 275° at 2-mm pressure. Since many of the materials handled in research boil in this range, and the quantities mentioned are convenient for many types of research, this column, in 24-inch length, has been used for routine distillation in investigations carried out by the authors. Attention should be directed, especially, to the very high-boiling materials that may be handled in this column. The head is not suitable for distillation of materials boiling below the range mentioned above; for such relatively low-boiling materials a total reflux head, such as described below with the Vigreux column, should be attached to the Podbielniak column. This latter type of head is not suitable for materials boiling above about 150° at 5-mm pressure, especially with the small Podbielniak column, for the vapors do not reach the takeoff. With a larger column, and extensive insulation of the head, it is possible to use such a total reflux head with very high-boiling materials. The partial reflux head described below for

[2]W. J. Podbielniak, *Ind. Eng. Chem., Anal. Ed.*, **3**, 177 (1931); **5**, 119 (1933).

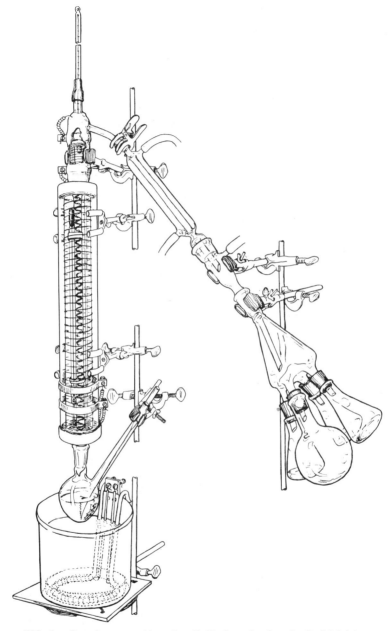

FIG. 2. Complete assemblage for distillation, showing the Podbielniak-type column with partial reflux head. Also illustrated are (a) the pear-shaped flask with side tubulature for capillary, (b) oil bath with "do-it-your-self" electric heating element, (c) the type of fraction changer known as a "pig" or "cow." The pig may have several more outlets if small tubes are used as receivers.

larger columns is not suitable for the Podbielniak column, for the amount of void in the head is too great for the small area of cross section through which vapor may pass in the column.

The complete setup for operation of the Podbielniak column, with all accessories for distillation at reduced pressure, is shown in Fig. 2. The construction of the column will be described in this section, while accessories will be described in a later section in this chapter.

The glass skeleton of the column may be visualized from Fig. 2. The fractionating section is an 8-mm outer-diameter Pyrex tube, with a 14/35 standard taper joint attached to the bottom. Pyrex tubing varies some from piece to piece, and it is best to select a "small" 8-mm tube.

The bottom of the joint is beveled at an angle and drawn to a short, fine tip at the lower side. The drip from this tip may be observed when a 14/20 joint is used on the flask, and there is a short neck between the bulb of the flask and the joint. A dripper at the top of the column has been found so very troublesome in construction and of so little practical value that it has been abandoned. To the top of the 8-mm tube is attached a 16-mm outer-diameter Pyrex tube, 100 mm in length; to the top of this tube is attached a Pyrex tube whose inner diameter is just large enough to allow the thermometer to pass through. The takeoff, attached with an inset, is about 20 mm from the top of the large tube. The head, with thermometer in proper position, is shown in Fig. 3. The standard taper joint shown in Fig. 3 has become preferred to the ball joint shown in Fig. 2. The lack of flexibility in the straight joint is a smaller disadvantage than the tendency of the ball joint to leak under vacuum. The thermometer should be placed slightly below the takeoff, as shown, to insure equilibrium with the vapor. It is also an advantage at the beginning of a distillation to have the boiling temperature register slightly before takeoff begins, so that any indicated readjustment of the controls may be made before actual takeoff begins. The condenser may be sealed to the takeoff tube, and the joint omitted; however, this makes the column unwieldy to handle, especially as the heater is being wound on the head. Furthermore, the type of takeoff system cannot be modified, e.g., by directly attaching a flask to receive solids.

The spiral may be inserted in the column either before or after the head is wound. A Nichrome or Chromel A wire is satisfactory if no acids or organic halides are distilled through the column, but tantalum wire is not excessively expensive and is highly desirable. During the distillation of a wide variety of organic compounds, over a period of thirty years, no attack on tantalum wire has been observed. The spiral is made from B. and S. (Brown and Sharpe) No. 18 wire (diameter 0.040 inches). The wire is first wound tightly (like thread on a spool) on a metal rod of 5/32-inch diameter. About 34 inches of wire will give a spiral 12 inches long, but it

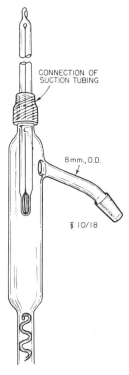

CONNECTION OF
SUCTION TUBING

8 mm., O.D.

⊼ 10/18

FIG. 3.   Detail of the partial reflux head for Podbielniak column.

is wisest to use about 36 inches of wire per foot of spiral to insure adequate length. It is better to waste a few inches of wire and insure adequate length to the spiral. The tight spiral is grasped at each end with pliers and stretched with an even pull until the length approaches that of the column. It is then checked for fit inside the Pyrex tube, and cautiously pulled out further until it barely slips in. The wire is held in the tube by friction, and near contact with the glass at all points is necessary for formation of a liquid film over the wire during fractionation. If the spiral did not pull out entirely smoothly, local sections may be carefully adjusted with the hands until the entire spiral is spaced fairly evenly. The spiral is then cut to the desired length, the ends are carefully turned in so that they do not project beyond the edge of the spiral, and one end of the wire is bent to form a hook (note top of wire in Fig. 3). A small copper wire with a loop at the end is passed through the column, the loop is placed on the hook at the end of the spiral, and the spiral is pulled into the column, with gentle pushing from the other end.

If the spiral cannot be pulled in without excessive stretching of the front end, the spiral is a trifle too large and should be adjusted by even stretching of the entire spiral. Pushing the spiral in is unsatisfactory, for this compresses it. Pulling it in as described stretches it slightly, so that when the tension is released the wire springs back slightly and fits snugly in the tube. After a little practice, using the cheap Nichrome wire, this method of fabrication and insertion of the spiral will be found rather easy. Our experience has found these spirals approximately as satisfactory as those made by the more elaborate procedure described by Podbielniak. There has been no difficulty in obtaining a spiral that will give a continuous liquid film when a little acetone is poured into the top of the column. Our tube and wire are slightly larger than those used by Podbielniak. This permits distillation of viscous materials, without flooding at full reflux.

The head is wound with a heating wire in much the same manner as described for the jacket. For use with a 24-volt transformer (described below, under "Accessories"), five feet of No. 24 Nichrome or Chromel A (about 8.5-ohms resistance) is suitable for distillations up to about 275°. This length includes the leads, which should be a total length of 4 inches or less. One or two turns of wire should pass above the takeoff. It is important that a piece of asbestos paper be placed between the wire and the ring seal at the takeoff. After the heater has been wound as described for the jacket, except that the wire is spaced approximately evenly, the wire is fixed in place with asbestos paper and water glass. *Care is always observed* to prevent large amounts of water glass from making direct contact with the Pyrex glass. This is especially important in the head.

After the water glass has dried briefly, the head is built up with wet asbestos paper until it is slightly too large to slip into the inner tube of the jacket. A thicker layer of insulation is undesirable. The jacket is slipped on the column and pressed against the bottom of the wet asbestos, thus shaping the bottom of the head insulation to fit against the jacket. After the asbestos has dried overnight, straps and terminals are attached as described for the jacket. The length required for the straps depends on the exact size to which the head is built up. The leads are attached to the terminals, and the straps covered with asbestos as described before. The terminals should not be placed so close together that a short can easily occur, and they should be covered with asbestos. A cut-away section of the head is shown as a part of Fig. 2. A smooth finish may be applied to the head if it is filled out evenly with wet asbestos paper pulp and then painted with water glass. This also gives a hard finish that is not easily damaged.

A cork that slips easily, but not too loosely, into the inner tube of the jacket is bored in the center with an 8-mm hole, and then split through the center, longitudinally. It is then placed on the column, just above the joint, and wired together with a piece of small Nichrome wire. In this operation, as well as in attaching the thermometer, care must be exercised to avoid breaking the small tube of the column. A total-immersion thermometer with bulb turned up is attached to the column with narrow strips of asbestos paper painted *lightly* with water glass, in such a position that the bulb is about 30 mm from the top of the jacket. Attachment of the thermometer with wire is not recommended, for breakage of the column is likely to result. Since the thermometer may tend to slip down, it is supported with a wire extending to the cork, as shown in Fig. 2, or with a collar of asbestos wound just below the thermometer. The asbestos strips should not obscure the thermometer scale, and the scale should be facing in a direction where it may be read without interference from the vertical strips of asbestos on the inner tube of the jacket. The cork at the bottom of the column and the careful fitting of the head insulation against the top of the jacket prevent air currents from rising through the jacket when it is heated. The partial-immersion thermometer in the head is attached with a short section of suction tubing.

In operation, the jacket is held with two clamps in a vertical position, and the column is held firmly against the jacket with a clamp on the head, as shown in Fig. 2. All clamps should be tightened securely, since any slippage is likely to result in breakage of the column. When a flask is being attached to or disengaged from the column, the head should be supported with one hand, to insure no turning of the column in the jacket.

Since the head of this column has no provision for cooling except by heat loss to the room, it is limited, as previously mentioned, to materials boiling above about 90° at 20-mm pressure. Actually, small lower-boiling fractions are removed with entire satisfaction, for appreciable quantities of material are required to heat the head sufficiently to give too little reflux. Also, where the separation is not difficult, lower-boiling materials may be satisfactorily distilled at somewhat lower column efficiency by underheating the jacket. The small size of the column reduces the need for high-capacity forced reflux. At higher temperatures, the desired reflux is obtained by heating the head just sufficiently to give distillation at an appropriate rate. The small size of the head and small holdup in the column make this column ideal for distillation of small amounts, and its construction is such that very high-boiling materials may be distilled. Our experience with various other types of heads has been unsatisfactory for distillation of small amounts of materials boiling above about 175° at 2-mm pressure. The temperature at which this column may be used is limited only by the thermal stability of the compounds being distilled.

The Vigreux Column with Total Reflux Head

Although the Vigreux column is appreciably less efficient, for a given length, than a packed column such as described in Chap. 5, it has the ad-

vantage of considerably less holdup. A packed column of one-meter length
has a holdup of about 10 ml; hence it is suitable only for relatively large-
scale laboratory work. Further, the Vigreux has a relatively large cross
section for vapor flow; hence, it is suitable for high-temperature and low-
pressure distillations. Construction of the fractionating zone involves only
glassblowing, and no further installations are necessary. Since the head
described here has no heater, this also involves no installation. For these
reasons, this column has been found the most satisfactory for routine
classroom work. The construction is illustrated in Fig. 4, which shows
the top of the column and head. The 16-mm size for the column, with
19/38 joint, is satisfactory. Indentations with a downward slant are believed
more effective than those extending in at right angles to the wall of the
tube. The efficiency of the column is improved by spacing the indentations
closely, but they must not be so close as to cause flooding at high reflux.

For fitting the Vigreux column into the jacket, the asbestos collars at
top and bottom are built up more on one side than the other, so as to

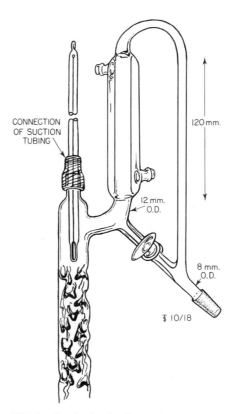

FIG. 4.   Total reflux head atop Vigreux column.

position the column in the jacket slightly to one side of the axis of the jacket. This allows room inside the jacket for the thermometer, placed beside the larger column in the manner that has been described for the Podbielniak column. The part of the head between the jacket and takeoff should be insulated with about $\frac{1}{4}$ inch of asbestos if high-boiling materials are to be distilled *in vacuo;* otherwise, the vapors will not reach the takeoff. The geometry of the glassware about the takeoff should be carefully designed, as illustrated in Fig. 4, to insure that the refluxing liquid runs into the takeoff. Otherwise, liquids that do not wet glass are likely to channel in such a way as to miss the takeoff. The capillary connection above the takeoff stopcock prevents excessive holdup, which would introduce some uncertainty as to the nature of the material at the beginning and end of a fraction.

Obviously, this type of head is the simplest to construct, and it is very useful, but it has certain disadvantages. The adjustment of rate of takeoff is usually rather troublesome, especially *in vacuo*, and, after rate is adjusted, it is likely to change. In vacuum distillation, any leakage at all through the stopcock will eventually introduce a bubble into the bore of the stopcock, and this often completely stops takeoff. Since the hot distillate is passing through the stopcock, this tends to dissolve the grease and cause the stopcock to leak. Also, the distillate becomes slightly contaminated. These latter difficulties are reduced, but by no means avoided, by use of silicone stopcock grease. A Teflon stopcock plug may be used without lubrication; however, it is difficult to obtain a sufficiently good fit to hold a vacuum without lubrication. Numerous improved devices have been described for regulating the takeoff from a total reflux head, but many are no more effective than a simple stopcock, and all the effective ones are too elaborate for classroom use. For research use, the partial reflux heads appear to have many advantages; however, discussion of the pros and cons of the various types of heads and columns is far beyond the scope of this book. The present objective is the description of simple types that will work, and brief citation of the more apparent advantages of each type.

The Partial Reflux Head for Larger Columns

This head is similar to that originally described by Lauflin, Nash, and Whitmore,[3] in that reflux is forced by means of a cold finger inserted in a well containing a high-boiling liquid such as dibutyl phthalate. Since this well is heated during distillation, use of mercury for the heat transfer constitutes a health hazard. The construction of the head is evident from Fig. 5. Extent of cooling is controlled by raising or lowering the cold fin-

[3]K. C. Lauflin, C. W. Nash, and F. C. Whitmore, *J. Am. Chem. Soc.*, **56**, 1396 (1934).

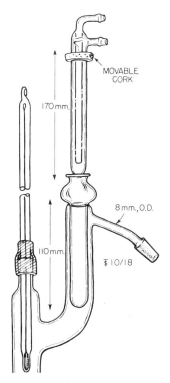

FIG. 5. Partial reflux head for larger columns.

ger in the well. A simple device for holding the cold finger at the desired level is the narrow cork ring shown in Fig. 5. The cork is loose enough to be slipped along on the cold finger, and may be held at the desired place with a tapered sliver of wood, such as a matchstick that has been sharpened at one end.

The cooling device is necessary only for low-boiling compounds; for higher-boiling compounds it is necessary to apply heat to the head as described for the Podbielniak column. Thus, the side neck containing the cold finger is wound with a heater and insulated lightly as described for the Podbielniak column. The heating element and insulation are not shown in Fig. 5. The winding procedure here is exactly the same as described for the Podbielniak column except that the larger size of the head necessitates a larger wattage heater. Three feet of No. 24 Nichrome or Chromel A wire is satisfactory. The side neck should be wound from take-off to junction with the column, and the asbestos insulation should cover all of the column protruding from the heated jacket. Otherwise, there may be difficulty in getting high-boiling liquids through the head, and the reflux will be affected by drafts.

Accessories for Fractional Distillation

In Fig. 2 is illustrated an assemblage of several of the accessories used in connection with fractional distillation. These and others are described below.

Flasks

Although columns sometimes have flasks sealed to them, their versatility is so limited that the flask is nearly always attached with a ground joint. A ball joint is preferred by some workers, but the orthodox standard taper joint is recommended as more satisfactory, especially as regards holding a vacuum. Since a capillary is desirable for any long distillation in a vacuum, the flask is provided with a side inlet (Fig. 2) through which a capillary is inserted and attached with a section of suction tubing. With this type of connection, there is essentially no contact of hot vapors with the rubber connections, and the same piece of rubber is often used for dozens of distillations. For flasks of 50-ml or less capacity, the pear shape shown in Fig. 2 is an advantage. For larger flasks, the conventional spherical flask is more convenient.

The joint for attaching the flask to the column may be lubricated lightly with silicone grease; however, when operating under vacuum, a leak is prone to develop at this point on account of the increased mobility and solubility of the grease on heating. *The best device for avoiding leakage at this joint is a Teflon sleeve.* Such thin sleeves of Teflon, tapered to fit the joint, may be purchased from laboratory supply houses.

Heating Baths

Heaters of the mantle type are not recommended for fractional distillation, for they cause serious overheating of the vapors when the flask is less than half full, and this makes proper fractionation very difficult. The electrically heated oil bath is very cheap and quite effective. For baths to be used at 200° or lower, an ordinary tin can, with the top cut out smoothly, is satisfactory. For higher temperatures, as well as lower ones, a steel beaker is highly recommended. The assemblage to be described below is shown as a part of Fig. 2.

A rectangular piece of transite, 30 × 40 mm, is bolted to the top of the container (can or steel beaker). To the upper half of the transite, projecting above the container, are attached two terminals. To these terminals are connected the leads from the Nichrome heater and the copper leads for attaching to a transformer. The wire in the heater should not be smaller than No. 26, for No. 28 burns out rapidly in this kind of usage. For a container of approximately 5 × 7 inches size, suitable for flasks up to 500 ml, 12 feet of No. 26 wire (about 32-ohms resistance) is a suitable heater. Sufficient wire is left for leads, and the remainder is wound on a piece of carbon such as used in arc lamps, held in place while it is heated to redness, and then quenched in water. This forms a springlike coil, which is pulled apart enough to separate the turns. (If an occasional turn touches the next, only the one turn is shorted out.) This heater is placed in the bottom of the container in a Pyrex Petri dish. (For larger containers, the bottom of a beaker of appropriate size is cut off.) The coil must be kept in position in some manner to prevent shorts; this is easily done by threading it on a piece of glass tubing bent in the proper shape, as shown in the illustration. Even better, on account of lack of fragility, is a piece of heavy copper wire with asbestos insulation. The Nichrome leads, coming up to the terminals are insulated with glass beads, ceramic rings, or pieces of Pyrex tubing. After materials are assembled, such a bath may be constructed in short time, and is useful for a variety of heating operations. Since it is internally heated and not insulated, it is rapidly responsive to changes in power input; however, the heat capacity of a bath of five inches, or larger size is sufficient to prevent fluctuations in response to minor air currents.

The heat-transfer medium in such a bath must be nonconducting, since the element is in the medium. Satisfactory bath oils for temperatures up to about 225° (250° for short periods) include hydrogenated cottonseed oil (solid at room temperature) and Ucon lubricant (liquid at room temperature; cf. page 302). For higher temperatures, where a salt bath is necessary, the simple heater described cannot be used. A commercial heater embedded in ceramic and sealed in metal may be put into the salt (such as the Aminco LoLag heater or the General Electric Calrod heater).

The heating bath is *best supported from the top*, rather than from beneath as shown in Fig. 2, for top support makes it nearly impossible to accidentally overturn the bath. This is especially important for a salt bath, which is dangerous at best (cf. Chap. 31). A steel beaker with flanged rim is readily supported at the top with an iron ring.

Transformers

The advantages of the variable transformer are so numerous that a rheostat should never be used for control of any heater. Transformers rated at 5 amperes are sufficient for control of heating baths large enough for 2-liter flasks, while a 3-ampere transformer (panel mounting is convenient) is sufficiently large for jackets less than a meter in length. Many makes of transformers on the market are excellent devices that may be expected to give an indefinite period of trouble-free service.

For the small heaters in the heads of the partial reflux columns, transformers operating at a maximum of 130 volts are not convenient on account of the large resistance required to give a low-wattage heater at high voltage. A 15-volt transformer, such as used for control of electric trains and other toys, may be used, but such devices contain rheostats that are a source of trouble. It is somewhat more expensive, but highly satisfactory to feed a voltage in the range of 16–24 volts from a small transformer with several fixed voltages (such as Model SC-5 of United Transformer Corp.) to the primary input of a 3-ampere variable transformer. This allows excellent control since the entire scale of the 3-ampere transformer covers the range of the low voltage applied.

Fraction Cutters

For distillation at atmospheric pressure, the changing of fractions is no problem, but in a vacuum distillation it is almost necessary to be able to change fractions without raising the pressure and thus interrupting the distillation. One type of fraction cutter is illustrated in Fig. 2; its construction is evident from the diagram. This device has the advantages that the distillate passes through no stopcock, and fractions may be changed without any interference with constant pressure in the system. It is limited to relatively small quantities (< 100 g/fraction) and no more than six or seven fractions. It should be operated in a position not too far from the vertical so that a full flask on the upper side will not throw too great a strain on the connecting tube, and flasks of more than 100-ml capacity should not be used. Fifty-ml Erlenmeyer flasks are convenient receivers; thousands have been evacuated without an accident. Evacuation of a larger Erlenmeyer flask is not wise; collapse of those larger than 125 ml is almost inevitable. Attachment of the flasks with ground joints instead of rubber stoppers is expensive and rather inconvenient.

A second type of conventional fraction cutter is shown in Fig. 6. This device has the advantage that receivers of any size and in any number may be used. Its chief disadvantage is that the distillate must pass through the stopcock, and even silicone grease is slowly dissolved. A further advantage is that distillate may be held above the stopcock whenever there is uncertainty as to whether or not the boiling point is changing. After the uncertainty has been resolved by continuation of distillation, the material held up can be put either in the fraction being collected or in the next fraction after flasks are changed. A study of the stopcock arrangement will make clear the sequence of operation for isolation of the receiver from the pump, letting air into the receiver for changing, and evacuation of the new flask while the distillation system is isolated from the pump. Any leaks in the fractionating system will cause a slight rise in pressure

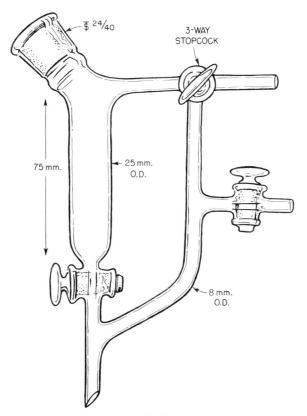

FIG. 6.   Fraction cutter for distillation at reduced pressure.

while the new flask is being evacuated, but this requires only a brief time, and the interference with column equilibrium is minor.

Operation of a Fractionating Column

Poor manipulation will defeat the best of fractionating equipment, and skillful operation will produce gratifying results with such simple equipment as described in this chapter. Operation of a column, like driving an automobile, must be learned by long practice, but proper instruction is a great help. An attempt will be made to set forth the principles most essential to a beginner in the art of fractional distillation.

As has been discussed in Chap. 5, the vapor in equilibrium with a two-component liquid mixture must be richer in the lower-boiling component than is the *liquid*. This is true, no matter whether the vapor was obtained by partial vaporization of the liquid, or the liquid was obtained by partial condensation of the vapor. The objective in a fractionating column is partial condensation of the ascending vapors, accompanied by partial revaporization of the returning liquid. Both processes tend to enrich the vapor in the lower-boiling component. This gives the same results as a series of redistillations, each of which causes further enrichment of the vapor in the lower-boiling component.

The number of "theoretical plates" in a column may be regarded as the number of times the first distillate from a mixture must be redistilled, with each redistillation applying only to the first distillate, in order to obtain the same results as achieved by one distillation through the column. Further, if the length of the fractionating zone in the column is divided by the number of theoretical plates, the "height equivalent to a theoretical plate" (H.E.T.P.) of the column may be obtained. For determination of the number of theoretical plates, the student is referred to laboratory texts of physical chemistry or chemical engineering. The organic chemist usually finds it sufficient for ordinary purposes in research and synthesis to determine how far apart components must boil before he can separate them satisfactorily in his column.

For most effective operation of a column, at least four conditions are desirable: (1) the exchange of heat between liquid and vapor in the column should be as near adiabatic as possible; (2) the column should spread the returning liquid over considerable surface so that exchange with the vapor is facilitated; (3) the *net* condensation in the column should be as near zero as possible for all net condensation should occur in the head; (4) ratio of reflux to takeoff should be high (5:1 or more) at all stages of the distillation where the mole fraction in the pot of the lowest-boiling constituent is low. The columns that have been described are designed to promote these conditions, but their effectiveness depends to a considerable extent on the manner of operation. There will next be described the procedure for starting up and carrying through a fractional distillation of two components. If more components are present, the procedure is simply continued. Distillation at reduced pressure will be discussed, since the problems encountered at atmospheric pressure are similar but more simple.

In starting a distillation at reduced pressure, the flask containing the material, with capillary in place, is attached to the column, and the fraction cutter with receivers is attached. If desired, solvent may be flash-distilled through the column by adding the solution from a dropping funnel attached to the side tube of the flask. After all solution has been added, the dropping funnel is replaced with the capillary, and last traces of solvent are distilled at reduced pressure with an aspirator, as usual in vacuum distillation. After all solvent has been removed, the oil pump is attached, and the material fractionated.

Pressure in the system is first adjusted to the desired value and the head is set for total (or maximum) reflux; then the flask is heated until the material begins to reflux into the column. Next, the column is heated until the refluxing liquid reaches the top of the column and the boiling point registers on the thermometer. The temperature at the top of the jacket (as recorded on the thermometer attached to the column) is then raised until it is just below or at the boiling point recorded by the thermometer in the vapor. In starting a distillation, the jacket should be heated cautiously until the boiling point registers at the top of the column, for, if the jacket is heated above the boiling point of the material reaching the top of the column, the vapors will be overheated and a temperature higher than the boiling point will be recorded. However, when the thermometer in the vapor registers a boiling point higher than the jacket temperature, superheating is not possible at that time. The jacket temperature may then be raised to a point just below the boiling point. Ideally, the temperature at the top of the jacket should be the same as the boiling point. In practice, essentially adiabatic conditions are realized if the jacket temperature is kept between the boiling point and 3° below the boiling point, except for very high boiling points. For boiling points above about 180° at 3 mm, it proves necessary to heat the jacket 2–5° above the boiling point (the larger differential as the boiling point becomes higher). This unexpected behavior is probably due to loss of heat from the column by direct radiation to the surroundings.

It should be mentioned, before proceeding, that if a high-boiling material is being distilled in the Podbielniak column with partial reflux head, it may be necessary to carefully heat the head before the vapors will reach the thermometer in the head. This should be done after the refluxing liquid has reached the top of the column, and with due caution against heating the vapors above the boiling point. In fact, throughout distillation in this type of column, precaution must be taken against overheating the head; it is highly recommended that the head be calibrated. This is done by putting an empty flask on the column, heating the head to various temperatures, and plotting a curve showing the relationship between head temperature and setting of the small transformer used for control of heat input to the head. If line voltage varies significantly, it is desirable that an ammeter (3-ampere range) also be included in the circuit. The calibration plot is then made for temperature of head against amperes. Such a calibration curve is indispensable for distillations at high temperatures and low pressures, for the head must be heated very nearly to the boiling point in order to get any distillation under such conditions.

After the column has been brought into equilibrium, as just described, the head is adjusted to give the desired rate of takeoff. The desired rate varies as the distillation proceeds; this will be discussed in the following paragraphs. At the beginning of the distillation, there is likely to be a small forerun; if that is the case, the vapor temperature will rise more or less rapidly until the first fraction is reached. This point is evidenced by the boiling point becoming constant or rising very slowly. Receivers are changed and the lower-boiling component is collected over the desired boiling-point range. For most purposes, a fraction collected over two or three degrees is of adequate purity (cf. discussion on page 335), but if especially pure material is desired a narrower cut may be taken. When the temperature begins to rise relatively rapidly, receivers are changed again, and an intermediate fraction is collected as the boiling point rises. When the boiling point levels off, the high-boiling fraction is collected over two or three degrees in another receiver. If the intermediate fraction is sufficiently large, it may be redistilled and more of the two fractions obtained from it. An idea of the separation that may be expected in the two-foot Vigreux column may be obtained from the distillation data for the preparation of ethyl hydrogen adipate, Chap. 37; and data obtained with the Podbielniak column are found under the preparation of diethyl cyclobutanedicarboxylate (Chap. 36).

During the distillation, a high rate of reflux should be maintained by heating the bath to a sufficiently high temperature to give as much reflux as the column can handle without flooding. This follows from the fact that a larger amount of liquid running down the column (and a proportional amount of vapor rising in the column) facilitates the heat exchange between liquid and vapor. The column must not be allowed to flood, however, for "slugs" of liquid in the column present very little surface for exchange with the vapor. If the column is always operated at full reflux in this manner, the actual reflux ratio is determined by the rate of takeoff. In the discussion to follow, a "very slow" rate of takeoff for the 16-mm Vigreux column will be regarded as 5–6 drops per minute, while about 40 drops per minute will be regarded as a "very fast" rate of takeoff. For the Podbielniak column, these rates should be divided by five.

Let us suppose that the mixture being distilled above in the Vigreux column consists of equimolar amounts of two substances boiling 30° apart. When the lower-boiling fraction first begins to distill, its mole fraction in the pot is then about 0.5, and the essentially pure lower-boiling component would be obtained at the top of the column with no difficulty; hence, there would be no object in taking off the distillate slowly. It may be taken off at a fast rate (20–30 drops per minute) without exceeding the rate at which it is being supplied at the top of the column. As this material is collected, however, while essentially all of the higher-boiling component is being left in the still, the mole fraction of the lower-boiling component in the pot is continually decreasing. Obviously, this continually increases the difficulty of fractionating out the pure lower-boiling substance by the time the vapor reaches the top of the column. There will eventually be reached a point where a mixture of the two substances is reaching the top of the column, and this will be evidenced by a rise in boiling point. When this occurs, the reflux ratio is increased by decreasing the rate of takeoff, thus increasing the efficiency of the column and also decreasing the rate at which the pure material must be supplied at the top in order to meet the rate of removal. This will make it possible to continue to collect the low-boiling fraction over a narrow range. As distillation continues, and the mole fraction of the lower-boiling component in the pot continues to decrease, a slower and slower rate of takeoff must be used in order to continue getting essentially pure lower-boiling component at the top of the column. Finally, this mole fraction becomes so unfavorable that the boiling point rises (indicating that a mixture is being collected) even at a very slow rate of takeoff; and this is the point at which fractions are changed and collection of the intermediate fraction is begun.

Throughout the distillation of the intermediate fraction, the rate of takeoff is kept very slow, for every drop of the intermediate fraction is a drop of the lower- and higher-boiling components that is not being obtained in the pure fractions. When the boiling point ceases to rise or rises very slowly, then the higher-boiling fraction is collected. At this point, if the mixture consists of only two components, the fractionation problem is solved, for everything left in the pot is the higher-boiling component; so forced reflux in the head is shut off and distillation is finished at as high a rate as would be used in a Claisen flask. If there is still a third component, the second component is collected according to the pattern described for the first component: rapidly so long as the temperature remains essentially constant, then more slowly until finally the intermediate is reached again while proceeding at a very slow rate of takeoff.

In summary, rate of takeoff is kept as fast as consistent with obtaining the necessary efficiency required to effect the separation required at each point during the distillation. In general, this is rapid during the first part of a fraction, slower as the end of the fraction is approached, with maximum slowness during collection of the intermediate fraction. If these principles are followed, fractional distillation through an efficient column may be accomplished without expenditure of an undue amount of time. The time for student distillation of the mixture obtained in the ethyl hydrogen adipate preparation is 5–7 hours. The percentage of a fraction that may be collected rapidly depends on the relationship between the efficiency of the column and the difference in boiling point between the compounds being separated. Thus, the more efficient the column, the more rapidly may the separation of a given mixture be accomplished. A limiting factor is the labor of installing and operating more efficient or longer columns; the ultimate limiting factor is the maximum efficiency that has thus far been obtained in a column. Further, the time consumed in constructing more efficient columns must be balanced against the time involved in slow distillation and redistillation of intermediate fractions.

As a general working basis, a separation may be regarded as "satisfactory" if a single distillation yields at least 80% of the components in narrow-boiling fractions. For proper interpretation of the term "narrow-boiling fraction," the *relationship of purity to the boiling range* of a fraction should be considered. In the discussion above, it has been stated that a fraction with a boiling range of two or three degrees is ordinarily considered rather pure. Although this is true for the case under discussion, a general statement must be qualified by pointing out that the homogeneity of a cut with a given boiling range depends on how far apart are the boiling points of the substances being separated. It is clear that if two substances boil two degrees apart, then a fraction boiling over two degrees might be a 1:1 mixture of these two substances. In the extreme case, two substances may have the same boiling point, or form a constant-boiling mixture (azeotrope). If substances boil as much as 20° apart, then fractions collected over a range of one degree on either side of the true boiling points are of a high degree of purity. For substances boiling as little as 10° apart, if high purity is desired, a boiling range of less than one degree is required. In cases where very high purity is required, such cuts as just mentioned should be redistilled and essentially constant-boiling fractions collected. It should be remembered, however, that in vacuum distillation the maintenance of absolutely constant pressure and complete avoidance of overheating of vapors is difficult. This renders less reliable the judgment of purity by size of boiling range, especially where the separation involves substances boiling rather close together. In such cases, it is well to receive the distillate in small arbitrary fractions and judge the composition of these fractions by the use of some other physical property. Various physical properties have been used, including index of refraction, optical rotation, infrared or ultraviolet absorption, and neutral equivalent; however, gas phase chromatography is nearly always the most effective method of assessment of purity of distillation fractions. Glpc may be used not only for establishing the purity of a homogeneous fraction, but also for determining the exact composition of less pure or intermediate fractions. The data on intermediate fractions are indispensable in judging which fractions are worthwhile for redistillation.

Problems Encountered During Fractionation

A few problems (or situations) encountered during fractionation should be discussed.

1. For a given heat input at the bath and jacket, the rate of reflux will be increased if the rate of takeoff is decreased. Thus, when the rate of

takeoff is reduced near the end of a fraction, a slight lowering of bath temperature may be necessary to avoid flooding of the column. Conversely, when the rate of takeoff is increased suddenly, as when a fraction is reached, heat input into the bath should be increased.

2. As a lower-boiling component is removed from the mixture, by fractionation, the boiling point of the mixture in the pot rises; thus, the bath temperature must be raised to maintain a constant heat input into the pot, for the rate of heat input into the pot depends on the temperature differential between the bath and the contents of the pot. Furthermore, the temperature at the bottom of the column becomes higher, while the temperature as recorded at the top of the column by the thermometer on the column remains about constant. Eventually, as more of the lower-boiling component is removed, the temperature at the top of the jacket may begin to rise without the heat input to the column being increased. Soon after this occurs, the boiling point usually begins to rise, and collection of the intermediate fraction is begun. A proper understanding and careful observation of these phenomena are a great aid in realizing the correct operation of the column.

As the boiling point rises during the collection of the intermediate fraction, it will be necessary to increase power input to the jacket in order to hold its temperature just below the boiling point.

3. If the components being separated boil as much as 40° apart, a variation of the behavior described in (2) above will usually be observed. In this instance, the separation will be so easy that essentially all the lower-boiling component will be stripped out while the boiling point remains essentially constant. Eventually, the top part of the column will begin to run dry, and distillation will slow up and finally stop, while the reflux in the bottom part of the column will be heavy. The vapor temperature may begin to drop until it is below the temperature of the top of the jacket. If the bath temperature is increased, the column may become flooded at the bottom, while insufficient vapor reaches the top to register the equilibrium boiling point. In this situation, the power input to the jacket must be carefully increased until reflux again reaches the top of the column and the boiling point begins to rise. The jacket temperature is then carefully raised just behind the boiling temperature, until the boiling point becomes constant as the next component distills. In such instances as this, the intermediate fraction will be very small. In the Podbielniak column, such an intermediate may be only 0.1–0.2 g. It is illuminating to distill such a mixture in a Claisen flask and discover that the boiling point rises more or less regularly from the boiling point of the lower component to that of the upper.

4. If a properly constructed column is flooding near the top, and there is very little reflux at the bottom, it is indicated that the jacket tempera-

ture is too high. On the other hand, if there is normal heavy reflux at the bottom of the column, and there is flooding at the top, the jacket temperature is probably correct, but the bath temperature is too high. If the column is flooding near the bottom, and there is little reflux near the top, the jacket temperature is too low. One such circumstance is described in (3) above.

5. The "holdup" of a column is the amount of liquid in the column during operating reflux, and the ultimate minimum intermediate fraction that may be obtained is not equal to but is a function of this holdup. This is why a small-diameter column, such as the Podbielniak column, should be used for distillation of small amounts, and a packed column should be used only for relatively large amounts. It is not necessary, however, to lose an amount of the last fraction equal to the holdup of the column, for the column may be "stripped." For this operation, the bath temperature is kept sufficiently high to distill most of the volatile component from any nonvolatile residue, and the jacket temperature is carefully raised above the boiling point of the component being collected. The contents of the column are thus distilled in much the same manner as material is distilled from a Claisen flask. If the jacket temperature is raised slowly, to avoid overheating, all the contents of the column may be distilled while the boiling point is watched to make certain that no higher-boiling component is coming over. By the use of this technique, distillation of 10 g of material through the Podbielniak column has yielded up to 9.8 g of distillate. This recovery is at least as good as may be obtained in a Claisen flask.

This discussion of fractional distillation may seem long, but it actually deals only with the *principles* of fractional distillation. Any new mixture may present new problems, but if these principles are well understood, the student should be able to solve the problems which arise. Even an experienced operator sometimes finds it necessary to throw all his fractions together and try again.

Mechanical Stirring

33

Mechanical stirring is essential to best yields in a large variety of reactions, especially in those carried out in heterogeneous systems and in those where a local high concentration of starting material and product is undesirable. In some reactions, the yield is improved significantly by increasing the efficiency of the mechanical stirring. In the present chapter will be described various types of equipment suitable for laboratory work.

Magnetic Stirrers

If a magnet is rotated beneath a flask and sufficiently close to it so as to spin a magnetized bar inside the flask, stirring may be accomplished with no direct connection between the stirrer in the flask and motor that spins the external magnet. Such a device is especially useful in a completely sealed system, whether the system be under vacuum or under pressure. The magnetic stirrer is also used for simple stirring of reactions under reflux in instances where no heterogeneous material must be intimately mixed, and the mixture is not excessively viscous. Various shapes and sizes of magnetized stirring bars may be purchased, and they may be obtained in either glass or Teflon seals, for protection against the reaction mixture. There are also available from laboratory supply houses combined stirrers and hot plates, which are often convenient for heating with stirring.

For large numbers of organic reactions, especially those where good stirring of heterogeneous mixtures is required, the magnetically coupled stirrer gives insufficient mixing. In such cases, some type of stirring blade on a shaft is directly coupled to a motor. Since such stirrers are satisfactory for all types of reactions except those in a sealed system, they are used rather routinely by most chemists. For stirring under reflux, they are more troublesome to assemble than the magnetic stirrer, for some type of vapor seal must be used; however, once the equipment is assembled, it is convenient to utilize. Several variations in components of these stirrers will be described.

Stirring Motors

For general use in organic synthesis, a stirring motor should be portable and have at least two other characteristics: (1) it should have considerable power, even at low speed, and (2) it should be possible to vary the speed without stopping the motor or changing the position of the drive shaft. These two features are essential, for heavy sludges are often encountered, and these sludges often develop as the reaction proceeds, thus requiring an increase in motor power. In other instances, high speed is desirable at certain stages of the reaction and not at others.

The lightweight, direct-drive motors, controlled by a small rheostat, have very limited use. A direct-drive motor of $\frac{1}{30}$ horsepower is sufficiently powerful to be useful for many mixing operations; however, even a motor of this size tends to overheat when subjected to significant load at low speed. In addition, the current required by a $\frac{1}{30}$ horsepower motor is too great for control by an inexpensive rheostat. Best control is secured by use of a 1.5-ampere variable transformer (cf. Chap. 32). In order to allow convenient clamping of the motor with apparatus, a half-inch rod should be threaded directly into the motor housing if it is sufficiently heavy. Otherwise, the motor may be mounted on a base plate which is attached to the rod. It is usually better, and of little expense, to use some type of stirring motor whose power is improved by use of gears, pulleys, or some other device.

An excellent laboratory stirring motor depending on a belt drive with a 4:1 pulley ratio has been described;[1] however, this motor is not sold by laboratory supply houses. It is necessary to have castings made for the pulley and shaft housing, and to assemble the parts in a machine shop. It is usually more convenient, and little more costly, to buy one of the several satisfactory motors available from supply houses. The satisfactory commercially available motors gain power by use either of gears or of a friction drive. In the first type, speed is varied with a rheostat, hence power is less at low speed but remains adequate for most purposes. In the friction-drive motor, which retails at a higher price than many of the gear-drive motors, a constant-speed induction motor is employed and speed is varied

[1] E. B. Hershberg, *Ind. Eng. Chem., Anal. Ed.,* **12,** 293 (1940).

by use of a cone for one side of the friction drive. The ratio is controlled by moving the drive wheel along this cone; so power is greater at low speed. An *additional advantage* of this type of stirrer is that the induction motor is sparkless, hence relatively safe for use in an atmosphere containing explosive or combustible gases. A turbine driven by compressed air is even more reliable than the induction motor in hazardous situations; however, the air turbine is difficult to control at low speed. Although the alteration of motor speed by variation of input voltage is cheap and convenient, as cited above, motors subject to this type of control contain brushes which generate sparks. *If hydrogen or other combustible gases are evolved during a reaction, they should be diverted from proximity to a brush motor.*

In case extremely high stirrer speeds are required, as when making sodium dispersions, a special motor and stirring assembly must be purchased.

Stirring Blades

Stirrers of the propeller type, such as illustrated for use in electrolytic reductions (Fig. 39-3) are useful for stirring in tubes or beakers, but they are of little value for stirring in a flask. The width of blade that will pass the neck of the flask is not sufficient to stir the large volume of the flask effectively. There must be used some device that will pass through a small neck but will sweep out a large periphery on rotation. A very simple device that will accomplish this is the bent glass tube shown in Fig. 1. This stirrer is sufficiently effective for most operations and can be made in a few minutes from a glass tube, by use of a Bunsen burner. A particular virtue of this type of stirrer is its effectiveness in stirring up metal or other heavy material sitting on the bottom of a round-bottomed flask. The angle and length of the bends depend on the size of the flask in which the stirrer is to be used. A glass tube with sealed ends is preferred to a solid rod. The tube is essentially as strong as the rod and much lighter; thus, it is less likely to break a flask if it is dropped against the bottom.

A still more efficient type of stirrer is the wire stirrer described by Hershberg.[2] This is illustrated in Fig. 38-1. The loop is made of Pyrex glass, and the wire is bent over a cork borer of suitable size. For all types of alkaline reactions, Nichrome and Chromel A wire, B. and S. No. 18, are suitable, but acidic media attack this wire. Hydrobromic acid or bromine solutions are especially corrosive to this alloy. Hydrochloric acid, as used in a Clemmensen reduction, attacks the wire slowly; its use in such reactions is practical, for replacement is inexpensive. Tantalum wire of No. 18 gage is resistant to nearly all mixtures, including hot sulfuric and nitric

[2]E. B. Hershberg, *Ind. Eng. Chem., Anal. Ed.,* **8,** 313 (1936).

FIG. 1.   Simple glass stirrer.

acids, and it is not excessively expensive. *Tantalum should not be used in any type of reduction*, either acid or alkaline, for it is embrittled by this treatment so that it may be crumbled in the hand.

Various types of glass stirrers with blades that may be turned or folded for insertion in narrow necks have been marketed, but these are always unsatisfactory. They are both expensive and fragile. Similar stirrers with Teflon blades are more satisfactory, for Teflon is not fragile; however, they are more expensive to construct than tantalum wire stirrers (the Teflon blade requires careful machining) and appear to offer no advantages unless for reductions.

The mode of attachment of the stirrer shaft to the drive shaft of the motor should be mentioned. *The use of a chuck is rarely convenient*, especially if the stirrer must be lined up in a mercury seal or other device for stirring a mixture under reflux. The rigidity of such an attachment is the chief difficulty. If the drive shaft is inserted into a small one-hole rubber stopper, and the stirrer shaft inserted in the other end of the stopper, the attachment is sufficiently strong and somewhat flexible. A piece of suction tubing may also be used, but may be too flexible for use when very heavy mixtures are stirred. The stirrer shaft should always be supported by one or two bearings, as described in a later section.

Vapor Seals

It is very often desirable to stir a reaction under reflux; hence, some type of vapor seal must be used around the shaft of the stirrer. The simplest such seal is shown in Fig. 2; the construction is evident from the illustration. There must be some type of lubricant to allow the stirrer shaft to slip freely in the rubber connection. Glycerol is fairly effective, but silicone stopcock grease is probably best. This type of seal is suitable for brief stirring operations, but is not entirely dependable for stirring operations lasting

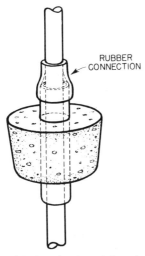

FIG. 2. Simple seal for stirring under reflux or in a closed system.

FIG. 3. Improved seal for stirring under reflux or in a closed system.

several hours. A common difficulty is the sticking of the rubber to the shaft, which causes the stirrer to stop or the rubber connection to wear and allow escape of vapors. A further difficulty is attack of vapors (especially benzene or toluene) on the rubber connection. This causes the rubber to swell and allow escape of vapors. The effectiveness of this type of seal is greatly improved by addition of the simple cup[3] shown in Fig. 3, especially if attack

[3]This improvement of the simple seal was described to the authors by Prof. G. M. Kosolapoff of the Alabama Institute of Technology.

by solvent vapor is avoided by use of a piece of silicone rubber. The cup accomplishes two very useful functions: (1) it may be spaced above the lower tube to give exactly the desired amount of contact between the stirrer shaft and the rubber connector; (2) a few drops of silicone oil or glycerol in the cup assure an inexhaustible supply of lubricant for long stirring operations. This type of seal may be used under a modest amount of pressure and it will hold a vacuum rather well. It may well be the most desirable seal for most stirring operations. Of course it may be readily attached to a ground joint.

A ball joint may be used as a stirrer seal if one side of the joint is fixed to the flask and the other side, fixed to the stirrer shaft, turns against the joint on the flask. This seal has been described in *Organic Syntheses*.[4] Even with the most careful adjustment of this seal, and lubrication with silicone oil, there is considerable drag on the stirring motor, and heat is generated by the friction between the parts of the seal. It is imperative that a small ball joint be used (size 18/9). The seal illustrated in Fig. 3 appears to offer significant advantages over the ball-joint seal.

The mercury seal is highly regarded by many chemists, for it has no moving parts that need touch each other. If the shaft is supported by bearings, to be described below, the seal may be lined up to run quietly and smoothly. The vapor path is blocked by a suitable quantity of mercury in the seal. The chief disadvantage of the seal is that mercury may be thrown from it at high stirrer speeds, or if the assembly of it is careless. Of course this constitutes a health hazard. A design of seal which has been found to function quite well is shown in Fig. 4 (a). The Teflon ring at the bottom, which may be easily fabricated by drilling a rod and sawing it in sections, gives support to the stirrer shaft near the bottom. This feature is especially desirable when heavy sludges are stirred. The mercury container is made relatively tall in order to minimize the tendency for mercury to be thrown out. A smooth lower edge on the top piece to the seal also minimizes splashing of mercury. At high speed, a layer of mineral oil on top of the mercury prevents splashing rather positively.

In the seal shown in Fig. 4 (a), it is important that the top piece, which is attached to the stirrer shaft, have an upper constricted part which fits the stirrer shaft reasonably well. If this upper tube is also parallel to and centered with the larger tube forming the bottom of the top piece, then correct line-up of this piece becomes intrinsic with proper line-up of the shaft. Of course all stirrer shafts used with a seal must be the same size in order to fit the top piece of the seal.

The seal shown in Fig. 4 (b) is constructed without the ground joint. In this case, a stopper is attached to the lower part of the inner tube, and this

[4]*Org. Syntheses,* **33**, 80 (1953).

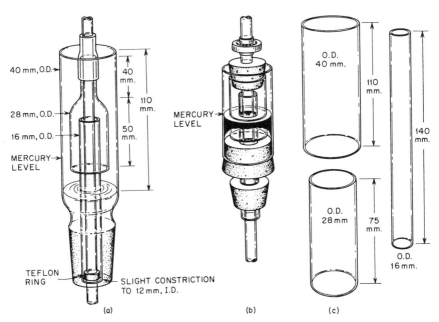

FIG. 4. Mercury seals: (a) improved type, (b) simple type. Tubing required for the simple seal is shown in (c).

inner tube is made slightly longer so as to extend 15–20 mm beyond the stopper.

Shaft Bearings

Since unground ball bearings are so inexpensive, there seems little justification for using such devices as glass tubes for bearings. The Nice bearing, No. 400-6, is an inexpensive bearing that is of a convenient size for stirrer shafts of 5–8-mm diameter. If packed occasionally with vaseline, such bearings last indefinitely, even when used around corrosive vapors. More expensive ground bearings, such as SKF bearings, offer no additional advantage for ordinary laboratory stirring. Unless the bottom of the stirrer shaft is supported by a Teflon bearing, as shown in Fig. 4 (a), *two* bearings should always be used to support the stirrer shaft. One bearing should be near the attachment to the stirring motor, and the other should be just above the seal. Of various methods that have been tried for attaching the bearing to the shaft, the most convenient seems to be that of winding a collar of adhesive tape around the shaft until the bearing will just slip over the tape. The bearing is then held in an ordinary laboratory clamp.

After the stirrer shaft is lined up very carefully in the seal by proper positioning of the clamps holding the bearings, the stirring motor is clamped in proper alignment just above the top of the stirrer shaft. The clamps holding the bearings are then loosened, the stirrer shaft is lifted and attached to the motor drive by the stopper or suction tubing, the motor is lowered to place the stirrer in the original proper position, and the bearings are again clamped. This sequence of lining up a seal will be found superior to many others.

Stirring Under Pressure or Vacuum

As has been mentioned, stirring under a vacuum or a few pounds of pressure may be accomplished with the simple seal shown in Fig. 3, or with the ball-joint seal. This may also be accomplished by use of the commercial seals in which a ground shaft operates inside a ground sleeve (an old hypodermic syringe may be adapted to such use). This arrangement permits stirring with somewhat greater pressure on the system; however, such ground seals are rather expensive and impose considerable drag on the motor.

Another type of stirrer seal that permits pressure is one in which the outer tube is metal and the shaft passes through a packed gland of the type used in valves. This stirrer is rather expensive, and it must be driven by a relatively powerful motor; however, it is not as easily damaged as the ground-glass seals. Such stirrers are used in commercially designed autoclaves which may be operated at pressures up to 1,000 pounds per square inch.

In instances where light stirring suffices, the previously described magnetically driven stirrer is most convenient in a sealed system.

Enolate Condensations

34

A large number of very important synthetic reactions may be included in the category, enolate condensations. This includes the aldol condensation, Knoevenagel reaction, Claisen ester condensation, Stobbe reaction, Michael condensation, and many others. These reactions have in common a key step in which an enolate ion attacks the carbon in a carbonyl group or other polar unsaturated group (in the Michael reaction, the beta carbon is attacked in a 1,4-addition). Various "name reactions" merely involve use of different components in this same general reaction. The Knoevenagel and Michael reactions are discussed in the present chapter as representative illustrations of the enolate condensations. Displacement reactions of the enolate ion, as represented by the alkylation of malonic ester, are discussed in Chapter 36.

Knoevenagel Reaction

The Knoevenagel type of condensation between an aldehyde (or active ketone) and a compound containing a doubly activated methylene group may involve either one mole of active methylene compound per mole of aldehyde or two moles of active methylene compound per mole of aldehyde. The 1:1 or 1:2 reaction may be favored by proper choice of catalyst, solvent, temperature, and ratio of reagents. Considerable experimentation is often necessary to determine conditions favorable to one reaction or the other, and the alternate reaction is always a side reaction. The present illustration is condensation of formaldehyde with diethyl malonate, and the best conditions for obtaining the desired *tetraethyl 1,1,3,3-propane-*

tetracarboxylate may be summarized in the following net reaction:

$$
CH_2O + 2CH_2(CO_2C_2H_5)_2 \xrightarrow[KCl]{(C_2H_5)_2NH} \begin{array}{c} CH(CO_2C_2H_5)_2 \\ | \\ CH_2 \\ | \\ CH(CO_2C_2H_5)_2 \end{array} + H_2O \quad (34\text{-}1)
$$

Formalin

Under these conditions, it has been found possible to obtain yields of tetra-ester in the range 80–85%. If the small amount of potassium chloride is omitted, the yield is consistently near 60% as has been previously reported.[1] A high-yield process using alcoholic potassium hydroxide has been reported,[2] but we have experienced difficulty in reproducing these results in this laboratory.

The function of the potassium chloride in increasing the yield of the desired product is obscure, but the value of this catalyst has been verified in more than 100 runs. It results in a large decrease in the amount of higher molecular weight material obtained (cf. side reactions, below). Possible effects of other salts have not been investigated. It should be emphasized that the significant effect of potassium chloride in this preparation is an

$$
CH_2O + \begin{array}{c} CO_2C_2H_5 \\ | \\ CH_2 \\ | \\ CO_2C_2H_5 \end{array} \rightarrow \begin{array}{c} CO_2C_2H_5 \\ | \\ HOCH_2-CH \\ | \\ CO_2C_2H_5 \end{array} \xrightarrow{-H_2O} \begin{array}{c} CO_2C_2H_5 \\ | \\ CH_2=C \\ | \\ CO_2C_2H_5 \end{array} \quad (34\text{-}2)
$$

I

$$
\begin{array}{c} CO_2C_2H_5 \\ | \\ CH_2 \\ | \\ CO_2C_2H_5 \end{array} + \begin{array}{c} CO_2C_2H_5 \\ | \\ C-CO_2C_2H_5 \\ \| \\ CH_2 \end{array} \rightarrow \begin{array}{c} CH(CO_2C_2H_5)_2 \\ | \\ CH_2 \\ | \\ CH(CO_2C_2H_5)_2 \end{array} \quad (34\text{-}3)
$$

II

$$
\begin{array}{c} CH(CO_2C_2H_5)_2 \\ | \\ CH_2 \\ | \\ CH(CO_2C_2H_5)_2 \end{array} \xrightarrow{CH_2=C(CO_2C_2H_5)_2} \begin{array}{c} CH(CO_2C_2H_5)_2 \\ | \\ CH_2 \\ | \\ C(CO_2C_2H_5)_2 \\ | \\ CH_2 \\ | \\ CH(CO_2C_2H_5)_2 \end{array} \quad (34\text{-}4)
$$

$$\downarrow CH_2O$$

$$
\begin{array}{c} CH(CO_2C_2H_5)_2 \\ | \\ CH_2 \\ | \\ HOCH_2-C(CO_2C_2H_5)_2 \end{array}
$$

III

IV

[1] T. J. Otterbacher, *Org. Syntheses,* **Coll. Vol. I,** 290 (1941).
[2] K. N. Welch, *J. Chem. Soc.,* 673 (1931).

excellent illustration of how the direction of a Knoevenagel reaction may be greatly influenced by apparently minor changes in conditions.

Side reactions encountered in this preparation may best be discussed by consideration of the steps involved in the over-all reaction expressed in Eq. 1, and the further reactions which the tetra-ester may undergo. All the additions shown in Eqs. 2–4 actually occur by way of initial attack of the enolate ion. Equation 2 shows the primary reaction to give the 1:1 condensation product, the methylenemalonic ester, I. Dehydration of a hydroxy ester in alkaline solution is not a common reaction, but occurs in structures such as the present one because of the rather high acidity of the alpha hydrogen in the malonic ester. The reaction shown in Eq. 3 is actually a Michael condensation (cf. next section), in that the enolate ion attacks, not the carbonyl group, but the beta carbon, so that a 1,4-addition occurs. Rearrangement of the enol initially formed, to the keto form, yields the desired product, II. Further condensation of ester II may lead to either a hexa-ester (IV) or a hydroxy ester (III). Similar condensations can continue and lead to still higher molecular weight products. Thus, *by-products whose separation must be considered* are methylenemalonic ester (I), the hydroxy tetra-ester (III), the hexa-ester (IV), and nonvolatile higher molecular-weight products.

Separation of the products of the condensation reaction may be satisfactorily accomplished by simple distillation in a Claisen flask, for ester I boils much lower than II, and ester IV boils much higher. Ester III is not separated from the desired product (II) by this simple distillation, but it is most convenient to accept contamination with this hydroxy ester and remove its hydrolytic product from the glutaric anhydride obtained after hydrolysis of the crude ester.

Glutaric anhydride is prepared from the tetra-ester, II, by the widely used process of hydrolysis and decarboxylation of a malonic ester (Eq. 5).

$$
\begin{array}{c}
CH(CO_2C_2H_5)_2 \\
| \\
CH_2 \\
| \\
CH(CO_2C_2H_5)_2
\end{array}
\;+\;4H_2O \;\xrightarrow{\;H^+\;}\;
\begin{array}{c}
CH(CO_2H)_2 \\
| \\
CH_2 \\
| \\
CH(CO_2H)_2
\end{array}
\;+\;4C_2H_5OH
\qquad(34\text{-}5)
$$

$$
\underset{V}{} \xrightarrow{\;\Delta\;}
\begin{array}{c}
CH_2{-}CO_2H \\
| \\
CH_2 \\
| \\
CH_2{-}CO_2H
\end{array}
\\
\underset{VI}{}
$$

Malonic esters of higher molecular weight that are less soluble in water are best saponified in alcoholic potassium hydroxide. The reaction mixture is then diluted with water, and the organic acid is precipitated by acidification of the soap solution. This process is not convenient in the present instance, for the tetra-acid, V, is very soluble in water. When the hydrolysis is carried out in aqueous hydrochloric acid, however, evaporation of the reaction mixture to dryness leaves a residue of the tetra-acid, V, usually mixed with some of the di-acid, VI. Decarboxylation of V occurs to some extent in the boiling hydrochloric acid, but complete decarboxylation is assured by heating the residue to about 200°. In some instances (cf. Chap. 36), essentially no decarboxylation occurs in the boiling hydrochloric acid.

The crude glutaric acid, obtained as just described, may be purified by recrystallization from benzene, but for preparation of the anhydride (Eq. 6) it is convenient to heat the crude acid with acetic anhydride and then distill the reaction mixture to yield glutaric anhydride, VII.

$$
\begin{array}{ccc}
\underset{|}{CH_2-CO_2H} & \underset{\diagdown}{CH_3-C}{\overset{\diagup O}{}} & \underset{\diagdown}{CH_2-C}{\overset{\diagup O}{}} \\
\underset{|}{CH_2} & + \quad O & \rightarrow CH_2 \qquad O \; + \; 2CH_3-CO_2H \quad (34\text{-}6) \\
CH_2-CO_2H & \underset{\diagup}{CH_3-C}{\underset{\diagdown O}{}} & \underset{\diagup}{CH_2-C}{\underset{\diagdown O}{}} \\
& & \text{VII}
\end{array}
$$

The principal *side reaction* in this process is probably linear polymerization of the glutaric acid to a high molecular weight anhydride, and this is left as a residue in the distillation procedure. There must be considered, however, the fate of the hydroxy ester, III, which is an impurity in the tetra-ester, II, used as starting material. When the hydroxy ester is put through the above process along with the tetra-ester, the product obtained from the hydroxy ester is α-methyleneglutaric anhydride, VIII.

$$
\begin{array}{c}
\underset{\diagup}{CH_2-C}{\overset{\diagup O}{}} \\
CH_2 \qquad O \\
\underset{\|}{C}-C{\overset{\diagdown O}{}} \\
CH_2 \\
\text{VIII}
\end{array}
$$

α-Methyleneglutaric acid, precursor to the anhydride VIII, may form by way of hydrolysis of the tetra-ester, III, followed by decarboxylation, then dehydration of the hydroxymethyleneglutaric acid. In the related Döbner reaction, however, evidence has been presented[3] that the mono-anion of the hydroxymalonic acid undergoes concerted elimination of carbon dioxide and hydroxide ion, as shown in Eq. 7, to yield the α,β-unsaturated acid. Decarboxylation of the malonic acid structure at the other end of the molecule would proceed in a normal manner to yield the α-methyleneglutaric acid.

[3] E. J. Corey, *J. Amer. Chem. Soc.*, **74**, 5897 (1952).

$$\begin{array}{ccc} \underset{\displaystyle |}{CH(CO_2H)_2} & \underset{\displaystyle |}{CH(CO_2H)_2} & + \ ^-OH \\ \underset{\displaystyle |}{CH_2} & \to & \underset{\displaystyle |}{CH_2} & + \ CO_2 \\ HO-CH_2-\underset{\displaystyle \underset{\displaystyle \underset{O}{\overset{\|}{C}}-O^-}{|}}{C}-CO_2H & CH_2=C-CO_2H \end{array} \qquad (34\text{-}7)$$

α-Methyleneglutaric anhydride is not readily separated from glutaric anhydride by distillation; however, it may be easily separated by crystallization. The impurity is present in relatively small amount and is more soluble than is glutaric anhydride. It has not been possible to find a single solvent suitable for the crystallization, but a mixture of benzene and ether is quite satisfactory. Since anhydrides react with both alcohol and water, both of which are present in commercial ether, it is advisable to use absolute ether for the crystallization.

It is of interest that the best preparation of α-methyleneglutaric acid is by way of a Knoevenagel condensation nearly identical with the presently described one, except that piperidine is used as catalyst. A yield of 20%, based on starting diethyl malonate, has been reported.[4]

Michael Condensation

The distinguishing feature of the Michael condensation is that an α,β-unsaturated compound (usually a carbonyl compound) is used, and addition occurs in the 1,4-manner so that the enolate ion adds to the carbon beta to the carbonyl. The present illustration of this reaction is a particularly interesting one, since the α,β-unsaturated compound is acrylonitrile, where the activating group is cyano instead of carbonyl. In most instances, the Michael condensation occurs readily only when the carbon to which addition occurs is activated by two unsaturated groups, as in diethyl malonate or ethyl acetoacetate. Acrylonitrile is so reactive, however, that it will add to a carbon activated by only one unsaturated grouping.

2-β-Cyanoethyl-2-ethylhexanal is prepared according to the procedure outlined in Eq. 8. This synthesis was first reported by Bruson and Riener,[5] who used 50% potassium hydroxide as catalyst. With the aqueous potassium hydroxide as catalyst, condensations of acrylonitrile with 2-ethylhexanal and with several ketones have been carried out at Berkeley; however, the procedure has proved to give erratic results. In a majority of runs, the reaction started promptly and proceeded exothermally, but occasionally it failed to occur, no matter how persistent the efforts to induce it.

[4]E. R. Buchman, A. O. Reims, and M. J. Schlatter, *J. Amer. Chem. Soc.*, **64**, 2703 (1942).

[5]H. A. Bruson and T. W. Riener, *J. Amer. Chem. Soc.*, **64**, 2850 (1942).

$$
\begin{array}{c}
\underset{\overset{|}{\text{C}_2\text{H}_5}}{\text{C}_4\text{H}_9-\text{CH}-\text{CHO}} \\
+ \\
\text{CH}_2{=}\text{CH}-\text{CN}
\end{array}
\xrightarrow[\text{glyme as}]{\text{solid KOH}}
\left[
\begin{array}{c}
\overset{\text{C}_2\text{H}_5}{\underset{|}{}} \\
\text{C}_4\text{H}_9-\text{C}-\text{CHO} \\
| \\
\text{CH}_2\text{CH}{=}\text{C}{=}\text{NH}
\end{array}
\right]
\quad (34\text{-}8)
$$

$$
\begin{array}{c}
\downarrow \\
\text{C}_2\text{H}_5 \\
| \\
\text{C}_4\text{H}_9-\text{C}-\text{CHO} \\
| \\
\text{CH}_2\text{CH}_2-\text{CN} \\
\text{IX}
\end{array}
$$

On other occasions, reaction set in only after addition of a second or third portion of aqueous potassium hydroxide.

With the appearance of Jolly's work[6] reporting the remarkable increase in base strength of hydroxide when used in a nonhydroxylated solvent, this concept was applied to the cyanoethylation reaction with uniformly excellent results. Hydroxylated solvents, such as water or alcohols, strongly solvate the hydroxide ion and interfere with its electron-donating capacity, i.e., its base strength. Particularly good results are obtained when coarsely ground potassium hydroxide is used with glyme (1,2-dimethoxyethane) as solvent. The solid potassium hydroxide is insoluble in this solvent, but this does not appear to interfere with its effectiveness as a strongly basic catalyst.[7] The reaction as outlined in Eq. 8 proceeds rapidly to give a good yield in a few minutes, and no failures have been encountered.

It is apparent that aldol condensation of the aldehyde is a potential *side reaction* in the synthesis shown in Eq. 8; however, α-substituted aldehydes give a slow rate of aldol condensation with a small equilibrium constant, even with the highly basic catalyst used. If the reaction time is prolonged to several hours, the aldol condensation does become a serious side reaction. Polymerization of acrylonitrile is another side reaction, which is catalyzed by a variety of reagents, so it is imperative that scrupulously clean apparatus be used for the reaction. In addition, the acrylonitrile should not be distilled prior to use, for the commercial product normally contains a polymerization inhibitor (free radical scavenger).

Cyanoethylation of aldehydes and ketones is a reaction of general utility; however, if more than one hydrogen is adjacent to the carbonyl, polysubstitution becomes a serious side reaction. After one cyanoethyl has

[6] W. L. Jolly, *Inorg. Chem.*, **6**, 1435 (1967).

[7] Use of a solvent in which KOH is insoluble is especially effective in instances where water is formed in the reaction. Reagent grade KOH pellets contain about 15% water, reduced only slightly by fusion at 300°; nevertheless, the KOH pellets are an excellent dehydrating agent, so an excess may be used to absorb water formed during a reaction.

been substituted, e.g., in butyraldehyde:

$$
\begin{array}{c}
\text{H} \\
| \\
\text{C}_2\text{H}_5\text{—C—CHO} \\
| \\
\text{CH}_2\text{—CH}_2\text{—CN}
\end{array}
$$

the remaining α-hydrogen is more acidic than is the case for the unsubstituted aldehyde, because the resultant enolate ion is a more substituted alkene, hence of lower energy:

$$
\begin{array}{cc}
\text{C}_2\text{H}_5\text{—C}{=}\text{C}\overset{\displaystyle O^-}{\underset{\displaystyle H}{\diagup}} & \text{C}_2\text{H}_5\text{—C}{=}\text{C}\overset{\displaystyle O^-}{\underset{\displaystyle H}{\diagup}} \\
\;\;\;\;\;| & \;\;\;\;\;| \\
\;\;\;\;\text{H} & \;\;\;\text{CH}_2\text{—CH}_2\text{—CN}
\end{array}
$$

It follows that the enolate ion from the cyanoethylated aldehyde (formula on right above) will be formed preferentially to the unsubstituted enolate; hence, the second cyanoethylation is favored. If monocyanoethylation is the desired reaction, the best procedure is to employ a limited amount of acrylonitrile and recover ketone or aldehyde in case it is expensive.

It is of interest that the aldehydo group in compound IX is highly hindered and also has no alpha hydrogens. This renders it much more inert chemically than is common with most aldehydes. The nitrile grouping may be saponified to the acid by prolonged heating in strong alkali without the aldehyde grouping being affected. If this process is followed by oxidation of the aldehyde to carboxyl, an α,α-disubstituted glutaric acid is obtained.[5,8] Such structures are difficult to obtain by other methods.

EXPERIMENTAL PROCEDURES

Tetraethyl Propane-1,1,3,3-Tetracarboxylate (Knoevenagel reaction)

To a mixture of 160 g (151 ml, 1 mole) of diethyl malonate and 42 ml of 35% formalin (16 g, 0.53 mole of CH_2O) in a 500-ml round-bottomed flask, cooled to 5° in an ice bath, are added 2.5 g (3.5 ml) of diethylamine and 3 g of potassium chloride. The components are mixed well and then allowed to come to room temperature and stand for 15 hours or longer, after which the flask is heated under a reflux condenser on a steam bath for 6 hours. After cooling, the small aqueous layer is separated in a separatory funnel and the organic layer is distilled (without drying) under reduced pressure from a 250-ml Claisen flask. The system is first evacuated with a water pump, and the bath is heated fairly rapidly to a temperature of

---

[8]J. Cason, *J. Org. Chem.*, **13**, 227 (1948).

about 180° and held there until distillation becomes very slow. During this time, water, diethyl malonate, and diethyl methylenemalonate distill. After air has been let into the system, a new receiver is attached to the Claisen flask, and the system is evacuated with an oil pump. A pressure of 4 mm or less is recommended, and the bath temperature is raised sufficiently to cause rather rapid distillation. An intermediate fraction is collected until the boiling point becomes fairly constant; then receivers are changed again and the tetra-ester is collected over a range of about 5° (Note 1). The entire distillation operation requires 2–3 hours. It may be interrupted at any time if desired. Toward the end, the bath temperature must be raised 20–30° in order to remove the last of the tetra-ester. Boiling points reported for this ester are 159–163° (3 mm), 168–171° (4 mm). The average yield is 80–85%.

Glutaric Anhydride

A mixture of 100 g (0.3 mole) of the above ester, 100 ml of concentrated hydrochloric acid, and 100 ml of water is placed in a 500-ml three-necked flask that is fitted with a mercury-sealed stirrer (cf. Chap. 33) and reflux condenser. The flask is heated in an oil bath while the mixture is stirred. The temperature of the bath is raised (to about 115°) until the mixture starts to reflux; refluxing with stirring is continued until the mixture becomes homogeneous (2–3 hours, usually). The stirrer is then removed, boiling chips are added to the flask, and it is arranged for distillation. The bath temperature is raised and the mixture is distilled to dryness, with a bath temperature up to about 200° for 20–30 minutes for final drying and decarboxylation.

The flask is now removed from the oil bath, and to the dry residue (molten when hot) of crude glutaric acid there is added 60 ml of acetic anhydride. The flask is closed with a calcium chloride tube and heated, with occasional swirling, on a steam bath for 1 hour. After the flask has been cooled with the calcium chloride tube attached, its contents are poured into a 250-ml Claisen flask. The three-necked flask is rinsed with a 5-ml portion of benzene that is added to the Claisen flask.

The contents of the Claisen flask are now distilled at reduced pressure, as the system is first evacuated with a water pump. After acetic acid and excess acetic anhydride have been removed (during removal of solvent, the manometer is kept turned off except for an occasional check on the pressure) the bath temperature is raised until the vapor temperature reaches the boiling point of glutaric anhydride (165–168° at 21 mm). If the water pump will not give a pressure below 30 mm, an oil pump may be used after the bath has been heated to about 180° with the water-pump vacuum. After receivers have been changed, the product is collected. The yield of crude glutaric anhydride, which solidifies almost completely in the receiver, is 20–25 g (58–73%). *Reserve* about 0.1 g of this product for the Baeyer test (see below).

The anhydride is crystallized from benzene-ether, and, since commercial ether contains some water and alcohol, it is imperative that the mixture not be heated or allowed to stand overnight after the ether is added. It is best to use absolute ether (cf. Chap. 38). The crude anhydride is melted and poured into a 250-ml Erlenmeyer flask. Forty-five ml of benzene is poured into the receiver to dissolve residual anhydride, and then poured into the Erlenmeyer flask. The anhydride is dissolved by gentle heating on a hot plate or steam bath. The warm solution is swirled while 150 ml of ether is added to it fairly rapidly (*NO FLAMES!*). The mixture is swirled a moment to insure good mixing. If the anhydride does not begin to crystallize at once or tends to oil out, the flask is scratched until crystallization sets in. After crystallization has started, if any oil has separated, the flask is warmed gently until the oil (but not all the crystals) has dissolved. The flask is then corked and allowed to stand undisturbed for about 30 minutes. Beautiful needles of glutaric anhydride separate. The flask is finally cooled for about 45 minutes in a *good* ice-salt bath (– 10° or less). The crystals are collected by suction filtration and washed with cold ether. After drying in a vacuum desiccator (Note 2), the melting point is determined. The yield of snow-white product melting at about 55–56° is 45–55%, based on crude tetra-ester. Very little pure product is obtainable from the mother liquor. Place the mother liquor in the bottle provided for it. If material in the mother liquor is converted to the diethyl esters, diethyl α-methyleneglutarate may be separated by distillation in a very efficient column (cf. footnote 4, this chapter).

Baeyer Tests

The crude anhydride contains some α-methyleneglutaric anhydride, which is largely removed by crystallization. Perform a Baeyer test for unsaturation on a sample of crude and one of pure anhydride as follows:

In about 1 ml of acetone and 1 ml of methanol, dissolve about 0.1 g of the sample. Add 2% aqueous potassium permanganate *dropwise* until a purple color persists for 2–3 minutes. Record the number of drops required in each case.

NOTES

1. Distillation of material with a boiling point this high offers some difficulties, because of the tendency for the vapors to condense without reaching the takeoff.

The discussion of this matter in Chap. 31 should be studied carefully before this distillation is attempted.

2. Drying in a vacuum desiccator is quite convenient and rapid in most instances, although removal of large amounts of water is best accomplished by heating at atmospheric pressure. Transfer of heat through the vacuum to supply the large heat of vaporization of water is a slow process if considerable quantities of water are involved. For drying materials sensitive to air (anhydrides react with the moisture in air), the vacuum desiccator is imperative. Vacuum ovens (metal vacuum desiccators arranged for heating) are very useful for higher-melting materials.

Since solvent is always being removed when a desiccator is evacuated (otherwise there would be no drying to do), the desiccator should *always* be evacuated with a water pump unless the oil pump is protected by a cold trap. (Dry Ice and acetone are used to cool the trap; *liquid air should never be used in such applications*, for an explosion often results from contact of organic vapors with liquid air, and an accident may lead to such a contact.) It should be remembered that an evacuated desiccator is under a pressure of about 15 pounds per square inch, so the top should never be slid off until after air has been let in slowly through the stopcock.

After a desiccator is evacuated, the stopcock is closed, the pump is disconnected, and the material is left to dry in the closed desiccator. A desiccator that will not hold a vacuum indefinitely (many weeks) is of little value, and the leak should be located and corrected by regrinding the poor surface.

The most useful absorbent for drying organic materials is concentrated sulfuric acid, for it will absorb water and all organic solvents except hydrocarbons and their halogen derivatives. Sulfuric acid oxidizes acetone and sulfur dioxide is liberated, so a small vessel of solid sodium or potassium hydroxide should be kept on the plate of the desiccator (the sulfuric acid is placed in the bottom). Hydrocarbons are absorbed by paraffin shavings; when these solvents are used, a vessel of paraffin shavings should be placed in the desiccator. The paraffin shavings should be replaced whenever they become "melted down" from the absorption of solvent. A desiccator containing sulfuric acid in the bottom and small vessels of sodium hydroxide and paraffin shavings on the plate is equipped for nearly any drying purpose.

A desiccator containing concentrated sulfuric acid should not be evacuated to pressures below about 5 mm, for the acid becomes appreciably volatile at such pressures. Also, acid-sensitive substances should not be stored for long periods over sulfuric acid.

2-β-Cyanoethyl-2-Ethylhexanal

A 500-ml three-necked flask, equipped with ground-glass joints, is fitted with a sealed mechanical stirrer, a reflux condenser, and a 250-ml dropping funnel. All items of this equipment should have been scrupulously cleaned. The apparatus is arranged so that it may be either heated with a steam bath or cooled with an ice-water bath. In the flask are placed 200 ml of glyme

(1,2-dimethoxyethane) and 3 g of solid KOH (85% KOH, 15% water) which has been weighed rapidly (accuracy not important) and then quickly crushed in a small mortar and added to the reaction flask before it becomes sticky from absorption of water from the air. In the dropping funnel are placed 38 g (47.2 ml) of acrylonitrile and 77 g (94 ml) of freshly distilled 2-ethylhexanal (Note 1). The two substances are mixed well by removing the funnel from the flask and swirling it.

The contents of the flask are heated to boiling on a steam bath as an ice-water cooling bath is prepared, then the heating bath is removed, the mixture is stirred vigorously so as to disperse the KOH, and about 5 ml of the aldehyde-nitrile mixture is added from the dropping funnel. If the exothermic reaction that ensues threatens to cause flooding of the condenser, the cooling bath is applied as necessary. The remainder of the aldehyde-nitrile mixture is added as rapidly as consistent with control of the reaction by application of the cooling bath, as vigorous stirring is continued. Addition normally requires only about 5 minutes. When addition has been completed, stirring is continued for an additional 10 minutes. As soon as spontaneous reflux abates, heat is applied with a steam bath. At the completion of the heating period, the mixture is cooled promptly to about room temperature, then poured into a 1-liter separatory funnel containing about 200 ml of water and 100 ml of technical mixed hexanes. Sufficient aqueous hydrochloric acid (about 3 N) is added to render the aqueous layer acidic to Congo red, after thorough shaking. The aqueous layer is drawn off into a 500-ml separatory funnel and extracted with an additional 50 ml of hexane. The two hexane solutions, kept in the two funnels, are washed in sequence with two 100-ml portions of water. In such an operation, the first extract is washed with a portion of water, the layers are allowed to separate, then the water is run into the second funnel, and the second extract is washed with this same water, after which the water layer is discarded. The procedure is then repeated with the second portion of water. This simple countercurrent extraction gives quantitative recovery of the product, and washes it thoroughly.

With hexane extracts, drying before distillation is accomplished satisfactorily by simple filtration through a layer of anhydrous sodium sulfate contained in a gravity filter of suitable size. The first extract is applied first, then the second, then a few milliliters of wash solvent. The filtrate is collected in a 500-ml Erlenmeyer flask equipped with a ground joint, and the bulk of the solvent is distilled from this flask through a simple gooseneck (or distillation head, if desired), with heating on a hot plate or on a steam bath. The residue is poured (*NO FLAMES!*) into a 250-ml Claisen flask equipped with a capillary and ready for vacuum distillation. A very little solvent (2–5 ml) may be used to avoid loss on transfer. The residual solvent is distilled at reduced pressure, with use of an aspirator to secure the vacuum. The receiving flask is cooled with water, as usual, during the solvent distillation; however, little, if any, hexane will condense in the flask, and the pressure cannot be reduced to that obtainable with an aspirator (20–30 mm) until the hexane has been removed. After all hexane has been distilled (as evidenced by a drop in pressure), the heating bath is raised to about 150° (may have already been raised to this temperature), and the pressure is *cautiously* reduced to less than 10 mm (not less than 3 mm) with the oil pump. Too sudden a drop in pressure may cause a sudden surge of material to froth into the receiving flask. If material should froth over into the receiver, the distillation must be interrupted, air let into the system, all distillate returned to the distilling flask, and a clean receiving flask substituted. If there is a small forerun, this must be removed before the product is collected over a range of about 5° or less (reported boiling point is 135° / 4 mm). The product should be stored in a narrow-mouthed bottle closed with a clean rubber stopper. The yield is in the range 60–70%.

Both the IR spectrum and the glpc tracing should be determined and attached in your notebook. In the IR spectrum, there should be observed the nitrile absorption at about 4.35 μ and the much stronger carbonyl absorption at about 5.80 μ.

At the highest settings on the Carle Basic Gas Chromatograph, the cyano aldehyde does not have an excessively long retention time on a silicone column (about 9.2 minutes). A sample of 2-ethylhexanal should also be injected in order to determine its retention time (about 3.2 minutes), and the tracing from the product should be examined for traces of the starting material.

The significant residue remaining from distillation of the cyano aldehyde consists largely of hydroxy aldehyde from aldol condensation. Although this product is not of interest to the current preparation, it may be distilled at a boiling point of about 192° /4 mm.

NOTE

1. 2-Ethylhexanal, like other aliphatic aldehydes, is easily oxidized to the acid and is also subject to polymerization on standing. Polymerization is much slower with α-substituted aldehydes than with unsubstituted aldehydes, but old samples of 2-ethylhexanal will contain appreciable polymer, so the material used in the preparation should be freshly distilled. The boiling point is reported as 70° /30 mm; the sample used should be collected over a range of about two degrees. If not used promptly, it should be stored in a flask stoppered with a clean rubber stopper.

Synthesis of Nitriles by Displacement of Halogen

35

Nitriles are sometimes made by dehydration of amides, especially in instances where the corresponding acid is readily available. Such a preparation is illustrated in Chap. 13. In instances where the primary alkyl halide with one less carbon is easily available, displacement of the halogen by cyanide is nearly always the preferred method of synthesis. As will be developed subsequently in this chapter, this synthesis is less satisfactory for secondary alkyl halides, and fails for tertiary alkyl halides. Aromatic halides may be converted to nitriles, but not by a normal S_N2 reaction; the conversion is accomplished by heating the aryl halide with cuprous cyanide in a high-boiling solvent such as dimethylformamide. The present chapter is directed specifically to preparation of the mono- and dinitriles from pentamethylene dichloride; however, the same techniques apply to synthesis of other nitriles. This method is the most widely applied synthesis of aliphatic nitriles.

Nitriles have several applications as intermediates in synthesis, such as hydrolysis to an amide, hydrolysis to an acid, reduction to an amine, reduction to an aldehyde, and conversion to a ketone by reaction with a Grignard or lithium reagent. Hydrolysis to an acid is a widely applied sequence, and is discussed in the present chapter.

Classical methods for accomplishing a simple displacement of halogen by cyanide involved heating the reactants in a reasonably good ionizing solvent which would dissolve both the organic halide and the sodium or potassium cyanide. Ethanol containing a small amount of water was the most widely utilized solvent, but completion of the displacement of bromide required eight hours or longer of heating under reflux. Displacement of chloride was so slow as to be impractical unless about one-fourth mole equivalent of potassium iodide was included in order to give displacement of chloride by iodide. This synthesis, as well as many others (cf. Chap. 36), has been greatly accelerated and improved by use of dimethyl sulfoxide[1] (DMSO), CH_3—S—CH_3, as solvent. The remarkable

$$\underset{\displaystyle O}{\overset{\displaystyle \downarrow}{}}$$

effect of this solvent in accelerating rates of displacement reactions, first reported[2] in 1960, has been ascribed to the near-absence of solvation of anions by DMSO. This leaves the anion unobstructed in its attack on a nucleophile. In the case of a base such as hydroxide or methoxide, the base-strength (electron-donating capability) is increased by a factor of many powers of ten. The importance of this phenomenon in generating enolate ions will be developed in Chap. 36. For the displacement of halogen by cyanide, the reaction is accelerated to the point that displacement of chloride is essentially complete in about one hour at 80°. Bromide is displaced at about one hundred times the rate of chloride, so displacement of bromide is complete in a few minutes at 60°.

Heptanedinitrile (pentamethylene dicyanide) is prepared in a two-step sequence (Eqs. 1, 2) from 1,5-dichloropentane. The rate constant for the

$$Cl—(CH_2)_5—Cl + NaCN \rightarrow Cl—(CH_2)_5—CN + NaCl \qquad (35\text{-}1)$$

$$Cl—(CH_2)_5—CN + NaCN \rightarrow NC—(CH_2)_5—CN + NaCl \qquad (35\text{-}2)$$

second step should be the same as for the first step, since the two functional groups are not sufficiently close together to permit a neighboring group effect (anchimeric effect). Thus, as soon as any chloronitrile is formed it reacts further to yield dinitrile. If the dinitrile is the desired product, at least two moles of cyanide per mole of dihalide is used.

If *6-chlorohexanenitrile* is the desired product, Eq. 1 is the *main reaction* and Eq. 2 becomes a *side reaction*, thus only about one mole

---

[1]There have been large numbers of reports of assorted physiological effects of DMSO, many of them alleged to be spectacularly beneficial; however, the discovery that it has a damaging effect on the lens of the eye in experimental animals has depressed investigation of use of the substance as a therapeutic agent. Any investigation must be authorized by the U.S. Public Health Service. An additional problem is the appearance of the vile-smelling dimethyl sulfide in the breath of a person soon after DMSO is ingested, or even applied to the skin. A much more serious objection to allowing significant amounts of DMSO on the skin is its ability to render the skin permeable to many chemical compounds. Substances ordinarily regarded as harmless on the skin become dangerous toxic agents when the nonpermeability of the skin has been destroyed by application of DMSO. Thus, the substance should be kept off the hands; if it is accidentally spilled on the skin, the area should be washed promptly using a detergent.

[2]R. A. Smiley and C. Arnold, *J. Org. Chem.,* **25,** 257 (1960); L. Friedman and H. Schechter, *J. Org. Chem.,* **25,** 877 (1960).

equivalent of cyanide is used. Since the rate constants for the two steps should be the same, as mentioned above, it would seem impossible for the reaction mixture to contain a higher yield of chloronitrile than about 33%. Nevertheless, it proves possible, in DMSO as solvent, to isolate yields of 6-chlorohexanenitrile amounting to 50% or more. Indeed, work-up and gas chromatography of samples of the reaction mixture at time intervals during the reaction reveals the fact that very little dinitrile is formed until about one-fourth the dichloride is converted to chloronitrile. Considerable investigation has eliminated most of the possible explanations of this phenomenon. The most plausible explanation which has not been eliminated is that the two-phase reaction mixture has a ratio of cyanide to dichloride in one phase which is significantly higher than is the ratio of cyanide to chloronitrile in either phase. In any case, a surprisingly good yield of chloronitrile may be obtained. It proves most convenient to use a slight excess (over one mole equivalent) of cyanide and run the reaction for only a few minutes at about 80°.

If pure and dry DMSO is used as solvent, there are no nucleophiles in the reaction except cyanide ion, and the only *side reaction* (except Eq. 2 in chloronitrile preparation) arises from the ambident nature of the cyanide ion. With primary halides, the isonitrile is formed (Eq. 3) in very

$$Cl-(CH_2)_5-Cl + {}^-CN \rightarrow Cl-(CH_2)_5-\overset{+}{N}\equiv C^- + {}^-Cl \qquad (35\text{-}3)$$

small amount, which is fortunate on account of its vile odor. With secondary halides, isonitrile formation becomes serious, but in DMSO solvent moderate yields of secondary alkyl cyanides are still attainable. With tertiary halides, the principle products are isonitrile and alkene, both of which products probably arise by way of dissociation of the *tert*-alkyl halide (S_N1 reaction route). In no case has it been possible to secure an S_N2 displacement in a tertiary halide, even with DMSO as solvent.

Since only traces of isonitrile are formed from primary halides, it is statistically improbable that di-isonitrile would be formed; however, the cyanoisonitrile could be formed (Eq. 4).

$$Cl-(CH_2)_5-CN + {}^-CN \rightarrow {}^-C\equiv\overset{+}{N}-(CH_2)_5-CN + {}^-Cl \qquad (35\text{-}4)$$

If the DMSO is not dry, other side reactions become possible, as outlined in Eqs. 5 and 6 for reaction of the dichloride. Since the

$$KCN + H_2O \rightleftarrows KOH + HCN \qquad (35\text{-}5)$$

$$Cl-(CH_2)_5-Cl + {}^-OH \longrightarrow \begin{cases} Cl-(CH_2)_5-OH + {}^-Cl \\ Cl-(CH_2)_3-CH = CH_2 + HOH + Cl^- \end{cases} \qquad (35\text{-}6)$$

chloronitrile may react similarly, there remains a halogen present to give the side reaction even after one halogen has reacted as desired (Eq. 1);

therefore, dryness of the solvent becomes much more important with a dihalide than is the case with a monohalide. Indeed, for displacement of a monohalide by cyanide in DMSO solvent, scrupulous dryness of the solvent is not necessary in order to obtain an excellent yield of nitrile.

Distillation is used for *isolation and purification* of either the dinitrile or chloronitrile. In the former case, simple distillation is adequate, but the chloronitrile must be separated from dichloride and dinitrile by fractional distillation in a fractionating column. With either of the columns described in Chap. 32, separation is rather simple, for the components of the mixture boil about 50° apart.

Hydrolysis of the nitrile to give amide or carboxylate anion may occur during its preparation if water is present in the solvent; however, this reaction is not significant with amounts of water accidentally present in the DMSO. In case hydrolysis is desired, it is very rapid in DMSO solvent if water and alkali are added. In the present instance, however, hydrolysis of heptanedinitrile is most conveniently accomplished, not in DMSO, but in water solution, on account of the solubility of the product in water. Isolation could not be accomplished by diluting the reaction mixture with water. *Pimelic acid* is conveniently obtained as outlined in Eq. 7. The

$$NC-(CH_2)_5-CN + H_2O \xrightarrow[\substack{\text{hydrochloric} \\ \text{acid; heat}}]{\text{conc.}} HO_2C-(CH_2)_5-CO_2H + NH_4Cl \quad (35\text{-}7)$$

product is crystallized from the reaction mixture in good yield by simply cooling. This constitutes the best available synthesis of pimelic acid.

EXPERIMENTAL PROCEDURES

Heptanedinitrile

A 500-ml round-bottomed flask with ground-glass center neck and side tubes (cf. Appendix I) is dried thoroughly and equipped with a sealed mechanical stirrer in the center neck, a calcium chloride drying tube in one side neck, and a thermometer in the other side neck. The thermometer should extend into the stirred liquid during reaction, but not into the path of the stirrer. The clamps holding the flask are loosened so that the flask may be removed from the stirrer assembly, and the flask is charged (Note 1) in the order specified with 70 g of 1,5-dichloropentane, 52 g of sodium cyanide (Note 2) which has been ground in a mortar then dried in an oven or vacuum desiccator, and 200 ml of dried DMSO (Note 3). The stirrer is run fast enough to mix well the partially insoluble sodium cyanide, and the flask is heated to about 60°. At this point the heat is removed, for the exothermic reaction causes a rapid rise in temperature.

At about 70°, the reaction is cooled in a bath of cold water sufficiently to hold the temperature below 80°. When the heat of reaction no longer keeps the temperature above 75° (usually no more than 10 minutes), heat is cautiously applied in order to raise the temperature to about 100°. After a reaction time of 25 minutes at about 100° the flask is cooled in a pan of water to about room temperature. The cooled reaction mixture is poured into a liter separatory funnel containing 300 ml of water and 300 ml of saturated aqueous sodium chloride solution. The product is extracted with a 150-ml portion of benzene, a part of which is used to rinse the reaction flask. The aqueous phase is carefully separated, then extracted with two additional portions of benzene (100, 50 ml) in order to recover the rather soluble dinitrile. The second and third extracts are combined, but kept separate from the first extract. The two extracts in sequence are shaken for a few minutes with a 100-ml portion of 6N hydrochloric acid in order to hydrolyze and remove any isonitrile. The phases are separated carefully each time, then a final wash is made with a mixture of 25 ml of water and 75 ml of saturated aqueous sodium chloride. If final separations are made carefully, drying is accomplished by simple distillation since benzene and water form a minimum-boiling azeotrope.

The combined extracts are distilled from a 500-ml Erlenmeyer flask, preferably with heating on an electric hot plate, but in any case with precaution against fire. When distillation becomes slow (and without over-heating the residue), the residue is poured (*No flames!*) into a 125-ml Claisen flask, which has been equipped with a capillary for vacuum distillation. Not more than 5 ml of benzene is used to rinse the Erlenmeyer flask. The flask is heated in an oil bath as usual for distillation at reduced pressure, and the last traces of solvent are removed as the system is evacuated with a water pump. The bath is heated to about 150°, and last traces of solvent are distilled until its complete removal is indicated by a drop in pressure to the minimum attainable with the water pump. The heating bath is then lowered from the flask, the pressure is cautiously reduced with an oil pump to about 4 mm, and the bath is raised again. If any forerun distills as the boiling point rises to about 145°, before the product is collected, the bath is lowered, air is let into the system, and a new tared receiver is attached. The heptanedinitrile is collected over a boiling range of about three degrees; its boiling point is reported as 149° (4 mm). The yield of colorless or slightly brown dinitrile is 49–55 g (80–90%).

NOTES

1. If larger runs are carried out according to this procedure, there may be difficulty in controlling the exothermic reaction, in which case the dichloride

may be added to the stirred mixture from a separatory funnel during a few minutes. The reaction is not harmed by temperature as high as 140°; however, the lower temperature is recommended in order to allow easier control of heat evolution.

2. Potassium cyanide is not satisfactory in this procedure when a *bromide* is used for the reaction; its use will lead to a maximum yield of about 35%. Potassium cyanide is considerably less soluble in DMSO than is sodium cyanide, but a more serious factor is the extremely low solubility of potassium cyanide in DMSO saturated with potassium bromide. After about one-third the bromide has been displaced, the amount of solvent that is used becomes saturated with potassium bromide formed in the reaction. This renders the potassium cyanide so insoluble that further displacement is extremely slow. In the case of chlorides, this phenomenon has not been investigated, but potassium chloride may generate the same difficulty.

Since *cyanides are highly toxic* (50–100 mg cause death), they should be handled with caution, as regards ingestion. If any salt is spilled it should be cleaned up at once and washed down the drain with adequate water. The aqueous phase from which the product is extracted should also be washed down the drain. Of course the hands should be rinsed well, especially before eating. There is no significant amount of hydrogen cyanide evolved in this reaction (e.g., from Eq. 5), so it need not be carried out in a forced-draft hood.

3. DMSO may be dried conveniently in either of two ways. A portion may be simply distilled at reduced pressure and the product collected over a range of about two degrees [reported b.p. 85° (20 mm)]. This is satisfactory because DMSO does not form an azeotrope with water (at least, not one boiling near DMSO). A somewhat more laborious method, which gives a very pure and dry sample, consists of fractional freezing. A suitable quantity of commercial product, contained in an Erlenmeyer flask, is placed in a refrigerator until about one-fourth or one-third is frozen (few hours required, depending on volume of material). The crystals are pressed out on a Büchner funnel, with suction as usual in filtration, and the product is placed in a desiccator to melt. When this method is utilized, the filtrates are collected and eventually distilled.

For the present reaction, distillation of the DMSO is recommended. Since it is hygroscopic, the distilled product should be protected from moist air until used.

6-Chlorohexanenitrile

The reaction is carried out as described for preparation of the dinitrile, but with the following quantities: 70 g of 1,5-dichloropentane, 29 g of ground and dried sodium cyanide, and 150 ml of dried DMSO. After the initial exothermic reaction subsides, subsequent heating is at 75–80°, and *total reaction time is only 15 minutes.* Longer heating or higher temperature will lower yield of chloronitrile in favor of dinitrile.

For work-up, the reaction mixture is poured into 200 ml of water and 200 ml of saturated aqueous sodium chloride solution. Extraction is with three portions of benzene (100, 100, 50 ml), and wash of the extracts is with 100 ml of 6N hydrochloric acid, then the mixture of 25 ml of water and 75 ml of saturated aqueous sodium chloride. Solvent is distilled as described for the dinitrile, but the residue of product is poured into a 125-ml flask equipped with ground joint for attachment to the Vigreux fractionating column and side tube fitted with a capillary (cf. Chap. 32). Before this distillation is attempted, Chap. 32 should be reviewed carefully. Also, an instructor should be present at the time the distillation is started and reference should be made to Note 4 of ethyl hydrogen adipate preparation (Chap. 37).

After the last of the solvent has been removed at reduced pressure, the mixture remaining consists largely of 1,5-dichloropentane, b.p. 56° (5 mm), 6-chlorohexanenitrile, b.p. 100° (5 mm), and heptanedinitrile, b.p. 152° (5 mm). Accurate reproduction of boiling points at reduced pressure is difficult, and a pressure differing somewhat from 5 mm may be convenient; however, the cited boiling points allow sufficient anticipation of the locations of the main fractions. The intermediate fractions should be quite small, no more than about 2 g. The yield of 6-chlorohexanenitrile is 26–29.5 g (40–45%), and there is recovered 12–15 g of dinitrile. The three major fractions should be turned in, properly labeled.

The infrared spectrum of the chloronitrile and dinitrile should be determined, and the stronger absorption at 4.35 μ in the dinitrile should be noted. If thin films are used (thus not necessarily of same thickness for the two compounds), comparison of the nitrile absorption with the C—H absorption in the same spectrum may be used for determining the relative strength of the nitrile absorption in the two compounds.

Glpc should be applied to the three major fractions, in order to assess the effectiveness of your fractional distillation. Small peaks due to impurities are generally noted in the glpc tracings: (1) at a time shorter than the dichloride, and believed to be an impurity in this starting material; (2) at a time about midway between the dichloride and chloronitrile. The latter impurity has not been investigated, but it may be an alcohol resulting from hydrolysis by traces of water in the reaction mixture.

It is also of interest to collect the intermediate between the chloronitrile and dinitrile fractions in three parts and compare the glpc tracings for the sequential intermediate fractions in order to observe the change in composition with boiling point. The Ƌ settings on the Carle Basic Gas Chromatograph should prove satisfactory, although the dinitrile will give a moderately long retention time.   •

Pimelic Acid

In a 500-ml Erlenmeyer flask (Note 1) are placed 45 g of heptanedinitrile and 125 ml of concentrated hydrochloric acid. The mixture is heated under reflux, preferably on a hot plate, for 3 hours (Note 2). Since hydrogen chloride is evolved at first, the reaction should be carried out in a hood, or the condenser should be connected to a gas trap (Fig. 8-1 or 8-5). The hot reaction mixture is poured into a 500-ml beaker, and the flask is rinsed with about 10 ml of hot water. As the beaker is cooled in water the contents are stirred vigorously by hand in an effort to prevent the separating pimelic acid from setting to a dense cake. After the mixture has reached room temperature and the major portion of the acid has crystallized, it is allowed to stand for at least 1 hour, preferably overnight. Any lumps are broken up in the beaker (with care against breaking the beaker), then the semisolid mass is collected on a Büchner funnel and drained as well as possible, with pressing of the filter cake. After drainage is complete, the crystals are returned to the beaker and stirred thoroughly with about 75 ml of cold water. The mass of crystals is again returned to the Büchner funnel and pressed well, then washed on the funnel with about 50 ml of cold water. If this washing procedure is properly carried out, the white product is essentially pure and nearly free of ammonium chloride. After drying to constant weight, the yield is 53.5–55.5 g (91–94%), m.p. 102–103°. The aqueous filtrate contains ammonium chloride and a small amount of pimelic acid, but additional pimelic acid can be separated from the ammonium chloride only with great difficulty.

About 2 g of the pimelic acid is recrystallized from water. The weight and melting point of this purified sample are determined, and it is turned in separately, properly labelled. The melting point is usually unaffected by this crystallization, but traces of ammonium chloride are removed.

NOTES

1. A ground-jointed connection to the condenser is highly desirable, for if a cork is used coloring matter is extracted from it and the pimelic acid becomes discolored. Usually, the color may be removed by recrystallization from water.

2. Heating on a hot plate is preferable to heating with a flame, especially if a solid separates (see below). It is well to place one or two small (about 1-cm square) pieces of asbestos paper between the hot plate and the flask. Occasionally, a flask set directly on a hot plate will crack; however, covering the entire hot plate with a piece of asbestos paper is quite undesirable. The objective is to heat the flask with the hot plate, not insulate the flask from the heat source.

The heating period need not be continuous; however, if it is interrupted (and occasionally if it is not) pimelamide separates from the solution and causes uncontrollable bumping. This difficulty is easily resolved by adding a few milliliters of water through the condenser in order to redissolve the amide.

Alkylation of Malonic Ester

36

The alkylation of a malonic ester, usually diethyl malonate, assumes considerable importance because of the variety of uses of the alkylated malonic esters. β-Keto esters undergo a similar alkylation. The key step in the reaction is displacement of halogen from an alkyl halide by the enolate ion of the malonate. This is a simple displacement (S_N2 reaction), with no complication by assistance of the leaving group from solvent or other reagents. There has not been observed an occurrence of rearrangement such as would result from formation of an intermediate carbonium ion. Although this means that tertiary halides and aryl halides are not sufficiently reactive for this displacement, the absence of rearrangement or of racemization of optical centers vastly increases the utility of the process. The scope of the reaction is further increased by the fact that alkylation may be accomplished, not only with simple alkyl halides, but with a variety of polyfunctional compounds containing halogen. The present illustrations permit the development of most of the principles involved in this reaction.

Conversion of Malonic Ester to the Enolate Ion

Since the synthesis of an alkylated malonic ester involves a displacement by the enolate ion of the ester, it is apparent that the first step in the process must be formation of the enolate ion. Malonic ester is converted more or less completely to its metallic enolate by reaction with a sufficiently strong base. An alkoxide is usually basic enough to accomplish the conversion, and a typical process is outlined in Eq. 1. The associated enolate, with the metal chelated between the carbonyl oxygens, is probably

$$C_2H_5O-\underset{\underset{O}{\parallel}}{C}\underset{CH_2}{\diagup}\underset{\underset{O}{\parallel}}{C}-OC_2H_5 + NaOC_2H_5 \;\rightleftharpoons\; C_2H_5O\diagup\underset{\underset{O}{\parallel}}{C}\underset{CH}{\diagdown}\underset{\underset{O}{\diagdown}}{C}\diagup OC_2H_5$$

$$\underset{Na}{}$$

$$+ \; C_2H_5OH \qquad (36\text{-}1)$$

the principal species present in solution; however, the resonance-stabilized enolate ion, formed by dissociation of the metallic enolate, is the nucleophile which accomplishes the desired displacement. Examination of the principal resonance forms (formulas A, B, and C) of this ion suggests

$$
\begin{array}{ccc}
\underset{\text{CH}}{\overset{\displaystyle OC_2H_5}{\underset{\diagdown}{\overset{\diagup}{|}}}} & & \\
\end{array}
$$

(A)   (B)   (C)

that either oxygen or carbon may be specifically involved in the displacement. In practice, the new bond is nearly always formed at carbon in malonic ester, although reactions are known in which a part of the substitution occurs on oxygen. In enolate ions from other species than malonic esters, all or most of the substitution may occur at oxygen.

In formation of an enolate ion, at least two factors are of importance: displacement of the equilibrium in Eq. 1 as far forward as possible, and as much ionization as possible of the metallic enolate. These factors are especially important because presence of base in the solution (ethoxide in Eq. 1) at the time that the alkyl halide is added generates an opportunity for side reactions to occur between the base and the alkyl halide (see below). Low molecular weight alcohols are moderately good ionizing solvents, and there has been widespread use of the alcohol as solvent which is the conjugate acid of the alkoxide used as base. Of course addition of large amounts of this alcohol as solvent displaces the equilibrium in Eq. 1 to the left and thus decreases the percentage conversion to enolate. For unsubstituted malonic esters, this shift in equilibrium proves tolerable in terms of yield when primary alkyl halides are used for the displacement, so ethanol has been widely used as solvent for the reaction. This procedure, which may now be termed as the "classical" one, is illustrated in the present chapter by alkylation of malonic ester with 1,3-dibromopropane.

If the alkylation of malonic ester is carried out in some good ionizing solvent other than the conjugate acid corresponding to the base used to get the enolate ion, improved results should ensue. The improvement

should be especially noteworthy in instances where hindrance in the enolate ion, as in an alkylmalonic ester, favors side reactions of the base with
the alkyl halide. Solvents that have been found useful include dimethylformamide, 1,2-dimethoxyethane (glyme; cf. Chap. 34), and dimethyl-
sulfoxide (DMSO). Of these, DMSO is especially advantageous for two
reasons: its inability to solvate anions increases rate of displacement reactions, as discussed in Chap. 35; the same feeble solvating capacity
greatly increases the base strength of the alkoxide, and thus displaces the
equilibrium in Eq. 1 to the right, as is desirable. The combination of these
factors makes practical the use of alkyl chlorides in displacement by the
enolate ion. The procedure is illustrated in the present chapter in conversion of malonic ester to the enolate ion with sodium methoxide and
alkylation with 6-chlorohexanenitrile. Although sodium methoxide is a
weaker base than ethoxide, and much weaker than *t*-butoxide, in DMSO
methoxide is an entirely satisfactory base. An advantage of methoxide is
its commercial availability at a modest price. If methoxide is used,
dimethyl malonate must be used, for use of diethyl malonate would result
in extremely rapid base-catalyzed trans-esterification, and the product
would be a mixture of esters. The alkoxide and the alcohol moiety in
the ester must always correspond if mixtures are to be avoided.

Other bases which are stronger than alkoxides have frequently been
used to form the enolate ion so that the equilibrium in Eq. 1 will be shifted
essentially entirely forward. With DMSO as solvent, however, the easily
manipulated sodium methoxide seems likely to be a sufficiently strong
base for most applications. Hydroxide is strong enough as a base (cf. Chap.
34); however, it is not useful when esters are reactants, for saponification
of the ester occurs. The anion of a carboxylic acid is such a weak acid as to
be of no value for conversion to the enolate. Formation of the enolate ion
would give a species of obviously high energy, with two charges in over-
lapping orbitals.

Dimethyl 6-cyanohexane-1,1-dicarboxylate results from alkylation of
dimethyl malonate with 6-chlorohexanenitrile (Eqs. 2 and 3). In DMSO,

$$\underset{\underset{CO_2CH_3}{|}}{\overset{\overset{CO_2CH_3}{|}}{CH_2}} + {}^-OCH_3 \underset{solvent}{\overset{DMSO}{\rightleftarrows}} \underset{\underset{CO_2CH_3}{|}}{\overset{\overset{CO_2CH_3}{|}}{{}^-CH}} + HOCH_3 \qquad (36\text{-}2)$$

$$\underset{\underset{CO_2CH_3}{|}}{\overset{\overset{CO_2CH_3}{|}}{{}^-CH}} + Cl-(CH_2)_5-CN \overset{DMSO}{\longrightarrow} \underset{\underset{CO_2CH_3}{|}}{\overset{\overset{CO_2CH_3}{|}}{CH}}-(CH_2)_5-CN + Cl^- \qquad (36\text{-}3)$$

the rate is sufficiently enhanced to allow use of the chloride, but several
hours at 95° are required for the reaction. Displacement of a bromide is

complete in an hour or less at 60°. The lower temperature is required with bromides, for they react with DMSO at higher temperatures.

Several *side reactions* may occur during the alkylation process. As has been mentioned above, hydroxide will saponify malonic ester and give the acid anion which is useless for forming enolate ion. Water may be removed from the solvent by drying (simple distillation for DMSO), but handling of sodium methoxide must be in a dry box in order to avoid some conversion to sodium hydroxide from reaction with moisture in air. As a matter of fact, commercial sodium methoxide is unlikely to be free of hydroxide. Since both dimethyl malonate and sodium methoxide are much cheaper than the alkyl chloride used in this alkylation, excess of sodium methoxide and dimethyl malonate are used in order to avoid the inconvenience of working in a dry box. Furthermore, there is used an excess of malonic ester greater than that of methoxide, for this displaces the equilibrium in Eq. 2 forward so as to reduce the concentration of methoxide. In turn, this minimizes the side reactions shown in Eqs. 4 and 5 (ether synthesis and dehydrohalogenation).

$$Cl-(CH_2)_5-CN + {}^-OCH_3 \begin{cases} \rightarrow CH_3O-(CH_2)_5-CN + {}^-Cl & (36\text{-}4) \\ \rightarrow CH_2{=}CH-(CH_2)_3-CN + HOCH_3 + {}^-Cl & (36\text{-}5) \end{cases}$$

Still another side reaction becomes possible on account of the fact that the alkylmalonic ester is also an acid. As it accumulates in the reaction mixture it competes with the unalkylated ester for base. This equilibration may be represented as in Eq. 6. Since this equilibrium must develop as

$$\underset{\underset{CO_2CH_3}{|}}{\overset{\overset{CO_2CH_3}{|}}{{}^-CH}} + \underset{\underset{CO_2CH_3}{|}}{\overset{\overset{CO_2CH_3}{|}}{CH}}-(CH_2)_5-CN \rightleftarrows \underset{\underset{CO_2CH_3}{|}}{\overset{\overset{CO_2CH_3}{|}}{CH_2}} + {}^-\underset{\underset{CO_2CH_3}{|}}{\overset{\overset{CO_2CH_3}{|}}{C}}-(CH_2)_5-CN \quad (36\text{-}6)$$

soon as any substituted malonic ester is formed in the reaction, it follows that the alkyl halide and ion of the substituted malonic ester are in the reaction mixture at the same time. Thus, dialkylation can occur, as in Eq. 7, and the dialkylmalonate is always a by-product. This side reac-

$$\underset{\underset{CO_2CH_3}{|}}{\overset{\overset{CO_2CH_3}{|}}{{}^-C}} + Cl-(CH_2)_5-CN \rightarrow NC-(CH_2)_5-\underset{\underset{CO_2CH_3}{|}}{\overset{\overset{CO_2CH_3}{|}}{C}}-(CH_2)_5-CN + Br^- \quad (36\text{-}7)$$

tion is repressed, however, if the equilibrium in Eq. 6 is shifted to the left by use of excess of dimethyl malonate. Since other side reactions are also repressed by use of excess malonate (Eqs. 4 and 5), this practice is always advisable. Even if a cheap alkyl halide is being used, the excess malonic ester may be recovered. By following procedures indicated from the above discussion, yields of alkylmalonate as high as 80% may be realized.

If a monoalkylated malonic ester is used for a second alkylation, of course the side reaction resulting from occurrence of the reactions in Eqs. 6 and 7 is no longer possible. Also, the substituted malonic ester is more expensive, so use of a large excess of ester is indicated only if the halide is expensive and the excess ester is recovered. In such instances, it is likely to be desirable to prepare sodium ethoxide as in the next procedure, remove alcohol by distillation, and then proceed with alkylation in DMSO. This avoids waste of substituted malonic ester by reaction with the hydroxide normally present in commercial methoxide.

One of the most common utilizations of the substituted malonic esters is hydrolysis to a malonic acid and decarboxylation of the malonic acid by simple heating. Procedures for this sequence are included for both products prepared in the present chapter. *Hydrolysis of the dimethyl 6-cyanohexane-1,1-dicarboxylate* is accomplished most easily in aqueous hydrochloric acid, for the water-soluble tricarboxylic acid may be obtained by evaporation of the reaction mixture to dryness. Heating the residue gives suberic acid in nearly quantitative yield. Ammonium chloride (from hydrolysis of the nitrile) is removed by extraction with water.

Alkylation of malonic ester with 1,3-dibromopropane is subject to the same considerations that have been presented above; however, additional factors also apply. Since the two halogens in 1,3-dibromopropane must be replaced one at a time, the initial step in the alkylation is that shown in Eq. 8. The product of this initial step may engage in a second displacement, but it may also experience ion exchange with the malonate anion, to set up the equilibrium shown in the top line of Eq. 9. This is the same situation

$$
\begin{array}{c}
CO_2C_2H_5 \\
| \\
CH^- \\
| \\
CO_2C_2H_5
\end{array}
+ \; Br-(CH_2)_3-Br \;\rightarrow\;
\begin{array}{c}
CO_2C_2H_5 \\
| \\
CH-(CH_2)_3-Br \\
| \\
CO_2C_2H_5
\end{array}
+ \; Br^-
\qquad (36\text{-}8)
$$

$$
\begin{array}{c}
CO_2C_2H_5 \\
| \\
CH-(CH_2)_3-Br \\
| \\
CO_2C_2H_5
\end{array}
+
\begin{array}{c}
CO_2C_2H_5 \\
| \\
CH^- \\
| \\
CO_2C_2H_5
\end{array}
\; \overset{B}{\rightleftharpoons} \;
\begin{array}{c}
CO_2C_2H_5 \\
| \\
{}^-C-(CH_2)_3-Br \\
| \\
CO_2C_2H_5
\end{array}
+
\begin{array}{c}
CO_2C_2H_5 \\
| \\
CH_2 \\
| \\
CO_2C_2H_5
\end{array}
$$

$$
\downarrow A \qquad\qquad\qquad\qquad\qquad \downarrow C \qquad\qquad (36\text{-}9)
$$

$$
\begin{array}{c}
CO_2C_2H_5 \quad CO_2C_2H_5 \\
| \qquad\qquad | \\
CH-(CH_2)_3-CH \\
| \qquad\qquad | \\
CO_2C_2H_5 \quad CO_2C_2H_5
\end{array}
+ \; Br^-
\qquad\qquad
\begin{array}{c}
CO_2C_2H_5 \\
| \\
CH_2-C-CO_2C_2H_5 \\
| \\
CH_2-CH_2
\end{array}
+ \; Br^-
$$

as described in Eq. 6, except that the substituted ion appearing on the right contains bromine, which may be displaced either intramolecularly or intermolecularly. In spite of the formation of a four-membered ring, the intramolecular displacement (reaction C) proves to be much faster than displacement of the halogen by another ionic species, or formation of bis-3-bromopropylmalonic ester. Of course reaction A represents a normal displacement reaction. Since hydrolysis and decarboxylation of the tetra-ester resulting from reaction 9-A leads to pimelic acid, which is much more easily prepared by another route (cf. Chap. 35), it is obviously desirable to manipulate the conditions of this preparation to favor the sequence of reactions B and C. Hydrolysis and decarboxylation of the cyclic di-ester lead to cyclobutanecarboxylic acid, which is difficult to obtain by other routes. This acid is a convenient source of many cyclobutane derivatives. Furthermore, a study of these reactions is very instructive.

It will be noted that reactions 9-A and 9-C are not reversible, while reaction 9-B represents an equilibrium between the ion of malonic ester and the ion of the substituted malonic ester. It may be reasonably assumed that the rates of the reactions involved in equilibrium B are very much greater than those of reactions A and C. If we also assume that the rates of reactions A and C are of the same order of magnitude, it follows that the relative amounts of tetra-ester and cyclic di-ester will depend on the position of equilibrium B. A shift of this equilibrium to the right will favor the production of cyclic di-ester. It should be pointed out that the concentration of trimethylene dibromide has no effect on the relative production of the two esters. It may be seen that the production of a molecule of tetra-ester requires one trimethylene dibromide, two sodiums, and two malonic esters; and that the production of a molecule of cyclic ester requires one trimethylene dibromide, two sodiums, and one malonic ester. Thus, if an equivalent amount of sodium and malonic ester is used, a molecule of malonic ester is formed each time a molecule of cyclic ester is formed. As the malonic ester accumulates, equilibrium B is forced to the left, and the production of tetra-ester is favored. On the other hand, if this is avoided by the use of two equivalents of sodium ethoxide to one of malonic ester, the second equivalent of sodium ethoxide remains in the solution at the time addition of trimethylene dibromide is begun, for only one equivalent of sodium ethoxide can react with malonic ester. This means that side reactions analogous to those in Eqs. 4 and 5 will be favored. This dual difficulty is resolved if the second equivalent of sodium ethoxide is added concurrently with the trimethylene dibromide. In this manner the concentration of sodium ethoxide is never high, but it is added approximately at the rate at which malonic ester is formed in reaction B. Thus, the equilibrium is constantly pressed to the right, and reaction C becomes highly favored. A yield of 60% or more of cylic ester, based on trimethylene dibromide, may be obtained, and the yield of open-chain tetra-ester is reduced to about 10%. It is of interest that the conclusions reached in the present discussion are supported by the experimental results that have been obtained with different ratios of reagents, as summarized in Table I.

TABLE I

Alkylation of Malonic Ester with 1,3-Dibromopropane

Run No.	*Ratio of Reactants*			*Yields in Per Cent*[*]	
	Na	*M. E.*	*Dibromide*	*Di-ester*	*Tetra-ester*
1	2	2	1	43	18.5
2	2	3	1	24	52
3	3	3	1	53	16
4	2	1.5	1	54	12
5	2	1.2	1†	61	7

[*]All yields based on dibromide.

†In this run the dibromide was added concurrently with 0.8 equivalent (the amount in excess of malonic ester) of the sodium ethoxide.

EXPERIMENTAL PROCEDURES

Dimethyl 6-Cyanohexane-1,1-Dicarboxylate

A 500-ml three-necked flask (Note 1) is fitted with a sealed stirrer and a 125-ml dropping funnel. The second side neck is fitted with a T-tube large enough for passage of a thermometer, which is placed to extend into the stirred contents of the flask but not into the path of the stirrer. The side of the T-tube is attached to a calcium chloride drying tube. In the flask is placed 140 ml of dimethyl sulfoxide, dried (Note 2) and protected from moisture, followed by 16 g of sodium methoxide (Note 3). The stirrer is started and there is added from the dropping funnel 61 g of recently distilled dimethyl malonate (Note 4). This addition is made rapidly (1–2 minutes), then good stirring is continued for about 15 minutes in order to ensure conversion of the malonate to the anion. Next there is added from the dropping funnel 26 g of 6-chlorohexanenitrile, as rapidly as it will run in. About 2 ml of dry DMSO may be used to quantitatively rinse the funnel into the reaction mixture. The reaction mixture is stirred for 3–4 hours (Note 5) with heating on a steam bath.

After completion of the heating period, the reaction mixture is cooled in ice water, then poured slowly into about 600 ml of ice water contained in a 1-liter separatory funnel (Note 6). The product is extracted with about 100 ml of benzene, then the aqueous phase is run into a second separatory funnel and extracted with 50 ml of benzene. The extracts are washed in sequence with about 100 ml of water, as the phase separations are made carefully. As usual in recovery of a product, the solvent is distilled at atmospheric pressure, taking care not to overheat the residue, then the material is transferred to a Claisen flask. After the last of the solvent has been distilled at reduced pressure, the product is distilled and collected over a boiling range of about 5°; b. p. about 160° (5 mm). Yield is 70–80%. There may be a small amount of residual chloronitrile which appears in the low-boiling forerun, but the principal forerun should be the rather low-boiling dimethyl malonate (unless it was lost by hydrolysis).

As usual, the IR and glpc tracings for the product should be recorded. The ester and nitrile absorptions should be noted in the IR spectrum. At the highest settings of the Carle Basic Chromatograph, this product will appear at a rather long retention time. On another instrument, with a 5-foot column having 10% loading of silicone fluid as partitioning agent, retention time was 4.2 minutes at a temperature of 195°.

NOTES

1. The flask with ground joint and side tubes (Appendix I) may be used if a T-tube whose straight-through arm is the size of the side tube is attached to one side tube in a flush fit, using a large enough piece of rubber tubing. The piece of tubing must not fall in position to obstruct the region of the thermometer around 80°.

2. The DMSO is best dried by distillation, as described in a note to the heptanedinitrile preparation (Chap. 35).

3. Sodium methoxide rapidly absorbs water, which gives hydrolysis to sodium hydroxide, which in turn saponifies the malonic ester. For this reason and others (refer to discussion), an excess of malonic ester is used, and a substantial excess of sodium methoxide (based on chloronitrile) is also used. Nevertheless, it is imperative that the sodium methoxide be weighed rapidly in a small dry Erlenmeyer flask (more emphasis on speed than accuracy), stoppered except when material is being added. It is *especially important that the reagent bottle of sodium methoxide be open only when material is actually being removed.* Before the sodium methoxide is weighed, the reaction flask should contain the DMSO and be ready to receive the sodium methoxide.

4. Dimethyl malonate is sufficiently low-boiling [b.p. 180° (760 mm)] that distillation at atmospheric pressure is satisfactory. Best results are obtained if a Claisen flask is used, and it is heated in an oil bath. A receiver cooled as in vacuum distillation is a convenient condenser.

5. The progress of the reaction may be profitably followed by using glpc analysis to determine amount of chloronitrile surviving. For this purpose, an aliquot is withdrawn after addition of the chloronitrile and thorough mixing, but before heating is started. This serves as reference by providing area under the glpc

tracing when 100% of the chloronitrile is present. Aliquots withdrawn at later times (e.g., after 2, 3, and 4 hours) may be analyzed to provide the per cent of chloronitrile remaining. A 1-ml aliquot of the reaction mixture is of suitable size. Each aliquot is withdrawn through the arm from which the separatory funnel has been removed, as the stirrer is temporarily stopped. The side arm is then closed with a cork and the reaction is continued. The aliquot is run into about 5 ml of water contained in the smallest separatory funnel available, and the funnel is shaken for 2–3 minutes. The resultant mixture is extracted with 1.0 ml of benzene, and the extract is washed once with water, then carefully separated and run into a stoppered vial. Of course, greater precautions to secure precision would be adopted if accurate data such as for determination of a rate constant were required.

A 25-μl aliquot of the benzene extract is a suitable injection for analysis, using D settings on the Carle instrument. If the large amount of benzene fails to clear before the chloronitrile appears, the C settings will give better results because the chloronitrile will appear at a longer retention time. This work-up procedure for the aliquot is designed to give hydrolysis of the dimethyl malonate so that the resultant acid will be lost in the aqueous alkaline extract, along with the water-soluble DMSO. Thus, the glpc tracing should show no substance interfering with analysis for the chloronitrile. The alkylation product will appear at a very long retention time, and this broad band should be avoided in subsequent analyses for chloronitrile. Also, after the last injection the chromatograph should be left running sufficiently long to clear the alkylation product.

6. Alkaline hydrolysis proceeds at a remarkably rapid rate in DMSO solution, and there is a significant hazard that hydrolysis of the ester will occur during the dilution process; hence, the mixture should be kept cold, and the benzene extraction should be performed promptly.

Suberic Acid

The cyano ester is hydrolyzed by heating with hydrochloric acid under reflux, with stirring in a suitably sized three-necked flask. For each gram of cyano ester, 3 ml of concentrated hydrochloric acid and 2 ml of water are used. Hydrolysis is continued for at least 1 hour after the mixture has become homogeneous. The total time should not be less than 3 hours and is normally no more than 4 hours. The mixture now contains 1,1,6-tricarboxyhexane, resulting from the hydrolysis of both ester groups and the cyano group. This substance is rather soluble in water but crystallizes in small amount on cooling. When suberic acid is desired, there is no object in isolating this intermediate.

When hydrolysis is complete, an 8-mm gooseneck (or the distilling head with thermometer outlet plugged) is used to attach the condenser in position for distillation, and water is rapidly distilled. The bath is raised to 180–190° at the end, and stirring is continued to prevent bumping. After all water and alcohol have been distilled, the stirrer is stopped and decarboxylation is effected by continuing heating at 180–190° until gas evolution has ceased, usually after 60–90 minutes. The residue, consisting almost entirely of suberic acid and ammonium chloride, is cooled somewhat, and 100 ml of water is added. This mixture is heated under reflux, with stirring, for about 5 minutes to insure thorough extraction of ammonium chloride; then the mixture is cooled in water, with stirring, for about one-half hour or allowed to stand overnight. The product is collected and washed with several small portions of cold water. After drying, there is obtained a slightly gray product amounting to 90–95% of the theoretical amount, based on cyano ester, and melting at 139–141°. It is nearly pure suberic acid.

Pure suberic acid is readily obtained by one crystallization from water. There is used 10–12 ml of water per gram of acid, and the hot solution is filtered with a small amount of charcoal. The recovery of acid melting at 139–141.5° is better than 90%.

Diethyl Cyclobutanedicarboxylate

A one-liter three-necked flask is fitted with a mercury-sealed stirrer, a reflux condenser protected by a calcium chloride tube, and a 250-ml separatory funnel. To the stem of the separatory funnel there is attached with a rubber connection a piece of glass tubing of such length as just to reach to the bottom of the three-necked flask. The funnel is marked at a volume of 200 ml. A U-tube of 8-mm tubing whose span is wide enough to connect a 1-liter Erlenmeyer flask to the side neck of the three-necked flask is also prepared, to replace the separatory funnel.

The apparatus is set up with the reflux condenser and stirrer in place, and with the U-tube attached in place of the separatory funnel. In the 1-liter Erlenmeyer flask are placed 600 ml of commercial absolute alcohol, followed by 12 g of sodium (Note 1), then the flask is immediately attached to the U-tube and arranged for heating on a hot plate, which is *not turned on yet.* As soon as the vigorous reaction has subsided (*CAUTION! The evolved hydrogen passes out the condenser.*), the hot plate is turned on and about 500 ml of alcohol is distilled into the three-necked flask (Note 2). The distillate may be condensed in the condenser, or more rapidly by cooling the three-necked flask. After distillation is complete, the alcohol is cooled, with stirring, in an ice bath for about 5 minutes. As the ice bath is left in place, the U-tube and Erlenmeyer flask are removed, and 23 g of clean sodium, cut in relatively large pieces, is added to the distilled alcohol (*Caution against dropping sodium into the ice bath!*). The neck of the flask through which the sodium was added is immediately closed with a stopper, and the stirrer is started (*Hydrogen evolution!*). As soon as the dissolution of sodium becomes sluggish, the cooling bath is removed and stirring is continued until all the sodium has dissolved (Note

3). At this point the stirrer is stopped, and the separatory funnel with extended stem is attached. Gentle suction is applied to the top of the separatory funnel until the funnel is filled to the 200-ml line with the sodium ethoxide solution. The stopcock of the separatory funnel is closed, the liquid in the stem is shaken out, the stem extension is removed, and the funnel is returned to the flask. The top of the funnel is fitted with the calcium chloride tube from the condenser, and a 125-ml separatory funnel is attached to the top of the condenser (Note 4) by means of a channeled cork. A channeled cork has a groove cut in the side so that the system is not closed.

To the stirred mixture there is added from the funnel on top of the condenser 96 g of redistilled diethyl malonate (Note 5). The stirred reaction mixture is heated to gentle boiling with an oil bath heated on a hot plate, and 101 g of 1,3-dibromopropane is placed in the top separatory funnel. The contents of the two separatory funnels are now added concurrently to the boiling reaction mixture during a period of about 1 hour. An effort should be made to adjust the rates so that the two additions are made at a steady rate over the same period of time (remember that the volume of the sodium ethoxide solution is about four times that of the dibromide). After addition is complete, the drying tube is returned to the condenser, and the mixture is heated under reflux, with stirring, until a few drops of the reaction mixture added to about 0.5 ml of water do not turn phenolphthalein pink. Make tests at 30-minute intervals and record the time required. If the mixture has not become neutral after 90 minutes of additional heating, continue with the work-up, after making *slightly* acid with acetic acid (a slight excess of sodium may have been used).

After the mixture has become neutral, the position of the condenser is changed for distillation, and the temperature of the oil bath is raised sufficiently to distill alcohol fairly rapidly, as stirring is continued to prevent bumping. After most of the alcohol has been distilled (about 400 ml) the heating bath is removed and about 400 ml of water is added to the flask. The mixture is stirred briefly, then transferred to a separatory funnel, where the organic layer is separated. The aqueous layer is extracted with two 50-ml portions of benzene, as the layers are separated carefully so that drying of the extract will be accomplished by distillation of the benzene-water azeotrope. The extracts are added to the main portion of product contained in a 250-ml Claisen flask. After solvent has been removed at atmospheric pressure, the last traces are distilled at reduced pressure supplied by a water pump. Finally, the oil pump is attached and the product is distilled at a pressure of 10–15 mm. After a small forerun, the cyclic ester is collected over a range of about ten degrees. Its boiling point is 110° (15 mm). The yield is 55–65 g (55–65%) (Note 6).

The distillation residue consists largely of *tetraethyl pentane-1,1,5,5-tetracarboxylate*, which may be obtained in about 10% yield by distillation at low pressure, b.p. 190° (1.5 mm). This ester may be hydrolyzed as described for the preparation of glutaric acid in Chap. 34, and the tetra-acid may be decarboxylated, by heating at 200°, to yield pimelic acid.

NOTES

1. Sodium should be handled with extreme care, for it will ignite or explode on contact with water. It should not be handled with the hands. It is always stored under kerosene or mineral oil. This should be dried off with absorbent paper; then the sodium should be weighed rapidly and put into the reaction vessel. If clean sodium is desired for a reaction, the oxide should be sliced off the outside with a knife, and the scraps cut off should be returned to a scrap-sodium jar containing oil. Scrap sodium is suitable for drying alcohol or ether, if the oxide is scraped off.

This method of drying gives alcohol satisfactory for the present purpose, but alcohol so dried still contains traces of moisture.

2. When the reaction is carried beyond this point, it is advisable to continue until the final heating period is complete before allowing the reaction to stand overnight. The distilled alcohol may be allowed to stand without disadvantage if the system is closed except for the calcium chloride tube.

3. In case the sodium ethoxide is to be used in some other solvent such as DMSO or glyme, for reasons that have been discussed, alcohol is distilled at this point. This is conveniently accomplished by connecting to a side neck a condenser arranged for distillation, and heating the flask in an oil bath as the stirrer is operated to prevent bumping and the caking of the sodium ethoxide. The oil bath is finally heated to about 180° in order to remove essentially all the ethanol. The condenser is next replaced in an upright position, with calcium chloride tube in place, the heating bath is removed, and the flask is cooled to room temperature. Finally, the desired solvent is added, and the synthetic procedure is continued. Ordinarily, there is no advantage in removing last traces of ethanol at reduced pressure.

4. Placing a dropping funnel in the top of a condenser creates a rather unstable assembly with a high center of gravity. If the apparatus is assembled and handled with care, this is tolerable in the present case because the reagent in the dropping funnel is not corrosive. The unstable assembly may be avoided by use of a four-necked flask, or by placing in one neck an adapter which allows attachment of two dropping funnels.

5. Diethyl malonate, b.p. 199°, may be distilled at atmospheric pressure if heating is in an oil bath. Distillation at reduced pressure, b.p. 92° (15 mm), avoids high bath temperatures and may be more convenient.

6. This cyclic ester is pure enough for hydrolysis and decarboxylation to cyclobutanecarboxylic acid, but it contains small amounts of diethyl malonate, and sometimes trimethylene dibromide is present.

If desired, pure diethyl cyclobutanedicarboxylate may be obtained by distilling the products of the reaction through an efficient fractionating column. The following data were obtained by distillation through a two-foot Podbielniak column of the type described in Chap. 32:

Material	B.P. and Pressure	Weight
Forerun	56–116° (20 mm)	10.6 g
Cyclic ester	116–117° (20 mm)	60.8 g
Intermediate	117–186.5° (20–1.5 mm)	7.2 g
Tetra-ester	186.5–188° (1.5 mm)	13.4 g
Residue		5.2 g

If distillation is carried out in the Vigreux column, with total-reflux head, distillation of the high-boiling tetra-ester should not be attempted. The residue after removal of the first three fractions should be distilled from a Claisen flask.

The separation of diethyl malonate and diethyl cyclobutanedicarboxylate in the two-foot Podbielniak column is illustrated by the following data obtained by distillation of the products of Run 2, Table I:

Material	B.P. and Pressure	Weight
Diethyl malonate	91–92° (15 mm)	52.6 g
Intermediate	92–109° (15 mm)	2.7 g
Diethyl cyclobutanedicarboxylate	109–110° (15 mm)	12.1 g
Intermediate	110–182° (15–1.5 mm)	2.4 g
Tetra-ester	182–189° (1.5–2 mm)	46.8 g

Cyclobutanecarboxylic Acid

The total yield of cyclic ester is hydrolyzed by use of 3 ml of concentrated hydrochloric acid and 1.5 ml of water for each gram of ester. The mixture is heated in a three-necked flask of appropriate size under reflux, with stirring, in an oil bath. Heating is continued for at least 1 hour after the mixture becomes homogeneous. The total time is usually 3–5 hours. When hydrolysis is complete, the reflux condenser is replaced with a short distilling head attached to a condenser set for distillation. Distillation is carried out with stirring, and finally the bath is raised to a temperature (160–180°) at which the residual dicarboxylic acid is decarboxylated. When gas evolution has ceased (usually about 1 hour), the residue is cooled somewhat and poured into a 125-ml distilling flask. The product is distilled at atmospheric pressure, and received in a 125-ml Claisen flask. A small flame may be used for heating. The distillate is redistilled *in vacuo,* and the product is collected at 104–106° (21 mm). The yield is 65–75%, based on crude di-ester. The colorless product, which may become slightly discolored on standing, has an odor resembling that of butyric acid, but much less repugnant than that of valeric acid.

Half Esters of Dibasic Acids

37

The half esters of dibasic acids are important intermediates in a variety of organic syntheses, for it is often possible to carry out a reaction with one of the two functional groups and leave the other for subsequent manipulation. Since normal dibasic acids having ten or less carbon atoms are commercially available, and higher ones may be synthesized in several ways, half esters of the general formula, $HO_2C—(CH_2)_n—CO_2R$, are most widely used. Many substituted dibasic acids may be synthesized, and their half esters are also useful; however, unsymmetrical dibasic acids [such as $HO_2C—(CH_2)_2—CHR—(CH_2)_3—CO_2H$] present a problem, in that there are two isomeric half esters which are usually separable with great difficulty. Methyl or ethyl esters are nearly always used, since they are cheapest and most stable, but *sec*-butyl esters are sometimes used in order to develop steric hindrance at the ester site.

Among the many uses of the half esters may be mentioned Kolbe electrolysis to yield a higher di-ester,[1] and reaction of the silver salt with bromine to yield an ω-bromo ester.[2] Many of the more useful syntheses involve initial formation of the ester acid chloride by use of conventional reagents for forming acid chlorides, so an example of this conversion is described in the present chapter. The ester acid chloride may be used for acylation of a malonic ester or β-keto ester, for reaction with a cadmium reagent (cf.

[1] For synthesis of dimethyl octadecanedioate in 68–74% yields, refer to S. Swann, Jr., and W. E. Garrison, Jr., *Org. Syntheses*, **41**, 33 (1961).
[2] For synthesis of methyl 5-bromopentanoate in 52–54% yields, see C. F. H. Allen and C. V. Wilson, *Org. Syntheses*, **Coll. Vol. III**, 578 (1955).

Chap. 38), for synthesis of keto di-acids,[3] for acylation by the Friedel and Crafts reaction, and for other syntheses.

There are **three principal methods** for preparing half esters, two of which are illustrated in the present chapter. Proper choice of method will lead to rather good yields for compounds of various molecular weights, or with different numbers of carbon atoms between the carboxyl groups. For *succinic and glutaric acids*, which readily yield cyclic anhydrides, the preferred synthesis of half esters is reaction of the anhydride with an alcohol, according to Eq. 1.

$$
\begin{array}{c}
\overset{\displaystyle O}{\underset{\displaystyle C}{\diagup}} \\
(CH_2)_n \diagdown O + R\!-\!OH \rightarrow (CH_2)_n \\
\underset{\displaystyle C}{\diagdown} \\
O
\end{array}
\qquad
\begin{array}{c}
CO_2H \\
| \\
(CH_2)_n \\
| \\
CO_2R
\end{array}
\qquad (37\text{-}1)
$$

$n = 2 \text{ or } 3$

For preparation of *half esters of acids containing six to ten carbon* atoms (and more than three carbon atoms between the carboxyl groups), partial esterification is usually the most effective method. As shown in Eq. 2, the

$$
\begin{array}{c}
CO_2H \\
| \\
(CH_2)_n + R\!-\!OH \underset{\text{H}^+}{\overset{\text{H}^+}{\rightleftharpoons}} (CH_2)_n + H_2O \underset{\text{H}^+}{\overset{\text{ROH}}{\rightleftharpoons}} (CH_2)_n + H_2O \\
| \\
CO_2H
\end{array}
\qquad (37\text{-}2)
$$

with CO_2H, CO_2R, CO_2R, CO_2R columns and $n > 3$

half ester is also converted to di-ester; however this side reaction may be managed so that the yield is satisfactory, as discussed for the preparation of ethyl hydrogen adipate. Since the di-acid, half ester, and di-ester are best separated by fractional distillation, this method becomes progressively more awkward as the molecular weight goes beyond that of a half ester with eleven or twelve carbons.

For half esters of *di-acids with more than ten carbons*, the most convenient method is usually that involving controlled saponification of the di-ester. An effective method for control of the saponification is use of a metallic hydroxide and solvent combination that will cause precipitation of a salt of the half ester. Such a procedure is outlined in Eq. 3. Since barium hy-

$$
\begin{array}{c}
CO_2CH_3 \\
| \\
(CH_2)_n + Ba(OH)_2 \xrightarrow[\text{solvent}]{CH_3OH} (CH_2)_n \xrightarrow{\text{H}^+} (CH_2)_n \\
| \\
CO_2CH_3
\end{array}
\qquad (37\text{-}3)
$$

$n > 7$ (precipitate)

with columns $CO_2Ba_{\frac{1}{2}}$, CO_2CH_3 and CO_2H, CO_2CH_3

---

[3]This synthesis of a difficultly accessible type of compound involves conversion of the acid chloride to a ketene with base. The ketene dimerizes and may be hydrolyzed to a β-keto acid which readily decarboxylates to yield a ketone. For synthesis of 6-ketohendecanedioic acid, reference may be made to L. J. Durham, D. J. McLeod, and J. Cason, *Org. Syntheses*, **Coll. Vol. IV**, 555 (1963).

droxide is quite insoluble in higher alcohols, the methyl ester is always used in this procedure. If the ester of another alcohol is used, some base-catalyzed trans-esterification to the methyl ester will occur. This method fails with acids containing less than ten carbons, for the barium salt of the half ester becomes too soluble in methanol. For methyl hydrogen sebacate and higher half esters, the barium salt of the half ester is so insoluble in methanol that very little saponification to di-acid occurs. Typical of this procedure is synthesis of methyl hydrogen hendecanedioate[4] in 60–64% yields.

In synthesis of ethyl hydrogen malonate[5] in 75–82% yields, formation of the potassium salt of the half ester in ethanol solvent proved effective.

Methyl hydrogen succinate is prepared in excellent yield by the reaction shown in Eq. 1 ($R = CH_3$, $n = 2$). The yield in this preparation is slightly below quantitative, for the methyl hydrogen succinate is a sufficiently strong acid to catalyze its esterification with methanol at an appreciable rate. Under the most favorable conditions, all the anhydride may be converted according to Eq. 1, while only about 5% dimethyl succinate is formed by esterification of the half ester. These favorable results are obtained only when the conditions and time of heating are carefully defined. The di-ester may be efficiently removed in at least three ways (cf. "Experimental Procedures"), but if the half ester is to be converted to ester acid chloride, removal of di-ester is often omitted, for the ester group is inert towards many of the reagents that react with acid chlorides. If, however, a pure sample of ester acid chloride is desired, removal of di-ester from the half ester is imperative, for the ester acid chloride and di-ester have essentially identical boiling points.

Samples of half esters of dibasic acids should not be stored for long periods (months, that is), for disproportionation according to Eq. 4 occurs

$$2CH_3O_2C\text{—}(CH_2)_n\text{—}CO_2H \rightleftarrows CH_3O_2C\text{—}(CH_2)_n\text{—}CO_2CH_3 + HO_2C\text{—}(CH_2)_n\text{—}CO_2H$$

$$(37\text{-}4)$$

slowly. Naturally, liquid half esters disproportionate much more rapidly than solid ones. Old samples of half ester that have disproportionated in this manner may be readily purified by fractional distillation, for the components differ in boiling point by 35° or more. Disproportionation during distillation is not sufficiently rapid to seriously affect the purity of the half ester so obtained, unless it contains more than about twelve carbon atoms.

β-Methoxycarbonylpropionyl chloride, the acid chloride of methyl hydrogen succinate, may be prepared in high yield by treatment of the half ester with thionyl chloride (Eq. 5). If one assumes exclusion of moist air

[4]L. J. Durham, D. J. McLeod, and J. Cason, *Org. Syntheses*, **Coll. Vol. IV,** 635 (1963).

[5]R. E. Strube, *Org. Syntheses*, **Coll. Vol. IV,** 417 (1963).

$$\begin{array}{c} CH_2-CO_2H \\ | \\ CH_2-CO_2CH_3 \end{array} + SOCl_2 \rightarrow \begin{array}{c} CH_2-COCl \\ | \\ CH_2-CO_2CH_3 \end{array} + SO_2 + HCl \qquad (37\text{-}5)$$

from the reaction mixture, the principal *side reaction* in this preparation (cf. Chap. 11) is formation of dimeric anhydride, by the equilibrium reaction shown in Eq. 6. If two equivalents of thionyl chloride are used, this side

$$\begin{array}{c} CH_2-CO_2H \\ | \\ CH_2-CO_2CH_3 \end{array} + \begin{array}{c} CH_2-COCl \\ | \\ CH_2-CO_2CH_3 \end{array} \rightleftharpoons \begin{array}{c} CH_3O_2C-(CH_2)_2-C \overset{O}{\underset{\diagdown}{\diagup}} O \\ \\ CH_3O_2C-(CH_2)_2-C \underset{O}{\overset{\diagup}{\diagdown}} \end{array} + HCl \quad (37\text{-}6)$$

reaction is repressed almost entirely. Excess thionyl chloride displaces the equilibrium shown in Eq. 6 to the left, not only by removing carboxylic acid as in Eq. 5, but also by thus keeping up a good supply of hydrogen chloride.

Since β-methoxycarbonylpropionyl chloride is purified by distillation at reduced pressure, care must be exercised that heating is not excessive. Loss of carbon monoxide or hydrogen chloride may occur at temperatures above 170° (cf. Chap. 11); however, derivatives of succinic or glutaric acid form a cyclic anhydride (Eq. 7) with relative ease. Some substituted ester acid chlo-

$$\begin{array}{c} CH_2-COCl \\ | \\ CH_2-CO_2CH_3 \end{array} \xrightarrow{\text{heat}} \begin{array}{c} CH_2-C \overset{O}{\underset{\diagdown}{\diagup}} O \\ | \\ CH_2-C \underset{O}{\overset{\diagup}{\diagdown}} \end{array} + CH_3Cl \qquad (37\text{-}7)$$

rides of this type lose alkyl chloride so readily that distillation is not possible; however, the unsubstituted derivative may be safely distilled at bath temperatures below about 130°, unless nonvolatile mineral acid is present in the mixture. If the acid chloride is prepared with phosphorus pentachloride, which is very likely to contain traces of phosphoric acid, distillation must be at rather low pressure. The boiling point at 2.5 mm pressure is 58–59°.

Ethyl hydrogen adipate may be prepared by the procedure shown in Eq. 2 (R = C_2H_5, n = 4). The only significant *side reaction* in this preparation is the formation of di-ester, according to the second equilibrium shown in Eq. 2. In irreversible reactions, the product formed by reaction with one of two identical functional groups can rarely be isolated in yields as large as 35% (cf. chloronitrile synthesis in Chap. 35). In reversible reactions such as in Eq. 2, however, the process becomes much more amenable for two reasons. In the first place, any recovered starting material or di-ester may be re-used in subsequent preparations to yield more half ester. Furthermore, use of a properly selected amount of di-ester in the initial reaction mixture makes possible the conversion of di-acid to half ester in yields of 60% or more, as the amount of di-ester recovered remains about equal to that initially used. For good yields in this conversion, it is necessary to follow directions in which there are carefully specified both conditions and ratios of reactants, solvent, and acid catalyst. It has been found, however, that such directions as specified for ethyl hydrogen adipate may be successfully applied to other half esters containing no more than about eleven carbon atoms.

EXPERIMENTAL PROCEDURES

Methyl Hydrogen Succinate

In a 125-ml round-bottomed flask are placed 60 g of succinic anhydride and 30 ml of methanol, and the mixture is heated under reflux on a steam bath or boiling-water bath. After it has been heated for about 35 minutes, the mixture is swirled frequently until it becomes homogeneous (usually about 20 minutes); then the part of the flask containing the mixture is immersed completely in the steam or boiling-water bath (reflux stops at about this point). Heating is continued for an additional 30 minutes (total heating time about 85 minutes). Without further heating, a boiling chip is added to the mixture, the flask is immediately attached to a side-arm test tube or small distilling flask by means of a gooseneck, and the system is evacuated cautiously with a water pump. Finally, the pressure is taken down as low as possible with the water pump. Heating for about 10 minutes in vacuo results in the removal of most of the excess methanol.

The hot mixture is poured into a clean mortar of such a size that it will be no more than half full, and the mortar is placed in a shallow pan of water. As the mixture solidifies, it is broken away from the mortar with a metal spatula and stirred so that a massive cake does not form. Lack of careful attention at this point gives an unworkable cake. When all the material has crystallized and become hard, it is ground well with a pestle and dried overnight in a vacuum desiccator over sulfuric acid. The yield of crude half ester is quantitative (Note 1).

NOTE

1. This crude half ester contains about 5% di-ester (more, if the heating period is prolonged beyond that specified), which may be removed by drying to constant weight in a vacuum desiccator over sulfuric acid, at 10–15 mm pressure. This process usually requires about a week. The half ester may be obtained in a pure

condition, with more effort but less delay, either by fractional distillation through a half-meter column with partial reflux head or by crystallization from a mixture of ether (110 ml) and carbon disulfide (225 ml). *CAUTION! (Carbon disulfide is extremely flammable, may ignite on a steam bath.)* If distillation is used, a total reflux head must be avoided; the crystalline half ester will plug the reflux condenser.

β-Methoxycarbonylpropionyl Chloride

A 250-ml Claisen flask is equipped for vacuum distillation, with a stopper on the side arm for attachment to a 125-ml receiving flask. The stopper containing the capillary is removed and there is added to the flask (*HOOD!*) the total crude yield of methyl hydrogen succinate (0.6 mole) and 87 ml (1.2 mole) of a good grade of technical thionyl chloride (Note 1). The neck is closed with a solid rubber stopper, and a calcium chloride tube is attached to the side arm. The mixture is swirled until it becomes homogeneous and allowed to stand overnight or longer in the hood; there is a smooth evolution of hydrogen chloride and sulfur dioxide.

The calcium chloride tube is replaced by the receiving flask, which is water-cooled, and the Claisen flask is heated in an oil bath sufficiently to distill excess thionyl chloride. When the bath has been raised to about 120° (*NO HIGHER!*) and distillation has become very slow, the bath is lowered, the flame is extinguished, and 100 ml of thiophene-free benzene is added to the flask (Note 2). The stopper bearing the capillary is attached, and distillation is resumed at atmospheric pressure until most of the benzene has been distilled and the bath has been raised to about 120° again. Vacuum is then applied with a water pump, and the last traces of solvent are removed in vacuo. After receivers have been changed, the product is distilled, with use of a water pump (Note 3) if a pressure as low as 30 mm can be so obtained. Water is not turned on the receiver until the boiling point reaches that of the product. This procedure avoids condensation of traces of solvent that may come over first. The product boils at 92–93° (18 mm) or 94–95° (21 mm), and the yield is 81–84 g (90–93 %). It contains about 5% dimethyl succinate if crude half ester was used as starting material. Store in a bottle with a well-fitting glass stopper. The stopper usually becomes sealed with half ester formed from reaction of atmospheric moisture with the acid chloride, and it is necessary to warm carefully in order to melt the half ester before removing the stopper. This seal of half ester protects the acid chloride from further entrance of moisture, and samples may be stored for years without deterioration.

NOTES

1. For this preparation, a good grade (not dark yellow or red) of technical thionyl chloride may be used. For preparation of aromatic acid chlorides, and for

most research work, it is desirable to purify thionyl chloride. A major objective of this purification is removal of sulfuryl chloride, which is a chlorinating agent. This purification may be accomplished by fractional distillation; however, a highly efficient column is necessary, such as a three-foot column packed with glass helices, and provision must be made either to work in a hood or to absorb the sulfur dioxide which is liberated. About one-third of the distillate must be rejected as forerun, and the pure product collected over a 0.1° range. Usually, it is more convenient to use the chemical purification described in the next procedure.[6] The distillation may

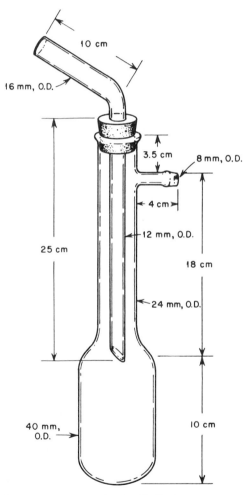

FIG. 1. Low temperature receiver for distillation at reduced pressure.

[6]The authors are indebted to Dr. W. Rigby, The University, Leeds, England, for this procedure, which appears to be the most convenient, effective method available for purification of thionyl chloride. Since our original correspondence with Dr. Rigby, the procedure has been published: *Chemistry and Industry*, 1508 (1969).

be more convenient for rather large amounts if the fractionating equipment is available.

2. Benzene is added to the flask and distilled in order to remove the last of the thionyl chloride before a vacuum is applied. *CAUTION!* If a vacuum is applied to remove the last traces of thionyl chloride, without distillation with benzene, any thionyl chloride that fails to condense in the receiver will pass out through the water pump, and in its course will *completely ruin all rubber tubing that it touches*. If a receiver of design such as shown in Fig. 1 is used, and is cooled in a Dry Ice-acetone bath contained in a Dewar flask, the last traces of thionyl chloride may be conveniently removed at reduced pressure. Of course the receiver is changed before the product is collected.

3. When an oil pump is used for distilling an acid chloride, it is imperative that the pump be protected by an adequate tower of flake sodium hydroxide. Some hydrogen chloride is always evolved, especially at the beginning of the distillation.

Purification of Thionyl Chloride[6]

The 250-ml flask (Note 1) with ground joint and side tubes (cf. Appendix I) is *set up in a fume hood* and arranged for distillation by attachment of the ground-jointed distilling head. A thermometer is not needed in the distilling head, so the thermometer outlet may be plugged with a short glass rod. The condenser should be attached to an adapter with a cork, and the adapter should extend into a 125-ml Erlenmeyer flask (Note 2). A thermometer is inserted in one side tube (Note 1) and positioned with the tip almost touching the bottom of the flask. The other side tube is plugged with a short glass rod. For heating with a burner, the flask is supported on a wire gauze which has placed on top of it a piece of asbestos paper with a 1-inch hole in its center. The object of the asbestos is to allow rapid input of heat to the contents of the flask, while preventing heat from the burner rising along the sides of the flask. If the walls of the flask are overheated, this causes decomposition that leads to a yellow product.

In the round-bottomed flask are placed 125 ml of technical thionyl chloride (handled entirely in the hood), and 6 ml of technical dipentene (sometimes called limonene). The materials are mixed, the flask is attached to the distillation head, and the thionyl chloride is distilled rapidly (Note 3). For this size run, no more than 10 minutes should be required for the distillation. The distillation is *stopped promptly* when the thermometer in the liquid reaches 84–86°. At this point the temperature begins to rise rapidly, and by 90° decomposition sets in, with gas evolution and distillation of yellow material.

The colorless product is obtained in about 80% yield, and is adequately pure for essentially all purposes. Any not used for the current preparation of an acid chloride should be placed in the glass-stoppered bottle, *stored in the hood* and marked "Thionyl Chloride, purified by Rigby method." This product contains traces of terpene derivatives which do not interfere with preparation of acid chlorides. On standing, the material may acquire a pale violet color, later fading to buff, but this also causes no problem in acid chloride preparation. If very pure material should be required, it may be obtained easily by allowing the above-described product to stand for one or two days, then distilling through a short column or simple distillation head. On account of traces of moisture on all glassware used, thionyl chloride always contains quantities of SO_2 and HCl, so boiling point is not meaningful until after degassing. The true b.p. is 76.7° (760 mm).

NOTES

1. Although thionyl chloride ruins all rubber that it touches, rubber connections are quite satisfactory for attaching tubes to this flask and distilling head by slip joints. The rubber will be ruined for future use, however, so sections of rubber tubing should be used, rather than the more expensive connectors described in Fig. 5-6.

2. Thionyl chloride reacts with moisture in air, but the products (SO_2, HCl) are gases which do not damage the reagent. Thus, the material is normally handled so as to minimize exposure to air, but a system which is closed except for a protective drying tube is used only when convenient or when the exposure is lengthy.

3. Larger amounts may be purified similarly, and a 500-ml batch may be distilled in about 20 minutes. Still larger batches, requiring longer distillation times, may be slightly discolored.

Ethyl Hydrogen Adipate

This preparation is carried out in a 250-ml round-bottomed flask equipped with a side tube for a capillary for vacuum distillation, and a 19/38 standard taper joint for later attachment to the fractionating column. In the flask are placed 42.5 g of adipic acid, 24 g of diethyl adipate (Note 1), 15 ml of di-*n*-butyl ether (Note 2), 7.5 ml of concentrated hydrochloric acid, and 25 ml (about 0.42 mole) of 95% ethanol. The side inlet is closed with a glass rod inserted through the rubber slip joint, a reflux condenser is attached to the joint, and the mixture is heated under reflux in an oil bath. The hot mixture is swirled frequently until it becomes homogeneous, then heated under reflux for two hours.

At the end of the heating period the flask is cooled somewhat, a *good* capillary is inserted in the side tube, and the flask is attached to a half-meter Vigreux column for distillation. Heating is with an electrically heated oil bath, and the pressure is reduced slowly with a *water pump*. Water, ethanol, hydrogen chloride, and di-*n*-butyl ether are removed at a pressure of about

100 mm. It is advisable to heat the column jacket to 70–80°. Lower pressure at the beginning promotes extensive bumping and frothing; however, there should be used a sufficiently high bath temperature to promote removal of the low-boiling material as rapidly as consistent with control of frothing (20–30 minutes usually). Excessive slowness at this point allows reversal of the equilibrium as the alcohol is removed.

When most of this low-boiling material has been distilled, it is removed from the system (Note 3), the pressure is gradually reduced to the minimum obtainable with the water pump (should be less than 40 mm), and the bath temperature is increased to the point where diethyl adipate is refluxing into the column. At this point the bath is temporarily turned off and allowed to cool somewhat, and a new receiver is attached. When the bath has cooled sufficiently to avoid violent boiling of the contents of the flask, the pressure is reduced with the oil pump to the range of 5–7 mm, and the mixture is fractionally distilled. *Before this distillation is attempted*, Chap. 32 should be studied with great care. The instructor or teaching assistant should be present when the distillation is started and it is advisable to make an appointment with him in advance. The following pattern of fractions should be collected (Note 4), although the specific boiling points observed may be somewhat different. Accurate determination of boiling points at reduced pressure is difficult.

1. Forerun, boiling point up to 118° (6 mm); very small fraction.
2. Diethyl adipate, b.p. 118–121° (6 mm); wt 20–25 g.
3. Intermediate fraction, wt 5–8 g.
4. Ethyl hydrogen adipate, b.p. 155–157° (6 mm); wt 28.5–34 g (55–65% based on adipic acid used).

As soon as the distillation is completed (*Caution*, Note 4), the flask should be detached from the column; the residue of adipic acid should be poured, while molten, into the Erlenmeyer flask marked "Residual Adipic Acid"; and the weight of recovered acid should be determined by difference.

Although boiling points at reduced pressure are not reproducible with great accuracy, your pattern should be similar to that indicated, and fractions 2 and 4 should be collected over approximately the ranges indicated. Fraction 4 may tend to solidify in the condenser, so the water should be turned off before this fraction is distilled. If trouble with solidification is encountered the solid may be safely melted by use of an infrared lamp, or steam may be passed through the condenser. Of course a total reflux column is not useful for distillation of solids; however, such a column is satisfactory for the present distillation. The half ester is sufficiently low-melting that there is a tendency towards crystalization only when rather pure half ester is distilling. At this point, there is no disadvantage to turning off the condenser water.

Turn in fractions 2 and 4, and pour fractions 1 and 3 in the bottles supplied for them on the reagent shelf. Calculate the yield of half ester on the basis of adipic acid used, neglecting recovered adipic acid (the residue) and any differences between di-ester used and recovered. Also calculate the per cent of adipic acid recovered, as well as the per cent of diethyl adipate recovered.

NOTES

1. If a few grams more or less of diethyl adipate are used, this is entirely satisfactory, for the exact amount of di-ester recovered from various runs is somewhat variable. If diethyl adipate is not available, it may be prepared rather easily from adipic acid by the procedure outlined in the following paragraphs. This is a characteristic procedure for acid-catalyzed simple esterification in high yield.

In a 125-ml Erlenmeyer flask are placed, in the order specified, 25 g of adipic acid, 55 ml of commercial absolute ethyl alcohol, and 5.5 ml of concentrated sulfuric acid. A condenser protected by a calcium chloride drying tube is attached to the flask, then the flask is warmed and swirled until the adipic acid dissolves and the sulfuric acid is well mixed. After addition of a boiling chip, the reaction mixture is heated under reflux on a steam bath or electric hot plate for one hour. The cooled reaction mixture is poured into about 200 ml of water contained in a separatory funnel, and the Erlenmeyer flask is rinsed with a little water and benzene. The product is extracted with two portions of benzene (60 ml, 20 ml), and the two extracts are retained in separate separatory funnels. The extracts are washed in sequence with a 50-ml portion of water, two portions (50 ml, 25 ml) of 5% aqueous sodium carbonate solution, and 50 ml of water. Final separations are made carefully so that azeotropic drying during distillation of benzene is adequate. There may be a tendency towards formation of emulsions during the alkaline extractions. For the present use of the di-ester, it is obvious that this extraction of small amounts of adipic acid and half ester is unnecessary, and its omission is recommended.

Benzene is distilled from the extract at atmospheric pressure, using an Erlenmeyer flask, until distillation becomes slow. If isolation of the ester is desirable, the residue is transferred to a 125-ml Claisen flask for distillation at reduced pressure. For the present use, it is convenient to transfer to the 250-ml flask in which the half ester is to be made. After last traces of benzene have been distilled at reduced pressure, the other components of the reaction are added, and the reaction is carried out as described.

2. Di-*n*-butyl ether is used as solvent in order to obtain a homogeneous reaction mixture.

3. If left in the system as the pressure is reduced, the volatile material will rapidly vaporize into the oil pump. The two-phase low-boiling distillate is separated in a separatory funnel, the ether phase is washed once with water, and the washed ether is placed in the bottle labeled "Recovered Wet Di-*n*-butyl Ether."

4. The fractional distillation for separation of the ethyl hydrogen adipate re-

quires more skillful operation of the equipment than does the fractionation described in Chap. 35, for the components of the presently encountered mixture boil only about 35° apart. Also, removal of the low-boiling components may present problems. Thus, it is highly advisable that an instructor be present when the distillation is undertaken.

Provided there is not being distilled a basic substance or mixture, such as an amine, it is not necessary to disconnect the distillation flask if the fractionation is interrupted; however, it is *very important* to lower the heating bath so that the flask and thermometer are out of the wax when it solidifies. The ground joint attaching the flask may become "stuck" but will ordinarily loosen again during the subsequent heating as the distillation is completed. When a distillation is completed, however, there should be *no delay* in lowering the bath, letting air into the system after a brief wait for vapor condensation, and detaching the distillation flask while it is still hot. As soon as the flask has been emptied, solvent should be added, the flask reconnected, and the solvent distilled to clean out the column, condenser, and receiver. If a flask is left attached it will nearly always be necessary to heat the joint before it can be disengaged, and sometimes the joint becomes permanently "frozen" because of tarry material in the distillation residue or too long standing in the tightly sealed condition resulting from heating under the pressure of the atmosphere. If a *joint becomes stuck*, do not risk breaking the column in attempting to loosen it; *consult the teaching assistant or instructor.*

The Grignard and Related Reactions

38

The Grignard reaction and several closely related reactions are probably more useful in synthesis than any other type of reaction except the reactions of enolate ions. The Grignard reaction is a rather expensive procedure, largely on account of the requirement of dry ether as solvent, so its principal application is to laboratory synthesis; however, certain expensive compounds are prepared industrially by a Grignard reaction.

Reactions closely related to the Grignard reactions are the Reformatsky reaction, the reactions utilizing organolithium reagents, and reactions utilizing organocadmium reagents. The present chapter includes procedures utilizing the Grignard reagent and the alkylcadmium reagent.

Grignard Reaction

The first step in any Grignard synthesis is the preparation of the Grignard reagent, according to the following simple equation:

$$RX + Mg \xrightarrow{\text{dry ether}} RMgX \qquad (38\text{-}1)$$

The Grignard reagent in solution is not the simple species indicated in Eq. 1, but rather a mixture of numerous species of varying molecular complexity. There are in solution the species, R_2Mg and MgX_2, in equilibrium under ordinary conditions with $2RMgX$. All of these species are complexed with the ether solvent, as well as with each other. It is probable, indeed, that little, if any, monomeric Grignard reagent is present in diethyl ether solvent. Principal species may be dimers, trimers, and so on, such as $R_2Mg \cdot MgX_2$. For simplicity in writing reactions, RMgX is commonly used, especially since the exact nature of the solution of a Grignard reagent is difficult to ascertain.

In practice, a Grignard reaction is carried out by treating an ether solution of the Grignard reagent with the component with which reaction is desired. Usually the reagent is prepared and used immediately in the flask in which it was prepared. It is stable to storage, however, in the absence of moisture and air, and ether solutions of some Grignard reagents are sometimes stored for use as needed. Solutions of some Grignard reagents are available commercially. The concentration of Grignard reagent may be determined by the careful addition of a measured aliquot of the solution to water, and titration with standard acid of the liberated base. The equation is:

$$2RMgX + 2H_2O \rightarrow 2RH + Mg(OH)_2 + MgX_2 \qquad (38\text{-}2)$$

The hydrocarbon is usually soluble in the ether phase, and titration of the two-phase solution offers no difficulties. It is seen that one mole of Grignard reagent liberates one *equivalent* of base. This determination is strictly accurate only if water and air have been excluded during the preparation and storage of the reagent.

In some reactions, it is useful to know when all Grignard reagent has been consumed, and in such instances the Gilman qualitative test[1] for Grignard reagent is useful. This is described in connection with the preparation of methyl 4-oxododecanoate, in this chapter.

The ether solvent is an integral part of the Grignard reagent, and one or two moles of ether are probably combined with the reagent by coordination of the ether with magnesium. It has been possible to prepare Grignard reagents in the absence of ether, but such preparations are of no synthetic significance, for satisfactory yields are obtained only when all or part of the solvent is an ether. It is sometimes necessary to add some benzene to keep the reagent in solution (cf. 1-naphthoic acid preparation). Diethyl ether is nearly always used because of its low cost and ease of removal from the reaction products, but when the product of the reaction is low boiling, di-*n*-butyl ether has been used to advantage.[2] In addition, it has been found possible to prepare several types of Grignard reagents in tetrahydrofuran, although it had not been possible to prepare those reagents in diethyl ether (cf. below).

Alkyl iodides, bromides, or chlorides, as well as aryl iodides or bromides, may be converted to Grignard reagents in diethyl ether. Aryl chlorides will not directly form Grignard reagents in diethyl ether solvent;

[1]H. Gilman and L. L. Heck, *J. Amer. Chem. Soc.*, **52**, 4949 (1930).

[2]C. R. Noller, *Org. Syntheses*, **Coll. Vol. II**, 478 (1943); J. Cason and R. L. Way, *J. Org. Chem.*, **14**, 31 (1949).

however, the arylmagnesium chlorides may be readily formed in tetra-hydrofuran as solvent.[3] It has also been found[4] that the monoacetylenic Grignard reagent may be formed in tetrahydrofuran, by reaction of acetylene with an alkylmagnesium halide. In diethyl ether, only the diacety-lenic Grignard reagent has been obtainable. Although the use of tetrahydrofuran has become of great utility for forming such Grignard reagents as just mentioned, it should also be pointed out that aryl chlorides will readily form lithium reagents by reaction with lithium metal in either diethyl ether or a hydrocarbon solvent such as hexane.[5] The lithium reagents usually give reactions very similar to those of Grignard reagents; however, in some instances the lithium reagents offer special advantages.

There is sometimes difficulty in "starting" formation of a Grignard re-agent, that is, initiating the reaction between magnesium and the halide. The difficulty in initiating the reaction increases in passing from the iodide to the bromide to the chloride, and the aryl halides are considerably more recalcitrant than the alkyl halides. The aryl bromide is about equal to the alkyl chloride in this regard. The most important factor in starting a Grignard reaction is complete dryness; the importance of dryness can hardly be overemphasized. Other devices used to start the reaction are mentioned in connection with the preparations. Once the reaction has started, it usually proceeds without difficulty, although alkyl chlorides usually react slowly. It should be mentioned that if any mercury is spilled from the mercury seal into a Grignard reaction, the magnesium is sur-face-amalgamated, and the reaction with the halide stops completely and permanently. The only cure is the removal of the amalgamated magnesium and any excess mercury, followed by the addition of a fresh equivalent of magnesium.

The *side reactions* commonly encountered in the preparation of a Grignard reagent are those outlined in Eqs. 3–6. Reaction 3 is avoided by the exclusion of moisture, including that in the air. Reactions 4 and 5 may be avoided by carrying out the reaction in an inert atmosphere such as nitrogen; however, ether vapor is reasonably effective in excluding air from the reaction flask if the reagent is not allowed to stand for a long period before use. In research work, the Grignard reaction is often carried out

[3]H. E. Ramsden, A. E. Balint, W. R. Whitford, J. J. Walburn, and R. Cserr, *J. Org. Chem.*, **22**, 1202 (1957).

[4] L. Skattebøl, E. R. H. Jones, and M. C. Whiting, *Org. Syntheses,* **39**, 56 (1959).

[5]It is sometimes an advantage to form the organolithium derivative indirectly by allow-ing a compound with an acidic hydrogen to undergo interchange with phenyllithium. For example, α- and γ-picolyllithium reagents, prepared in this manner from the corresponding picolines, may be used to synthesize a variety of pyridine derivatives. Typical procedures are described in the following publications: J. W. Hey and J. P. Wibaut, *Rec. trav. chim.*, **72**, 522 (1953); R. B. Woodward and E. C. Kornfield, *Org. Syntheses,* **Coll. Vol. III,** 413 (1955).

$$RMgX + H_2O \rightarrow RH + MgOHX \qquad (38\text{-}3)$$

$$2RMgX + O_2 \rightarrow 2ROMgX \qquad (38\text{-}4)$$

$$RMgX + CO_2 \rightarrow RCO_2MgX \qquad (38\text{-}5)$$

$$2RX + Mg \rightarrow R{-}R + MgX_2 \qquad (38\text{-}6)$$

in an atmosphere of nitrogen. A simple setup for such work is shown in Fig. 1. The connection with the top of the dropping funnel is necessary in order to equalize the pressure in the funnel with that in the flask. This apparatus is also useful for carrying out reactions between a Grignard

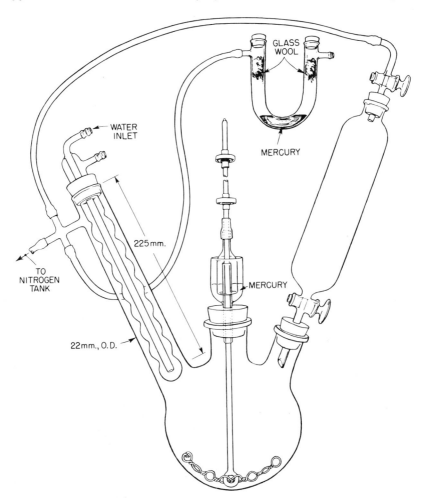

FIG. 1.   Apparatus for carrying out reactions in an inert atmosphere, with stirring under reflux.

reagent and a gas. The mercury valve permits a slight pressure of gas; if gas is being passed in faster than absorbed, this is evidenced by bubbling of the gas out the mercury valve. In case a reaction is to be carried out at low temperature, the cold-finger condenser may be removed and replaced by a thermometer extending into the liquid, without interference with maintenance of the atmosphere of nitrogen. In case the product of the reaction is a gas that is evolved, the outlet side of the mercury valve may be connected to a cold trap. It may be mentioned that this type of reaction flask is useful for numerous other reactions besides Grignard reactions. Various modifications of this flask prove convenient in certain situations. For example, the extended neck with cold-finger condenser may be replaced with an orthodox neck and some usual type of condenser, with a four-way tube atop the condenser. Another common modification is equalization of pressure in the dropping funnel by means of a small tube sealed to the funnel wall near the top and to the delivery tube below the stopcock. Of course the various connections may be made with ground joints to advantage.

Side reaction 6, above, is the coupling reaction or Wurtz reaction. It can never be avoided, but it is minimized by preventing local high concentrations of organic halide at the surface of the metal. This is accomplished by slow addition of the halide, with efficient stirring of the reaction mixture. A reasonable dilution of the reactants with ether helps, and in difficult cases (as when allyl bromide is used to form a Grignard reagent) a large excess of magnesium must be used. Ordinarily, 350–500 ml of ether per mole of reagent is used, and the time of addition should not be less than 1 hour. Iodides couple more readily than bromides; hence, they are not usually recommended for the preparation of a Grignard reagent. Certain metals and metallic salts promote coupling, presumably via radical information, and it has been found that an etched nichrome-wire stirrer promotes very serious coupling. A smooth nichrome-wire stirrer appears to be satisfactory, but the safest plan is to use a tantalum-wire, glass, or Teflon stirrer.

In the *preparation of 1-naphthoic acid* from 1-naphthylmagnesium bromide, the main reaction corresponds to Eq. 7.

$$+ \ CO_2 \rightarrow \qquad \xrightarrow{H^+} \qquad + \ ^+MgBr \qquad (38\text{-}7)$$

The principal *side reaction* encountered is further reaction to yield a ketone or tertiary alcohol (Eq. 8). Addition of water when the reaction is worked up yields the tertiary alcohol. This side reaction is minimized to a considerable extent by the insolubility of the bromomagnesium salt

$$RCO_2MgX + RMgX \rightarrow R-\overset{\underset{\|}{O}}{C}-R + MgX_2 + MgO$$

$$\downarrow RMgX$$

$$R_3COMgX \qquad (38\text{-}8)$$

of the acid. Use of the lithium derivative in this reaction leads largely to the indicated by-products, partly because of the solubility of the lithium salt of the acid. This side reaction is also minimized by the use of Dry Ice as a source of carbon dioxide, for it results in low temperature of reaction as well as in high concentration of carbon dioxide. It should be mentioned, however, that Dry Ice is not satisfactory for reaction with inert, relatively insoluble Grignard reagents, such as those of aliphatic bromides with 10 or more carbons. When *n*-tetradecylmagnesium bromide is treated with Dry Ice, the yield of pentadecanoic acid is only about 30%, even with a much larger excess of Dry Ice than indicated for the preparation of 1-naphthoic acid. With such Grignard reagents, the best procedure is to force the Grignard solution under nitrogen pressure into a pressure vessel, such as a bomb for high-pressure hydrogenation, charge the bomb with carbon dioxide from a high-pressure tank, and shake for several hours at room temperature. Good yields may be obtained in this way.

In the *preparation of 2-decanol*, the main reaction is that shown in Eq. 9.

$$C_8H_{17}-MgBr + CH_3-\overset{\underset{\|}{O}}{C}-H \rightarrow C_8H_{17}-\overset{\underset{|}{OMgBr}}{CH}-CH_3 \xrightarrow{H_2O} C_8H_{17}-\overset{\underset{|}{OH}}{CH}-CH_3$$

$$+ MgOHBr \quad (38\text{-}9)$$

The acetaldehyde must be freshly prepared by depolymerization of paraldehyde. Secondary alcohols may be obtained in good yields by this method when the reaction is properly carried out, but several *side reactions* must be considered (Eqs. 10–13). Reaction 10, reduction of the carbonyl

$$C_8H_{17}MgBr + CH_3CHO \rightarrow C_6H_{13}CH=CH_2 + CH_3CH_2OMgBr \quad (38\text{-}10)$$

$$R-\overset{\underset{|}{OMgBr}}{CH}-CH_3 + CH_3CHO \rightarrow R-\overset{\underset{\|}{O}}{C}-CH_3 + CH_3CH_2OMgBr \quad (38\text{-}11)$$

$$RMgBr + CH_3CHO \rightarrow RH + CH_2=CHOMgBr \quad (38\text{-}12)$$

$$CH_2=CHOMgBr + CH_3CHO \rightarrow CH_3-\overset{\underset{|}{OMgBr}}{CH}-CH_2-CHO \quad (38\text{-}13)$$

group, always occurs to some extent unless the Grignard reagent is from an aryl halide or has no hydrogens on the carbon adjacent to the carbon bearing magnesium. The beta hydrogens are involved in the reduction. Aryl halides may have hydrogen on this adjacent carbon and still not give reduction, for the resultant hydrocarbon (refer to Eq. 10) would have a triple bond in the aromatic ring, and this would generate an intolerable strain in the six-atom ring.

Conversion of some carbonyl compound to the magnesium enolate (Eq. 12) also occurs to some extent unless there are no hydrogens on the carbon alpha to carbonyl. When water is added in work-up of the reaction, the carbonyl compound is regenerated from the enolate, but the corresponding amount of Grignard reagent is wasted as hydrocarbon.

Neither reduction nor enolization (Eqs. 10 and 12) are serious side reactions unless hindered molecules are involved in the reaction. It will be noted that in the desired reaction (Eq. 9) an alkyl group becomes attached to the carbonyl carbon, whereas reaction 10 involves attaching only a hydrogen to the carbonyl carbon, and reaction 12 involves only the oxygen. It follows that steric hindrance favors the side reactions. In instances where poor yields are obtained in the Grignard reaction, on account of steric hindrance, much better yields may sometimes be obtained by the use of the lithium reagent. Good yields of tertiary alcohols from a hindered ketone and a lithium reagent have been reported.[6]

Reaction 11, like reaction 10, results from the reducing action of a Grignard reagent. This reaction is slow in comparison with the main reaction and also involves a product of the main reaction. Thus, it may be avoided almost completely by adding the aldehyde to the Grignard reagent at low temperature, and avoiding excess aldehyde. Since the yield of Grignard reagent from bromide is about 90%, the optimum equivalency of bromide is slightly in excess of that of aldehyde. Reaction 13 is simply the aldol condensation of the aldehyde with the magnesium enolate. This reaction is minimized by adding the aldehyde to the Grignard reagent and operating at a sufficiently low temperature to make the rate of the aldol condensation very low.

It is common practice, when adding water to decompose the Grignard complex (Eq. 9), to add enough mineral acid to neutralize the resultant magnesium hydroxide; otherwise, the magnesium hydroxide promotes a frothy unworkable emulsion. In the presently described reaction, use of acid is satisfactory; however, some alcohols (e.g., tertiary alcohols or secondary benzyl alcohols) are readily dehydrated in presence of mineral acid. In case acid-sensitive alcohols are being prepared, the Grignard reaction mixture should be worked up by addition of a saturated solution of ammonium chloride. If just enough ammonium chloride solution is added to furnish only slightly more than the stoichiometric amount of water (Eq. 9), the mass of ammonium and magnesium salts precipitates

[6]G. Vavon and H. Colin, *Compt. Rend.*, **222**, 801 (1946).

in a form which is readily removed by filtration. This procedure is actually quite convenient for work-up of a Grignard reaction, even when there is no objection to mineral acid.

The above-discussed illustrations of the Grignard reaction involve many of the difficulties and side reactions encountered in running these reactions, but other types of side reactions are encountered in other Grignard preparations. Although the Grignard is the most widely useful of synthetic reactions, it is apparent that optimum results may be obtained only if the reaction is well understood by the operator.

Organocadmium Reagents

The cadmium reagents, which are usually prepared from the corresponding Grignard reagents, are very useful for the preparation of nearly all types of ketones, but are especially useful for the preparation of aliphatic keto esters. The special virtue of the cadmium reagents lies in the fact that they react vigorously with acid chlorides of all types, even highly hindered ones, but add sluggishly or not at all to multiple bonds. The organocadmium reaction is presently illustrated by the preparation of *methyl 4-oxodode-canoate* according to the scheme outlined in Eqs. 14 and 15. Since the

$$2C_8H_{17}MgBr + CdCl_2 \rightarrow (C_8H_{17})_2Cd + MgBr_2 + MgCl_2 \qquad (38\text{-}14)$$

$$(C_8H_{17})_2Cd + 2Cl\underset{\underset{O}{\|}}{-C}-(CH_2)_2-CO_2CH_3 \rightarrow$$

$$2C_8H_{17}\underset{\underset{O}{\|}}{-C}-(CH_2)_2-CO_2CH_3 + CdCl_2 \qquad (38\text{-}15)$$

entire sequence, including the preparation of the Grignard reagent, is carried out in one flask, without isolation of intermediates, this preparation is equivalent to a single step. All other useful methods for making aliphatic keto esters involve several steps and usually give less than one half the yield obtained by the use of the cadmium reagent. If the Grignard reagent is used in place of the cadmium reagent, the yield of keto ester is nearly zero, for the Grignard reagent reacts rapidly with both keto and ester groups. For this reason, it is important that the Grignard reagent be converted completely to cadmium reagent. Completion of this conversion is checked by use of the qualitative test for Grignard reagent. Since this test depends on reaction with the carbonyl group in Michler's ketone, the cadmium reagent does not give a positive test.

An organozinc reagent may be prepared from the Grignard reagent and zinc chloride, in a manner entirely analogous to the preparation of a cadmium reagent. In instances where a direct comparison of the two reagents is available, the cadmium reagent appears to give a better yield of ketone, probably because of the slower reaction of the cadmium reagent with carbonyl groups. Also, the extreme hygroscopicity of anhydrous zinc chloride is an inconvenience. There has been reported,[7] however, one significant advantage of the zinc reagent. This is the greater thermal stability of such reagents, which permits use in synthesis of *sec*-alkylzinc compounds. The cadmium reagent containing an aryl group or a primary alkyl group is moderately stable to heat (cf. below under side reactions), but the secondary and tertiary alkylcadmium reagents are unstable even at $0°$, hence are not useful in synthesis.

The side reactions encountered in the preparation of a Grignard reagent have been discussed previously, so there will be discussed here only those *side reactions* concerned with the *cadmium reaction* (Eqs. 16 and 17).

$$CH_3O_2C—(CH_2)_2—COCl + (C_2H_5)_2O \xrightarrow[\text{Mg salts}]{\text{anhydrous}}$$

$$CH_3O_2C—(CH_2)_2—CO_2C_2H_5 + C_2H_5Cl \quad (38\text{-}16)$$

$$\tfrac{1}{2}R_2Cd + R—\underset{\underset{OH}{|}}{C}{=}CH—CH_2—CO_2CH_3 \rightarrow$$

$$R—\underset{\underset{OCd_{\frac{1}{2}}}{|}}{C}{=}CH—CH_2—CO_2CH_3 + RH \quad (38\text{-}17)$$

There is an excellent opportunity for reaction 16, since a full molar equivalent of magnesium halide is present in the reaction mixture. This reaction is minimized by distilling ether from the reaction mixture and adding benzene before reaction with the acid chloride is carried out. In this way, di-ester formation is reduced to less than 5%. Reaction 17 is similar to the side reaction encountered in the Grignard reaction with acetaldehyde. Reaction with the enol is more serious in the cadmium reaction, especially if α-chloroketones are prepared from α-chloroacid chlorides. The formation of enolate appears less favored in benzene than in ether; therefore, benzene is an advantage for avoiding this side reaction, as well as reaction 16. An additional advantage of benzene is that a higher temperature may be obtained, and the reaction thus completed in shorter time. Frequently, in the final stage of the cadmium reaction, heavy sludges separate and tend to stop the stirrer. This difficulty is less pronounced in benzene, but a powerful stirring motor should always be used.

Although there are the above-cited advantages to the use of benzene as solvent in the cadmium reaction, caution must be exercised to avoid excessive thermal cracking (Eq. 18) of the cadmium reagent when this

$$(C_8H_{17})_2Cd \xrightarrow{\text{heat}} 2C_8H_{17}{\cdot} + Cd$$

$$\longrightarrow C_8H_{18} + C_6H_{13}—CH{=}CH_2 \quad (38\text{-}18)$$

[7] G. A. Schmidt and D. A. Shirley, *J. Amer. Chem. Soc.*, **71**, 3804 (1949).

higher-boiling solvent is used. The alkyl radicals initially formed by thermal dissociation rapidly disproportionate to an equimolar mixture of alkene and alkane, although some coupling to a higher alkane may occur. Since this is a cracking reaction, it is more rapid at a given temperature for a higher molecular weight alkyl group. For all alkyl groups, this reaction is rapid at 100°; hence, heating of the cadmium reagent on a steam bath after distillation of ether solvent must be avoided. For alkyl groups higher than butyl, the reaction is moderately rapid in boiling benzene, so excessive heating in that solvent should be avoided. For alkyl groups larger than decyl, a higher ratio of alkyl bromide should be used in the reaction to allow for losses according to Eq. 18. In any case in which an expensive acid chloride is used, excess of alkyl bromide may be used to advantage. In no instance is there any advantage to using more than 0.8 equivalent of acid chloride per equivalent of alkyl bromide. The maximum yield of cadmium reagent from alkyl bromide (via Grignard reagent) appears to be about 80%. Of course any loss by cracking further reduces the available cadmium reagent.

There is a finite rate of reaction of the cadmium reagent with a keto group, but this is usually a very minor side reaction. In case there is present a rather reactive ketone, especially a methyl ketone, it is not advisable to use an excess of cadmium reagent and prolong the reaction period. Addition to the keto group may occur.[8]

Although the ester acid chloride involved in the presently illustrated synthesis is a derivative of a symmetrical dibasic acid, it should be mentioned that the cadmium reagent gives rearranged products with the ester acid chloride of an unsymmetrical dibasic acid.[9]

EXPERIMENTAL PROCEDURES

Preparation of Absolute Ether (method of Hershberg and Newman)

Even a good grade of commercial ether contains considerable quantities of water and ethyl alcohol, along with traces of other substances. Both water and alcohol must be completely removed from ether before it is fit for use as a solvent in the Grignard reaction, or in certain other reactions, such as the Stephen reduction. Although anhydrous ether may

[8]C. H. Wang, R. Isensee, A. M. Griffith, and B. E. Christensen, *J. Amer. Chem. Soc.*, **69**, 1909 (1947).

[9]A leading reference in which there is discussed this novel rearrangement and its mechanism is J. Cason and R. D. Smith, *J. Org. Chem.*, **18**, 1201 (1953).

be bought, its quality is often poor and its price is always high; for these reasons, it is often prepared in the laboratory and stored over sodium. Various methods have been used for its preparation, but the following is recommended, not only because it is simple and rapid, but because it may be readily carried out on as large a scale as desired.

Procedure. In a one-liter round-bottomed flask is placed 500 ml of ordinary commercial ether (Note 1). A reflux condenser is attached to the flask, the flask is placed on a cork ring on the desk, and the condenser is supported in an upright position with a clamp. A 125-ml separatory funnel is supported in the top of the condenser with a channeled cork; then 25 ml of concentrated sulfuric acid is placed in the separatory funnel and allowed to drop into the ether during about 15 minutes. The ether refluxes during this operation, especially toward the end. After all the acid has been added and the ether has stopped refluxing, the condenser is arranged for distillation. As a precaution against entrainment during distillation, the tube connecting the flask to the condenser should have a bulb or a Kjeldahl trap incorporated into its upright portion. An adapter is attached to the lower end of the condenser, and a 500-ml Erlenmeyer flask is used as a receiver. The adapter should pass well into the receiver, and a piece of cotton should be stuffed around the adapter to cut down diffusion. In summer weather, the receiver should be immersed in an ice bath. After boiling chips have been added to the distilling flask, the ether is distilled from a water (or steam) bath, as care is taken that distillation is not so rapid that part of the ether passes the condenser as vapor. After about 400 ml of ether has been distilled, the distillation slows up markedly and should be stopped (Note 2). The distilled ether is treated with a small amount (3–4 g) of sodium wire (Note 3) and allowed to stand overnight in a flask which is closed with a *cork bearing a capillary*. After standing about 48 hours, all the water and alcohol have usually been converted to sodium hydroxide and sodium ethoxide. If there appears to be no sodium wire left, a second small portion is added; if any bubbling ensues, it is allowed to stand overnight (or until bubbling ceases) again. The ether is now filtered by gravity (Notes 1 and 4) into a dry bottle and stored over a little sodium wire. The bottle is best closed with a good cork covered with tin foil. A change of temperature sometimes causes a glass stopper to be blown out, and failure to discover this results in loss of the ether.

When anhydrous ether is being used, it should not be poured from one vessel to another any more than necessary, for *on exposure to air it evaporates rapidly, and much water condenses on the cooled surface.* The use of a siphon or a pipette is to be preferred (the pipette must be full or nearly so). In damp weather, pouring ether from one vessel to another may render the ether so damp that a Grignard reaction will not start in it.

NOTES

1. This quantity of ether constitutes a *very grave fire hazard!* All corks used in the distillation setup should be new, well-fitting, and carefully bored. If ground-jointed equipment is available for attaching the condenser to the distilling flask, it should be used. Very few substances are more highly flammable than ether; and ether vapors, being heavier than air, will sink to the desk top and roll along to your neighbor's burner. Precaution should be taken that vapors are not passing the condenser (detection through odor and visually by the different index of refraction); when ether is poured, no burner should be within 10 feet. (The hood is a safe place for this job.) When large quantities of ether are handled (and best with smaller quantities), steam or electric heating should always be used. Even an electric hot plate will occasionally ignite ether vapors. Ether should not be distilled from a flask placed on a hot plate, but from a water bath heated by the hot plate.

2. The residue should be poured carefully into the sink (keep the face back) and rinsed down with water. Under no condition should water be poured into the residue.

3. For precautions in handling sodium, refer to Note 1 to diethyl cyclobutanedicarboxylate preparation in Chap. 36. After a sodium press has been used, residual sodium should be removed from both die and punch with methyl or ethyl alcohol. These parts are then washed with water and dried. Under no circumstances should sodium be left in the press, for this practice is dangerous and also corrosive to the press.

4. The ether will become somewhat damp by exposure to air during the filtration process, so it should be allowed to stand overnight with sodium before it is used in the Grignard reaction. Part of the ether may be used without this final filtration into a bottle for storage, but if this is done, care must be exercised to avoid stirring up the sodium hydroxide and sodium ethoxide when the ether is removed.

When the ether is filtered into a bottle for storage, residual sodium wire, including any that may get on the filter, must be completely destroyed with alcohol before any water is added. Even a very small amount of sodium metal added to water usually starts a fire, by ignition or explosion of the hydrogen generated. In any case, bottles of ether or other solvent should not be in the vicinity when sodium is being handled or disposed of—there might be a mistake.

2-Decanol

A 500-ml three-necked flask is equipped with a mercury-sealed mechanical stirrer, a reflux condenser, and a 125-ml separatory funnel. If a nitrogen atmosphere is used, refer to Fig. 1. Rubber stoppers or ground joints are used for all connections, and the apparatus must be thoroughly dry. In the flask is placed 8.5 g (0.35 mole) of magnesium turnings. A calcium chloride tube is attached to the top of the condenser, the stopcock of

43.05 gm

32 ml

the separatory funnel is closed, mercury is placed in the seal, and the flask is heated gently all over with a soft (but not smoky) flame. This displaces moisture adsorbed on the surface of the flask; on cooling, dry air is drawn in through the calcium chloride tube. After the flask has cooled to approximately room temperature, 50 ml of anhydrous ether is placed in the separatory funnel, with a pipette, and is allowed to run into the flask. After 75 ml of ether and 67.5 g (60.6 ml, 0.35 mole) of *n*-octyl bromide have been placed in the separatory funnel and mixed by swirling, a cork is placed loosely in the top of the funnel. The stirrer is started, and about 10 ml of this mixture is allowed to run into the flask. If the reaction does not start in 2–3 minutes, the flask is warmed gently with a small flame (*ALL ETHER STOPPERED!*). After the reaction has definitely started (Note 1), the bromide solution is added at such a rate that all of it will have been added in about 1 hour. The heat of reaction will keep the solution refluxing gently. As soon as practical after the reaction has started, the preparation of acetaldehyde should be started as directed in Note 2.

After all the bromide solution has been added, the mixture is heated under reflux for about 15 minutes (Note 3); then the reaction mixture is cooled in ice and salt to −5°, and the condenser is replaced by a thermometer supported in a channeled cork so as to extend below the surface of the stirred liquid but not into the path of the stirrer. There is now added from the separatory funnel a solution of 13.9 g (18 ml, 0.318 mole) of freshly prepared acetaldehyde in 40 ml of anhydrous ether. During this addition the temperature should not be allowed to rise above 10°. With a good ice-salt bath, this addition can be made in 30–45 minutes. After all the acetaldehyde has been added, the solution is stirred an additional 5 minutes and then poured onto about 150 g of cracked ice contained in a one-liter beaker (*NO FLAMES!*). After this mixture has been stirred well, it is acidified carefully with about 100 ml of *cold* 15% sulfuric acid (9 ml of concentrated sulfuric acid in 90 ml of water). The aqueous layer is separated in a 500-ml separatory funnel and extracted with a 25-ml portion of *ordinary* ether. The total ether extract is dried for several hours over about 15 g of anhydrous potassium carbonate. (This also neutralizes any sulfuric acid present.)

As usual in removal of solvent, most of it is distilled at atmospheric pressure from an Erlenmeyer flask, using a simple gooseneck or distillation head. Since the solvent is ether in the present instance, heating must be on a steam bath or electric hot plate; also refer to precautions described in the procedure for preparation of absolute ether. When most of the ether has been distilled, the residue is poured (*CAUTION AGAINST FIRE!*) into a 125-ml Claisen flask equipped for vacuum distillation, and about 5 ml of benzene or acetone is used to rinse the Erlenmeyer flask. After last traces of solvent have been removed in the usual way, with evacuation by an aspirator, a little octane and octene will distill and be condensed in the water-cooled receiver. The boiling point will then rise rapidly to that of 2-decanol, which should be collected over a range of about 5°, after receivers have been changed. Either an aspirator or oil pump may be used for distillation of the alcohol, whose boiling point has been reported as 121° (25 mm). A yield of 75–85% should be received in a properly executed run. On a larger scale, in the hands of an experienced operator, this procedure is capable of giving a yield approaching 90%.

NOTES

1. The start of the reaction is evidenced by spontaneous boiling of the solution, with bubbles originating at the surface of the magnesium. Also, there is usually cloudiness or opalescence, sometimes followed by development of a dark color. It is imperative that the reaction be started before more halide is added, for not only will the yield be seriously lowered, but, also, the reaction is likely to get out of control if it starts after considerable halide has been added. If the apparatus and reagents are dry, alkyl bromides nearly always start readily, as indicated. Alkyl chlorides start with more difficulty, as do aryl bromides. Aryl chlorides cannot be started in diethyl ether solution (cf. earlier discussion). Iodides start more readily but give lower yields. Many tricks are used to start Grignard reactions, including the following: (1) crack a piece of magnesium under the surface of the ether with a stirring rod (taking care not to crack the flask), (2) add a crystal of iodine, or (3) add a few drops of ethyl iodide. If (2) is used, the final ether extract should be washed with a dilute solution of sodium bisulfite to remove the iodine. If ethyl iodide (or methyl iodide) is available, (3) is probably the easiest method and is also quite effective, for this substance forms a Grignard reagent very readily and promotes the formation of the desired Grignard reagent. In the present reaction, if the flask had been properly dried, these special devices are never necessary.

2. *Depolymerization of paraldehyde.* In a 200-ml round-bottomed flask are placed 55 ml of paraldehyde and 3 g of *p*-toluenesulfonic acid monohydrate; they are mixed well. The flask is arranged for distillation through a simple Vigreux or packed column about 18 inches long, and is heated on a wire gauze with a small flame. There is attached to the condenser as receiver a 50-ml distilling flask immersed in an ice-salt bath; a calcium chloride tube is attached to the side arm. The bottom of the condenser tube must extend to (but not into) the bulb of the receiver. It is usually necessary to extend the condenser tube by attaching a short piece of glass tubing by means of a rubber connection. Distillation is carried out at such a rate that the temperature at the top of the column does not rise above 35° and is stopped when the small residue begins to char. *Acetaldehyde is not only quite volatile but also highly flammable.* The apparatus is cleaned (while the acetaldehyde is kept cold), and the distillate is redistilled from the same apparatus. A water bath is used to heat the flask. The bath should not be overheated (its temperature is measured with a second thermometer), and the column is wound

with a piece of cloth that is kept moist with ice water. The fraction boiling at 20–25° is collected. Nearly all the material should distill in this range. It is most convenient to prepare the acetaldehyde during the preparation of the Grignard reagent and use it at once; however, the acetaldehyde may be kept one or two days if it is placed in a bottle with a well-fitting glass stopper and stored in the refrigerator. It should not be stored for long periods, for it repolymerizes on standing.

3. There is a small amount of residual magnesium, for the Wurtz reaction is always a side reaction, and this requires only one atom of magnesium for two moles of bromide. If the acetaldehyde is not ready at this point, there is no objection to stirring the Grignard solution longer than 15 minutes, while preparation of the acetaldehyde is completed. The Grignard solution may be kept overnight or longer if moisture is carefully excluded.

1-Naphthoic Acid

A one-liter, three-necked flask is equipped with a mercury-sealed stirrer, a reflux condenser, and a 500-ml separatory funnel. Rubber stoppers or glass joints are used for all connections. In the flask is placed 7.3 g (0.3 mole) of magnesium turnings. The flask is dried as described under preparation of 2-decanol. After the flask has cooled to approximately room temperature, a mixture of 4.5 g (3 ml, 0.022 mole) of 1-bromonaphthalene and 30 ml of anhydrous ether is placed in the separatory funnel, by means of a pipette, and allowed to run into the flask. A solution of 57.5 g (38 ml, 0.278 mole) of 1-bromonaphthalene, in 250 ml of ether and 60 ml of anhydrous thiophene-free benzene (Note 1), is next placed in the separatory funnel, and a cork is placed loosely in the top of the funnel. The stirrer is started and the flask is warmed gently with a small flame *(ALL ETHER STOPPERED!)*. As soon as reaction has definitely started (cf. Note 1 of 2-decanol preparation), the bromide solution is added at such a rate that addition is complete in about 1 hour. The heat of the reaction will keep the solution refluxing gently. After all the bromide solution has been added, the mixture is heated on a water bath for about 30 minutes (cf. Note 3 of 2-decanol preparation). The reaction mixture is cooled to slightly below room temperature before it is added to the carbon dioxide.

In a dry two-liter beaker is placed 80 g of Dry Ice, which has been weighed quite approximately (Note 2) and quickly broken up in a towel into small lumps. On account of the rapidity of moisture condensation, the crushed Dry Ice should not be exposed to air any more than necessary before the Grignard reagent is added. The solution of the Grignard reagent is poured onto the solid carbon dioxide slowly, with stirring, as the unreacted magnesium is retained in the flask. First a vigorous boiling occurs. The mixture is stirred and lumps are broken up until all the Dry Ice has evaporated.

Next, 200 g of ice is added, followed by 100 ml of water and 50 ml of concentrated hydrochloric acid. The mixture is stirred until most of the solid has dissolved and there is a separation into two layers; then the mixture is poured into a separatory funnel, and about 100 ml of ether is used to wash in the material adhering to the beaker. The mixture is shaken in the funnel until the solid has dissolved; more ether is added if necessary. The aqueous layer is separated and discarded, and the ethereal layer is washed with about 100 ml of water (Note 3). Next, the ether-benzene solution is extracted with 50 ml of 25% sodium hydroxide; this operation is repeated twice. The combined alkaline extracts are extracted with 50 ml of ether, and then heated on a hot plate to drive off dissolved solvent (Note 4). To the warm alkaline solution, 1.0 g of decolorizing carbon is added and the solution is filtered. The filtrate is cooled to room temperature and acidified with concentrated hydrochloric acid. After cooling, the crude acid is collected by suction filtration, washed, and dried.

The crude dried acid is dissolved in 120 ml of hot toluene, a small quantity of acetone is added, and the solution is decolorized with charcoal, filtered, and concentrated to a volume of 100 ml. After cooling, finally in ice, the acid is collected and dried. The average yield is 30 g (58%), m.p. 159–161°.

NOTES

1. Ordinary thiophene-free benzene contains traces of moisture; this can be removed by distilling slowly until the distillate is no longer cloudy, and using the residue. If the solvent is to be stored, it is best kept over sodium wire.

2. Dry Ice should be handled with a dry towel or with gloves. If it is held for long in the bare hand, it may cause frostbite. In case of such an injury, use the same treatment as for a burn.

3. If the ether-benzene solution is not entirely clear, it should be filtered before extraction with sodium hydroxide.

4. Diethyl ether is soluble in water to the extent of 8.3 g per 100 g of water. It is necessary, therefore, to warm the aqueous layer to boil out the dissolved ether so that when the alkaline solution is acidified, the desired product does not remain, in part, in solution. Care should be exercised in this operation, since the ether may foam and the vapors are flammable.

Methyl 4-Oxododecanoate

A one-liter three-necked flask is equipped with a mercury-sealed mechanical stirrer, a reflux condenser, and a 250-ml separatory funnel. Rubber stoppers or ground joints are used for all connections, and all apparatus must be thoroughly dry. In the flask is placed 9.7 g of magnesium turnings, then the equipment is dried as described in the preparation of 2-decanol. As also described in the 2-decanol preparation, a Grignard reagent is prepared from 77 g (69 ml) of *n*-octyl bromide in a total of 150 ml of anhydrous ether.

After all the bromide has been added, the solution of Grignard reagent is heated under reflux for about 10 minutes, and then cooled in an ice bath. After stirring, with cooling, has been continued for about 10 minutes, the separatory funnel is removed and 40.3 g of anhydrous cadmium chloride (Note 1) is added during 3–5 minutes. The most convenient method is to add the cadmium chloride in portions from a small Erlenmeyer flask. *(DO NOT ADD THE CADMIUM CHLORIDE ALL AT ONCE!)* The separatory funnel is replaced, the ice bath is removed, and stirring is continued for about 5 minutes, then the mixture is heated under reflux, with stirring, by use of a steam bath or a water bath heated on a hot plate. After a half hour, a Gilman test for Grignard reagent is made (Note 2), and if it is not negative, heating with stirring is continued; a Gilman test is then made at 15-minute intervals until a negative test is obtained. As soon as a negative test for Grignard reagent is obtained (Note 3), the reflux condenser is replaced by a gooseneck connected to a condenser set for distillation, and ether is distilled, as stirring is continued. Distillation is continued as the temperature of the water bath is raised until finally the water bath is heated to boiling. The residue in the flask becomes viscous and dark, and the power input to the stirring motor must be increased to maintain stirring. When distillation becomes slow (Note 4), 240 ml of dry, thiophene-free benzene (Note 5) is added promptly from the separatory funnel, with slowing of the stirrer to prevent undue splashing. The condenser is immediately shifted back to reflux position, and the reaction mixture is heated to boiling. There should be no delay about proceeding with addition of the ester acid chloride.

In the separatory funnel is placed a solution of 48.2 g of β-methoxycarbonylpropionyl chloride in 75 ml of the dry benzene. When the reaction mixture has been heated to boiling, the heating bath is removed and an ice-water bath is prepared (not too thick with ice—the flask should sink easily into the water). Any flames in the vicinity are extinguished, and the solution of ester acid chloride is added rapidly during 2–3 minutes unless the vigor of the reaction requires slowing of the addition rate. There may be a vigorous reaction after a brief induction period. The ice bath is used only as much as necessary to keep the reaction under control. Soon after addition is complete, the vigorous reaction abates, but spontaneous refluxing may continue for a few minutes. The mixture is finally heated under reflux, with stirring, for about 30 minutes. The organometallic complex is decomposed by the addition of ice to the stirred mixture while the flask is cooled with an ice bath; then sufficient cold 6N sulfuric acid is added to give two clear phases.

The reaction mixture is poured into a liter separatory funnel, and the water phase is allowed to run into a 500-ml separatory funnel, where it is extracted with the ether and benzene originally distilled from the reaction mixture. The benzene solution containing most of the product is washed with about 100 ml of water, and the same water is used to wash the second extract. Similarly, the two solutions are washed with 100-ml portions of 0.5 molar sodium carbonate solution, water, and saturated sodium chloride solution. (If emulsions are encountered, a few milliliters of methanol are added, with swirling.) Finally the benzene solutions are separated carefully, and solvent is distilled from an Erlenmeyer flask until distillation becomes slow. The residue is transferred to a 250-ml Claisen flask, last traces of solvent are removed in the usual manner with evacuation by an aspirator, and the residue is distilled at about 5 mm pressure. There will be a small amount of dimethyl succinate (present in the ester acid chloride) and methyl ethyl succinate (from reaction of the ester acid chloride with ether), distilling below 100° at 5 mm, and there will be some hexadecane (from coupling of the Grignard reagent), whose boiling point is 135° (5 mm). Since the desired keto ester boils at 148° (5 mm), hexadecane cannot be separated by distillation in a Claisen flask. If the Grignard reagent was properly prepared, however, there will be no more than 4–6 g of hexadecane, and the product collected at 135–150° (5 mm) is a reasonably good sample of keto ester (Note 6). A good sample collected in this range has n^{22}_D of 1.439–1.440. Samples containing more hydrocarbon have lower indices. Even poorer samples readily yield pure 4-oxododecanoic acid by the procedure described below.

The average yield of methyl 4-oxododecanoate is 39–48 g (55–65%, based on crude ester acid chloride). There is appreciable distillation residue. A sample of pure keto ester is readily obtained by distillation through a two-foot column, or by re-esterifying a sample of pure keto acid obtained by crystallization as described below.

4-Oxododecanoic Acid

This may be easily obtained from the ester, and is a suitable solid derivative. In 50 ml of 95% ethanol is dissolved 2.5 g of potassium hydroxide. This solution is added to 5 g of the keto ester contained in a 125-ml Erlenmeyer flask which is equipped with a ground joint for attaching a reflux condenser. The contents of the flask are heated on a hot plate under reflux for 20 minutes and then poured, while warm, into 200 ml of water. The flask is rinsed with a little water. The aqueous solution, which should be opalescent but clear, is made distinctly acid with concentrated hydrochloric acid. The acidified mixture is swirled, with cooling in water, for about 15 minutes to get the precipitated keto acid in a coagulated easily filtrable form. The product is collected by suction filtration on a small funnel, washed with water, dried, and then crystallized from hexane (Note 7). It will probably be necessary to filter from the hot solution a little inorganic salt occluded by the acid. After crystallization and collection of the crystals as usual, a very small amount is ground on a watch glass and allowed to dry while the main portion is crystallized again. The melting point of the material is taken after the first and second crystallizations; if there has been no appreciable rise in melting point, it may be assumed that the sample is pure. If there has been an appreciable rise in melting point (more than one degree), the sample should be recrystallized. This is the procedure used in preparing a sample of a new compound for analysis, except that, before a compound is analyzed, a hot solution of the pure substance is filtered to remove filter paper fibers and dust. The final crystallization is carried out in a carefully cleaned flask, and the increase in melting point after the final crystallization should be no more than about 0.2°.

Turn in your pure acid properly labeled. 4-Oxododecanoic acid melts at 78–79° (Note 6).

NOTES

1. Hydrated cadmium chloride is dried overnight in an oven at 110–120°; then the caked salt is ground *thoroughly* in a mortar (*protect the mouth and nose with a dust mask, to prevent sneezing*) and placed in a screw-capped bottle, which is returned to the oven (with cap off) for several hours. The bottle is then capped and stored in a desiccator over calcium chloride. The anhydrous salt does not absorb water rapidly and may be leisurely weighed and used in the air; however, it should not be stored outside a desiccator and should not be exposed to air unnecessarily while it is being used.

2. The Gilman test is positive for Grignard reagent but negative for cadmium reagent; hence, it is very useful in the present reaction. It is carried out as follows:

A sample of 0.5–1.0 ml of the reaction mixture is removed with a small bulb pipette with a wide-bore delivery tip, and placed in a dry 1.2 × 10 cm test tube containing an equal volume of a 1 per cent solution of Michler's ketone in dry benzene. The mixture is shaken for about 1 minute. About 0.5 ml of water is carefully added, and is followed by enough (a few drops) of a 0.2 per cent solution of iodine in acetic acid to give a clear two-phase solution. Finally, 2 ml of glacial acetic acid is added, and the solution is mixed well. The mixture is allowed to settle and the color noted. A positive test will have a characteristic blue-green color; a negative test is a shade of pale amber or yellow. As a check on the reagents, and to acquaint the operator with the appearance of a positive test, it is well to test the Grignard solution before the cadmium chloride is added.

3. The reaction may be interrupted at this point and allowed to stand overnight, or it may be interrupted at any time before a negative Gilman test is obtained but after all the bromide has been added. The system should be tight except for the calcium chloride tube, which admits only dry air. The gradual escape of ether vapor is reasonably effective in keeping air out. *Standing more than two or three days is not recommended.*

4. The residue should not be heated further after ether distillation becomes rather slow, for heating at 100° decomposes a dialkylcadmium to a mixture of alkene and alkane (Eq. 18).

5. A total of about 315 ml of dry, thiophene-free benzene is needed for this reaction. This is most easily dried by distillation of about 415 ml of benzene until 100 ml of distillate is collected. This removes all water as the azeotrope with benzene. The residue is cooled, while protected by a calcium chloride tube, and stored in a tightly stoppered flask or bottle (preferably the flask in which it was distilled, for all adsorbed moisture has been removed from this flask).

6. The described procedure may be applied to preparation of other keto esters, and usually the keto ester and hydrocarbon from coupling will not have such similar boiling points. For example, ethyl 6-oxotetradecanoate may be obtained in similar yield by allowing the octylcadmium reagent to react with the acid chloride from ethyl hydrogen adipate (cf. Chap. 37; preparation of the acid chloride is by the same procedure used for β-methoxycarbonylpropionyl chloride). In this instance, the keto ester boils at about 175° (5 mm); so separation of hexadecane by distillation in a Claisen flask is rather effective. Gas chromatography of samples of ethyl 6-oxotetradecanoate prepared in this manner showed presence of 0–4% of hexadecane and similar amounts of diethyl adipate. This keto ester has about the same index of refraction as the impure samples of methyl 4-oxododecanoate.

6-Oxotetradecanoic acid, obtained by saponification of the ester and recrystallization of the acid, has m.p. 71–72°.

7. Acetone is also a useful solvent for crystallization of aliphatic keto acids; however, in the present instance hexane is more effective on account of the great solubility of hexadecane in hexane.

Electrolytic Reduction
Synthesis of *p*-Benzoquinones

39

As mentioned in Chap. 24, the best yields of *p*-benzoquinones are obtained by oxidation of derivatives having amino or hydroxy groups in *para* positions. If the phenol is available as starting material, a high yield of *p*-aminophenol may be obtained by way of coupling and reduction, as outlined in Eq. 1. Conditions for this process have been worked out very

$$\text{(39-1)}$$

thoroughly.[1] Oxidation of the crude aminophenol often gives yields of quinone amounting to 80–95%, based on starting phenol. If the available starting material is a nitro compound, however, this is converted to a phenol with some difficulty. The amine may be obtained in high yield by reduction, but conversion of an amine to a phenol by the diazotization route (Chap. 25) often gives a yield no greater than 50–60%. Since a very

[1]L. I. Smith, J. W. Opie, S. Wawzonek, and W. W. Pritchard, *J. Org. Chem.*, **4**, 318 (1939).

wide variety of pure aromatic nitro compounds is available, the conversion of a nitro compound to the corresponding *p*-aminophenol becomes of much interest as an intermediate step in quinone synthesis.

An aromatic nitro compound may be reduced, under proper conditions, to the phenylhydroxylamine, and this derivative is easily rearranged under acid catalysis to the *p*-aminophenol. The most convenient and efficient method of accomplishing this two-step conversion is electrolytic reduction in acid solution, which yields the *p*-aminophenol directly. This process is illustrated in the present chapter by reduction of *o*-nitrotoluene. Oxidation of the resultant *p*-aminophenol to *p*-toluquinone is also described.

Preparation of *2-methyl-4-hydroxyaniline* (4-hydroxy-*o*-toluidine) may be represented as in Eq. 2. Although it is quite probable that the electrons

$$
\begin{array}{ccc}
\text{NO}_2 & \text{NHOH} & \text{NH}_2 \\
\end{array}
$$

$$
\underset{(4H^+ + 4e)}{+ \quad 4[H]} \longrightarrow \quad \xrightarrow{H^+} \qquad \qquad (39\text{-}2)
$$

$$
+ \text{ H}_2\text{O}
$$

supplied at the cathode attack the organic compound (the "depolarizer") directly, rather than reduce protons to hydrogen atoms, this point is difficult to establish with certainty. In any case, the stoichiometry may be conveniently considered by the designation in Eq. 2, and another half reaction at the anode may be considered for supply of the electrons. There may be several reactions occurring at the lead anode, but the processes shown in Eqs. 3 and 4 are probably the most important ones. Attack on the

$$
2\text{Pb} \longrightarrow 2\text{Pb}^{++} + 4e \qquad\qquad (39\text{-}3)
$$

$$
2\text{H}_2\text{O} \longrightarrow 4\text{H}^+ + \text{O}_2 + 4e \qquad\qquad (39\text{-}4)
$$

lead anode may be observed, as may evolution of gas.

The principal *side reaction*, so far as concerns the organic compound, is further reduction of the hydroxylamine to the amine, as in Eq. 5. The

$$
\begin{array}{cc}
\text{NHOH} & \text{NH}_2 \\
\end{array}
$$

$$
\underset{(2H^+ + 2e)}{+ \quad 2[H]} \longrightarrow \qquad\qquad + \text{ H}_2\text{O} \qquad\qquad (39\text{-}5)
$$

p-aminophenol is not further reduced under the conditions utilized. If the electric current is considered to be a reagent, then another possible side reaction is formation of hydrogen gas at the cathode (Eq. 6).

$$
2\text{H}^+ + 2e \longrightarrow \text{H}_2 \qquad\qquad (39\text{-}6)
$$

Reactions occurring at a cathode depend on the magnitude of the cathode potential (potential drop between the cathode and solution, usually measured with respect to a standard electrode); some reactions require a greater cathode potential than others. In the present instance, the reactions shown in Eqs. 2, 5, and 6 require progressively higher cathode potentials. In order to consider the factors involved in selective reduction, it should first be pointed out that the total potential applied to a cell, which we will designate as E_t, may be considered as consisting of three parts, as shown in Eq. 7, where E_c is the cathode potential, E_a is the

$$E_t = E_c + E_a + E_{ir} \qquad (39\text{-}7)$$

anode potential, and E_{ir} is the potential drop across the electrolyte in the cell. The last component of the potential drop is the only one subject to the relationship defined by Ohm's law ($E = ir$) for simple conduction. The magnitude of this potential drop is a function of the current flowing.

When a potential is applied to an electrolytic cell in which several reductions may occur, as in the present process, the relationship of cathode potential to current through the cell is represented in a somewhat idealized manner in Fig. 1. Until the cathode potential (E_c) reaches the value at

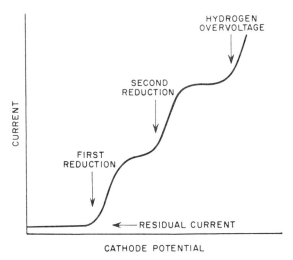

FIG. 1.   Relationship of cathode potential to current in an electrolytic cell.

which the first reduction can occur, the only current passing through the cell is the small current known as the residual current; therefore, E_{ir} remains very small, and the increase in the applied potential (E_t) must appear in E_c and E_a (cf. Eq. 7). At the point where the first reduction begins to occur, however, increase in applied potential does not continue to increase the cathode potential, for electrons no longer accumulate there; electrons may be accepted by the depolarizer so that reduction occurs.[2] As the applied potential is increased further, the increased supply of electrons gives more rapid reduction and current in the cell increases rapidly, as shown in Fig. 1; therefore, E_{ir} increases rapidly at this point. Cathode potential can be increased further, *so that the second reduction can begin to occur, only if the supply of electrons to the cathode exceeds the rate at which they can be accepted by the depolarizer.* If this rate is exceeded, then electrons will again accumulate at the cathode, and its potential will eventually rise to the point where the second reduction can occur. In a similar manner, the cathode potential may eventually be raised to a point (the hydrogen overvoltage) where hydrogen is discharged at the cathode as a result of reduction of protons (Eq. 6). This behavior of an electrolytic cell has several consequences which are of considerable interest if one is attempting to secure a first reduction (for example, Eq. 2) and avoid subsequent reductions (Eqs. 5 and 6). The first and second reductions, in the general case, need not be consecutive reactions. If reductions of different functional groups are involved, the principles remain the same.

Since the cathode potential is the fundamental factor determining which reactions may occur at the cathode, it is important to understand what influences determine this potential. It should be mentioned at the outset that if the hydrogen overvoltage should happen to fall between the potentials required for the first and second reductions, this would virtually guarantee that the second reduction could be avoided easily. Although the hydrogen overvoltage varies considerably for different metals (for example, it is low for platinum, high for lead and mercury), it is rarely, if ever, practical or possible to determine conditions where the hydrogen overvoltage happens to fall between the potentials for the two reductions of organic material. The principal concern with the hydrogen overvoltage is that it be *high enough to allow the desired reduction.* If hydrogen is discharged at a lower cathode potential than that required for the desired reduction, then the desired reduction can be accomplished only while hydrogen is being produced at the maximum rate of which the cell is capable. Frequently, cathodes are treated in special ways in an effort to raise the hydrogen overvoltage in respect to the potential required for a desired reduction. The efficacy of such methods is subject to some question, especially their reproducibility. For the present reduction, various metals are satisfactory for the cathode, even those of low hydrogen over-

---

[2]Of course reduction can occur, with flow of current through the cell, only if there is also a reaction occurring at the anode at the potential which has been attained at that electrode. Electrode potentials are influenced by the nature of the electrolyte; however, the nature of the metal comprising the electrode is an important factor. Lead anodes are satisfactory for a variety of electrolytic reductions, with various cathodes.

voltage such as platinum or copper. Nickel is unsatisfactory, probably because of rapid alteration of the surface in the strongly acidic catholyte.

From the above considerations, it follows that selectively securing a first reduction must depend on keeping the cathode potential high enough to give a good rate for the first reduction, but low enough to prevent the second reduction from occurring. The difficulty of accomplishing this depends, naturally, on the difference in potential required for the two reductions. If the difference is as much as about 0.2 volt, selective reduction may usually be accomplished rather effectively. The rate at which electrons may leave the cathode will obviously depend on how large is the cathode surface; therefore, *low current density* is frequently presented as the most important factor in keeping down the cathode potential and thus avoiding a second reduction. The size of the cathode is certainly important in determining how rapidly electrons may be fed into the reduction without raising the cathode potential to an undesirable value; however, *an equally important factor is the rate of supply of depolarizer to the cathode surface.* In practice, this means that good stirring is of foremost importance. Also important is design of the cathode and vessel in such manner that the stirring forces the solution of depolarizer over the cathode surface.

A second factor determining the amount of depolarizer available at the cathode surface is the concentration of the depolarizer in solution. Since it is common practice to carry out the reduction until all or most of the starting material is reduced, it follows that the concentration decreases steadily. As the concentration decreases, the rate of acceptance of electrons at the cathode surface must decrease, and E_{ir} must decrease accordingly; therefore, if the total applied potential (E_t) remains constant, E_c (also E_a) must increase. When E_c has increased to the value required for the second reduction, the side reaction begins to occur. From these considerations, it follows that the applied potential must be lowered as the reduction progresses, if E_c is to remain constant. If this is done, then the current will decrease during the reduction until only the residual current remains when all the depolarizer has been reduced.

The potential applied to a cell may be decreased manually during a reduction, so as to maintain a reasonably constant cathode potential; however, this is laborious and rather unsatisfactory. It is most practical to use a relatively elaborate device which automatically turns down the applied potential as required to maintain a constant cathode potential.

Although these important considerations in electrolytic reduction should be well understood, the present preparation has been so chosen that rather good yields may be obtained without the necessity for careful control of cathode potential. This becomes possible because the rate of rearrangement of the hydroxylamine (Eq. 2), under the conditions defined, goes at a sufficiently high rate to render further reduction of the hydroxylamine (Eq. 5) a minor side reaction, even when the cathode potential is high enough to give the second reduction. Since this factor renders careful control of cathode potential unnecessary for this specific reduction, a current of several amperes may be used in the small cell. It is also no disadvantage to use a battery charger as source of the applied d-c potential, in spite of the large fluctuation in voltage output of a battery charger.

Although the presently studied selective reduction is relatively insensitive to several factors controlling reduction, as has been discussed, it remains important to have a cathode of suitable geometry and to stir in a manner which will drive the solution rapidly over the cathode surface. This is especially important on account of the low solubility of *o*-nitrotoluene in the catholyte. Use of a homogenous solution containing acetic acid gives better yields[3]; however, the work-up becomes more laborious. The cathode design due to Harman,[3] as illustrated in Fig. 2, has been found quite satisfactory if there is used inside the cathode a rapidly rotated stirrer of the design shown in Fig. 3. It is best that the blades be pitched

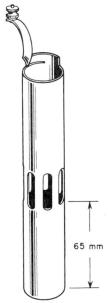

FIG. 2. Cathode for electrolytic reduction.

FIG. 3. Glass stirrer for narrow tubes.

65 mm

[3]R. E. Harman, *Org. Syntheses*, **35**, 22 (1955).

so that the liquid is driven up. Liquid then flows out through the slots, down outside the cathode, and beneath the cathode back into the center.

In order to accomplish an electrolytic reduction satisfactorily, it is usually necessary to operate in a two-compartment cell. This prevents material reduced at the cathode from coming into contact with the anode and becoming oxidized. It follows that the membrane or partition between the compartments must be sufficiently porous to allow free passage of small ions but reasonably resistant to diffusion of the organic materials. For small-scale laboratory work, a dense alundum extraction thimble makes a suitable catholyte compartment. If this is placed in a beaker of appropriate size, and inside a cylindrical anode, there results a satisfactory cell in which the distance between the electrodes is short enough to avoid excessive resistance in the solution. A complete setup for the reduction is shown in Fig. 4.

Oxidation of the 2-methyl-4-hydroxyaniline (4-hydroxy-*o*-toluidine) may be carried out in satisfactory yield by use of dichromate in acid solution (Eq. 8). The half reaction for reduction of the dichromate has

been presented previously as Eq. 15-5. Best yields are obtained in this particular oxidation at 5–10°; however, other aminophenols give better yields at other temperatures.[4] Although the aminophenol may be isolated after the reduction, if desired, such compounds are rather sensitive to air oxidation, and considerable loss is likely to be encountered during the isolation. In the present experiment, it is economical of time and material not to isolate the aminophenol. The reaction mixture from the reduction may be diluted, and the oxidation carried out directly by the addition of sodium dichromate. Ferric ion is also a satisfactory oxidizing agent, but in this instance dichromate gives a somewhat better yield.

Side reactions in preparation of benzoquinones by oxidation have been discussed in Chap. 24. Loss of material by overoxidation and opening the ring is minor in the present instance, where there are favorable *p*-substituents in the ring. Polymerization of radical intermediates is also relatively minor in the present case. Significant losses occur by polymerization of the quinone itself, for toluquinone is especially sensitive to polymerization by either acid or base catalysis. For this reason, it is *important* that the quinone not be left for prolonged periods in contact with

[4] R. E. Harman and J. Cason, *J. Org. Chem.*, **17**, 1058 (1952).

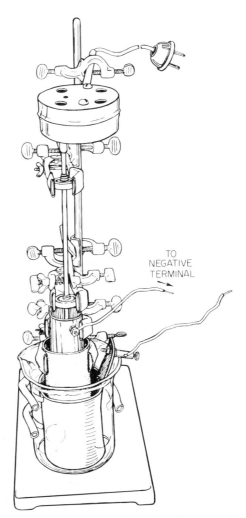

FIG. 4.   Assemblage of apparatus for small-scale electrolytic reduction.

the oxidizing medium, or in a crude state without purification. A pure sample of toluquinone is moderately stable to storage in absence of light, but crude samples usually decompose rapidly. Most quinones, even when pure, decompose to some extent on long storage. Since the decomposition products are polymeric in nature, purification by crystallization is likely to be ineffective, and steam distillation usually gives easy purification. The crude toluquinone obtained in the present experiment cannot be satisfactorily purified by crystallization, but steam distillation gives most of the material in a rather pure condition.

During all work with quinones, it should be remembered that they are relatively unstable compounds, especially sensitive to acids, bases, heat, and light. Success in their preparation and handling results only from rapid, careful work.

EXPERIMENTAL PROCEDURES

4-Hydroxy-o-Toluidine (not isolated)

A two-compartment electrolytic cell is set up as illustrated in Fig. 4, with a 400-ml beaker containing the anolyte and a 4.5 × 11 cm dense alundum extraction thimble (Note 1) inside the beaker to contain the catholyte. The cylindrical anode of lead is placed with the catholyte chamber inside it, and the specially designed copper cathode (Fig. 2) is placed in the center of the catholyte chamber. The thimble and the cathode are clamped securely in position, but care should be taken not to break the rather fragile alundum thimble. The bottom of the cathode should be about 5 mm above the bottom of the thimble, so that liquid may flow beneath the cathode. In the center of the cathode is placed a glass propeller-type stirrer that is turned at high speed. The shaft is supported with two ball bearings, and lined up carefully so that the blades do not strike the cathode. The negative terminal of the 6-volt battery is connected to the cathode, and a 0–5 amp ammeter is connected in series with the battery and a 25-ohm slide wire rheostat. A convenient substitute for battery and rheostat is a small (4-amp) battery charger, with a-c input voltage controlled by a variable transformer. This gives excellent control of the d-c output. The negative terminal of the battery charger may be located by use of the ammeter (Note 2). Diagrams for wiring are shown in Fig. 5.

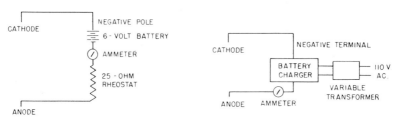

FIG. 5.   Circuit diagrams for electrolytic reduction.

Since four electrons are required for this reduction, the theoretical amount of current that must pass is calculated from the following formula:

$$\frac{4(\text{moles of nitro cpd.})(96{,}500 \text{ coulombs per equiv.})}{3{,}600 \text{ coulombs per amp hr}} = \text{amp hr required}$$

Some current is dissipated by over-reduction, especially near the end of the run when the concentration of *o*-nitrotoluene has become low. Also, the current usually drops slightly as the reduction progresses, so accuracy is decreased by the necessity for estimating the average current. Sufficient allowance is made for these variables if about 1.4 times the theoretical amount of current is passed through the cell. A current as high as 3–4 amp may be used if it can be obtained; however, if this much current is used it may become necessary to cool the cell somewhat in order to avoid excessive heating. It is an advantage if the cell warms to 30–35°, for solubility is increased, but higher temperatures cause excessive loss of water (which should be replaced, if this happens). The higher current density increases the need for excellent stirring, and towards the end of the reduction increases the side reaction (Eq. 5) slightly; therefore a current of 1–2 amp may give better results.

After the time that will be required for the reduction has been calculated the reaction is started at a time such that the operator can be present to turn off the reaction when the desired amount of current has been passed. A moderate excess of current over that recommended is no disadvantage; however, a large excess always leads to poor results. The most common difficulty is frothing of material out of the catholyte compartment by evolution of hydrogen, and this occasionally happens by the time 1.4 equivalents of current have been passed. If grossly excessive current is used, such products as sulfur and hydrogen sulfide may form, and these or other products destroy the aminophenol.

When the reduction is to be started, there is placed in the catholyte compartment 80 ml ($\pm$ 5 ml) (Note 1) of 75% (by weight) sulfuric acid (cf. Appendix III for data on concentrated sulfuric acid). Enough 75% sulfuric acid is placed in the anolyte compartment to make the level of acid the same as in the catholyte. *After* acid is placed in both compartments, there is added 10 g (0.073 mole) of commercial *o*-nitrotoluene to the catholyte. The stirrer is then started, proper positioning of the cathode is checked, the rheostat (or input voltage to the battery charger) is adjusted to give the desired current, and current is passed for the calculated length of time. The dark-colored but clear catholyte is then diluted for oxidation. It is not necessary to carry out the oxidation immediately, but the solution should be poured from the thimble immediately, for there is some diffusion of organic material through the walls of the thimble. If oxidation is not started soon after completion of reduction, the diluted catholyte (see below) should be stored in a stoppered flask in a refrigerator.

Toluquinone

The catholyte is poured into a one-liter Erlenmeyer flask, and the thimble is rinsed with water. The catholyte is finally diluted to about 500 ml and cooled in an ice bath. At a temperature of 5-10° there is added, with swirling and continued cooling, during about 5 minutes, a solution of 11.4 g (0.038 mole) of sodium dichromate dihydrate in 20 ml of water. The solution is then allowed to stand at room temperature for about 2 hours. If the mixture cannot be worked up at the end of the oxidation period, the flask should be placed in a refrigerator.

The precipitate of quinone and tar is collected by suction filtration, and the filtrate is extracted with three 50-ml portions of ether *(CAUTION!)*. The material filtered out is added to the ether extracts and shaken for several minutes; then the tar is removed by suction filtration and washed with several small portions of ether. The ether solution is placed in a 500-ml flask arranged for indirect steam distillation, but before steam is passed in, the ether is carefully distilled from a water bath. After ether has been distilled and receivers changed, the quinone is steam-distilled. Since toluquinone is rather soluble in hot water, very little condensation should be allowed in the distilling flask. When the rate of quinone distillation slows down (after 25-30 ml of distillate; Note 3), receivers are changed, and the remainder of the quinone is steam-distilled (no more than 75 ml total distillate usually required).

The first distillate is cooled in ice, and the bright-yellow toluquinone is collected by suction filtration, drained well, and dried in the dark in an evacuated desiccator over calcium chloride (Note 4). This sample weighs about 3 g and melts at 68-69°. The aqueous filtrate and second steam-distillate are combined and extracted with the ether distilled above, and then with a second 25-ml portion if the aqueous solution is still yellow. The total ether solution is shaken with about 50 ml of saturated sodium chloride solution, and the ether layer is separated very carefully. The ether is distilled from a water bath, and as much ether as possible is finally removed on a boiling-water bath. The residue is crystallized from a minimum amount (10-20 ml) of 50% aqueous ethanol. The product is collected after cooling in ice, washed with 50% aqueous ethanol, and dried as described above. This fraction weighs about 0.5 g, m.p. 65-66°, so the total yield is about 3.5 g (39% over-all, based on *o*-nitrotoluene).

If further purification of the low-melting fraction is desired, it should be steam-distilled again. If the procedure for this experiment is not followed carefully and skillfully, yields below 25% are commonly encountered.

The infrared spectrum of *p*-benzoquinones is of interest on account of the highly conjugated system of double bonds. For toluquinone, the carbonyl absorption is at 6.00 μ (in carbon tetrachloride solution), significantly longer wavelength than in the case of saturated ketones.

Toluquinone may be gas chromatographed on a silicone column, by injection in about 20% solution in ether. For the Carle instrument, c settings should be satisfactory.

NOTES

1. At least twice as large a run may be carried out in a 5 × 16.5 cm alundum thimble (Norton No. 10040 RA 98). When a different size run is made, whether or not in a thimble of different dimensions, care must be exercised that the amount of catholyte is such that the surface of the liquid is in the slots in the cathode (cf. Fig. 2). Otherwise, proper circulation of the catholyte over the surface of the cathode will not be realized. If a significantly larger thimble is used, of course a larger cathode is an advantage.

2. When the ammeter gives displacement of the needle in the proper direction (instead of below zero), the battery charger cable which is connected to the ammeter terminal marked + is the positive terminal of the battery charger. In making this test, of course current must flow through the cell, and for this purpose *it is important that the depolarizer be added to the catholyte.* With the copper cathode and lead anode, if electrolyte only is present in the cathode compartment *the cell will not conduct in the desired direction,* but will conduct in the opposite direction, i.e., with the lead electrode connected as cathode. Failure to recognize this phenomenon can, of course, lead to general confusion.

3. When a larger amount of distillate is collected in the first fraction, additional quinone is lost by solubility in the water. Only a part of this can be recovered by the subsequent work-up of the filtrate from the insoluble quinone. Thus, it becomes of importance to limit the first fraction to the volume that gives rapid distillation of quinone.

4. When drying a volatile material, the best method is use of a closed desiccator, evacuated if desired, containing an agent which will absorb the solvent but not the desired material. Thus, drying toluquinone over calcium chloride gives removal of water, without loss of toluquinone (except the vapor required to fill the desiccator). Drying over sulfuric acid would result in loss of all the toluquinone. When a volatile material is being dried in a vacuum desiccator, it is important that the pump not be left going longer than necessary to secure the desired vacuum. Also, the material should not be allowed to stand longer than necessary in the evacuated desiccator, for changes in room temperature may result in slow transfer of the material from the containing vessel to the walls of the desiccator.

APPENDICES

Equipment List

I

On pages 428–431 is listed locker equipment which is suitable for performing the experiments. The items marked with an asterisk are those equipped with standard taper (S.T.) ground-glass joints. The total cost of these items is about $35, and they replace items costing about half this sum. They eliminate 70–80% of the corks required for the course, and virtually all glass-bending is eliminated. Considerable economy has been achieved, with loss of essentially no utility, by using ground joints only where needed. In Figs. 1–3 are illustrated certain items of the equipment designed for maximum utility at minimum cost. A particularly convenient device is use of rubber slip joints for attachment of small tubes, thermometers, and separatory funnels, as illustrated in Fig. 4 (also cf. Fig. 5–6). This type of connection is, on the average, as convenient as a ground joint, and a ring of liquid that tends to collect inside the tube protects the rubber from attack by vapors. Lubrication with a trace of silicone oil, or glycerol, makes tubes slip readily into the rubber connection.

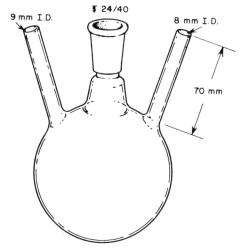

FIG. 1.   Round-bottomed flask with ground-jointed center neck, and side tubes. Side tubes are of slightly different size so that one conveniently accommodates a separatory funnel and the other a thermometer; cf. Fig. 4. For this application of a separatory funnel as a dropping funnel, it is necessary to avoid separatory funnels with very large delivery tubes (> 9 mm o.d.).

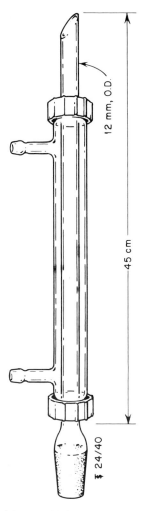

FIG. 2. Condenser with ground joint. When distilling heads are properly designed (cf. Fig. 3), the condenser with a single male joint may be used for reflux or distillation. For distillation, an adapter is attached to the small end by a cork, since no warm solvent is in contact with this connection. For reflux, a drying tube or gas trap may be attached by fitting a short section of small rubber tubing over a small glass tube and slipping it inside the condenser tube.

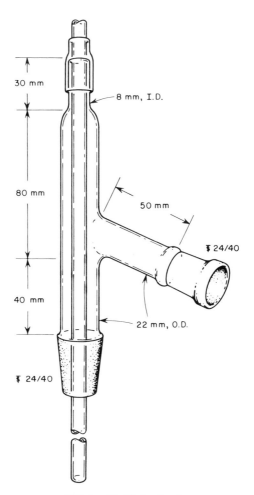

30 mm

8 mm, I.D.

80 mm

50 mm

₮ 24/40

40 mm

22 mm, O.D.

₮ 24/40

FIG. 3.   Distillation head.

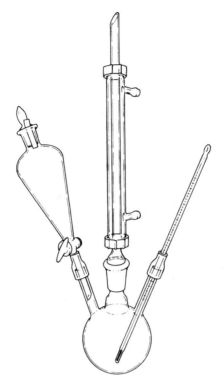

FIG. 4. Assembly of apparatus utilizing all outlets of the flask with side tubes.

If the ground-jointed equipment is not used, it should be replaced by the supplementary list placed after the principal list.

1 Adapter
6 Beakers; 50, 100, 150, 250, 400, 800 ml
5 Bottles, glass-stoppered; two 30, two 60, 120 ml
3 Bottles, wide-mouthed; two 60, 120 ml
1 Brush, test-tube
2 Burners, Bunsen
1 Burner, micro
1 Burner shield
5 Clamps; three 7″, two 9″
8 Clamp holders (5 for clamps, 3 for rings)
1 Cold-finger condenser (see Fig. 30–2)
1 Condenser, standard
1 *Condenser, S.T. 24/40 (see Fig. 2)
2 Cylinders, graduated; 25, 100 ml
1 Dropper, 1 ml with bulb (see Fig. 30–1)
3 pkg. Filter paper; 25, 70, 150 mm
3 Flasks, distilling; 25, 50, 125 ml
8 Flasks, Erlenmeyer; two 50, two 125, two 250, 500, 1000 ml
2 *Flasks, Erlenmeyer, S.T. 24/40; 250, 500 ml
1 Flask, filter, 500 ml
1 Flask, Kjeldahl, 30 ml
2 *Flasks, round-bottomed, S.T. 24/40; 100, 1000 ml
2 *Flasks, round-bottomed with side tubes, S.T. 24/40; 250, 500 ml (see Fig. 1)
1 *Fractionating column, S.T. 24/40, with packing and shield (see Fig. 5–4)
1 Funnel, Büchner, 75 mm
2 Funnels, glass, short-stem; 50, 80 mm
1 Funnel, Hirsch, No. 000A
1 Funnel, powder, 80 mm
3 Funnels, separatory; 125, 250, 500 ml
2 Gauzes, wire, 100–150 mm
1 Glass cutter
1 Glycerine bottle, 1 oz, equipped with applicator rod
1 *Head, distilling, S.T. 24/40 (see Fig. 3)
2 Boxes of matches, safety
1 Pipette, graduated, 10 ml
2 Rings, cork, 11 cm
3 Rings, iron, straight shank; 3″, two 4″
2 Rods, glass, for stirring

1 Scoopula
2 Screw clamps
1 Spatula, nickel, 6–8″
1 Sponge
2 Stewpans
5 Test tubes, 6″
1 Test-tube holder
1 Test-tube rack (wooden block with drilled holes)
1 Test tube, side-arm, 22 × 175 mm
2 Thermometers, 360°
2 Towels
1 Trap, gas (see Fig. 8–5)
1 Trap, safety, for filtration (see Fig. 3–3)
1 T-tube
1 Tube, for drying agent
4 ft Tubing, glass, 8 mm
1 Wash bottle, polyethylene, † 250 ml
2 Watch glasses, 100–125 mm
1 Wing-tip, for Bunsen burner

Supplementary list in lieu of S.T. equipment:

1 Condenser, standard
1 Flask, Erlenmeyer, 500 ml
2 Flasks, extraction; 250, 500 ml
4 Flasks, round-bottomed; 100, 250, 500, 1000 ml
1 Fractionating column, with packing and shield (like Fig. 5–4 except with 10-mm straight tube at bottom and 8-mm delivery tube)
1 Head, distillation
1 Head, steam distillation (like Fig. 3, except with 12-mm straight tube at bottom and 8-mm delivery tube)
4 ft Tubing, glass, 8 mm
4 ft Tubing, glass, 9 mm

Corks, cork borers, round file, and ring stands available in the laboratory.
Suitable lengths of rubber tubing issued to each student.
One gas chromatograph with accessories (cf. Chap. 4) is sufficient for a laboratory of 24 students.
Items required for thin sheet chromatography are listed in Chap. 7.

---

†The polyethylene wash bottle should have a tiny hole in the top so that the solvent will not be forced out when the room temperature rises. When the bottle is squeezed to eject solvent, a finger is placed over this hole.

Additional equipment required for advanced work in Chaps. 34–39:

Ground-jointed equipment is recommended for these operations; however, use of rubber stoppers or rubber slip joint connections is frequently a convenience and advantage in vacuum distillation (cf. Figs. 31–1, 31–7, 31–8). Alternate equipment without ground joints may be used, but it is not included in the following list.

2 Ball bearings
1 Condenser, S.T. 24/40 male
1 Desiccator, vacuum
2 Flasks, Claisen; 125, 250 ml
3 Flasks, distilling; 125, 250, 500 ml
2 Flasks, 3-necked, center S.T. 34/45, sides 24/40; 500, 1000 ml
2 Funnels, cylindrical, dropping, S.T. 24/40; 125, 250 ml
1 Funnel, separatory; 1000 ml
1 Hot plate, electric, 3-way heat or continuously adjustable
1 Motor, stirring, with transformer or rheostat control
2 Oil baths, in steel beakers, with supporting rings; 11, 16 cm
1 Pipette, graduated, 1 ml
1 Seal, mercury, S.T. 34/45, with Teflon O ring and fitting top-piece
   [Fig. 33–4 (a)]; S.T. 24/40 if used with side-tube flasks (Fig. 1)
2 Stirrer shafts, Hershberg, with tantalum wire blade to fit 500, 1000
   ml flasks (cf. Fig. 38–1)

Larger items of equipment may be shared by several students.
1 per 6 students; fractionating column and accessories:

   (a) Total reflux column with heated jacket (Chap. 32)
   (b) Vacuum pump (oil)
   (c) Fraction cutter (Fig. 32–6)
   (d) 6 Round-bottomed flasks; three 125 ml, three 250 ml, S.T. 19/38
        with side inlet for capillary (Fig. 32–2)
   (e) 3 Condensers for reflux with above flasks, S.T. 19/38 (for preparation of ethyl hydrogen adipate, Chap. 37)
   (f) Electrically heated oil bath (Fig. 32–2)
   (g) 2 Variable transformers, one for bath rated at 5–7.5 amp, one for
        jacket rated at 3 amp
   (h) Pressure regulator (Fig. 31–6) is optional

1 per 5 students; outfits for electrolytic reduction:
   (a) 6-Volt battery, or 6-volt 4-amp battery charger
   (b) D-c ammeter, 0–5 amp

   (c) Slide-wire resistor, 25-ohm; or variable transformer to control battery charger
   (d) Cathode, copper (Fig. 39–2)
   (e) Anode, lead
   (f) Glass propeller-type stirrer (Fig. 39–3)
   (g) Alundum extraction thimble, dense, 4.5 × 11 cm
   (h) Copper wire for connection of apparatus

1 per 3 students; vacuum pump (oil) in addition to those for columns, preferably mounted on carts and with a protecting tower of flake sodium hydroxide attached.

Time Required for Performance
of Experiments

II

The times given are required for setting up apparatus, performing the experiments, and cleaning apparatus. If local conditions involve delays at the stockroom window, or in other ways, allowance should be made for such consumption of the student's time. There must also be recognition of time devoted, during the laboratory, to lecture or quizzing. No allowance is made for time consumed during long reflux periods, long steam distillations, and similar operations, for it is expected that during such intervals the student will be occupied with cleaning apparatus from a previous experiment, setting up apparatus for the next experiment, or performing another experiment. A major cause of delay is drying of apparatus; so provision of a heated compressed air outlet is very helpful. For efficient operation in the laboratory, the student must plan his work in advance so that there will be few times when there is "nothing to do."

The times given are estimated to one-half of a 3-hour laboratory period, and based on average times required by students. If a single "long" laboratory period is used, $5\frac{1}{2}$ hours is approximately equivalent to two 3-hour periods; however, some additional planning is required to allow time for such things as drying of crystals. Of course, some students are able to work faster than others in the laboratory, and an experienced operator can perform the experiments in a much shorter time than indicated.

Under average conditions, about 1 hour is required for "checking out" a locker, but a minimum of 2–3 hours is likely to be required for putting the locker into condition for "checking in."

Experiment	*Time (3-hour periods)*
Melting points	1
Crystallization	$1\frac{1}{2}$
Distillation	3
First gas phase chromatography	1
Steam distillation	$2\frac{1}{2}$
Paper chromatography	2
Thin layer chromatography	2
Ethyl iodide	1
Butyl bromide	$1\frac{1}{2}$
Di-*n*-butyl ether	2
Cyclohexene	1
n-Butyryl chloride	$1\frac{1}{2}$
Methyl benzoate	2
Methyl salicylate	$2\frac{1}{2}$
Capramide	$2\frac{1}{2}$
Caprinitrile	$1\frac{1}{2}$
Azelaic acid	3
Cyclohexanone and tests	$2\frac{1}{2}$
Benzyl alcohol	$1\frac{1}{2}$
Pentaacetyl β-R-glucose	1
Osazones	$\frac{1}{2}$
Lactose	$1\frac{1}{2}$
Mucic acid	$\frac{1}{2}$
Bromobenzene and *p*-dibromobenzene	3
Bromination of chlorobenzene and glpc	3
Nitrobenzene	$1\frac{1}{2}$
m-Dinitrobenzene	1
o- and *p*-Nitrophenols	$3\frac{1}{2}$
Sodium *p*-toluenesulfonate	1
Aniline	2
Acetanilide	$\frac{1}{2}$
Sulfanilamide	2
p-Acetaminobenzenesulfonyl chloride	$1\frac{1}{2}$
Sulfathiazole	1
β-Benzoylpropionic acid	$1\frac{1}{2}$
γ-Phenylbutyric acid	$1\frac{1}{2}$
6-Bromotoluquinone	2
Phenanthraquinone	2
o-Bromochlorobenzene	$2\frac{1}{2}$
Guaiacol (*o*-methoxyphenol)	$2\frac{1}{2}$
Methyl orange	1
N-Methylpyrrole	2
2-Aminothiazole	$1\frac{1}{2}$
2-Amino-5-nitropyridine	$2\frac{1}{2}$
2-Amino-3-nitropyridine, additional	$\frac{1}{2}$
Quinaldine	3
2-Tribromomethylquinoline	1

Time allowed for *separation and identification* should be sufficient for exploration, and for trial and error. Some "unknowns" require much less than others, but extra time so generated can be used for optional work. It is recommended that three 3-hour laboratory periods be allowed per unknown, and one period for a separation.

Experiment	*Time*
First vacuum distillation	1
Tetraethyl propane-1,1,3,3-tetracarboxylate	2
Glutaric anhydride	$3\frac{1}{2}$
2-β-Cyanoethyl-2-ethylhexanal	$2\frac{1}{2}$
Heptanedinitrile	$2\frac{1}{2}$
6-Chlorohexanenitrile	$3\frac{1}{2}$
Pimelic acid	$1\frac{1}{2}$
Dimethyl 6-cyanohexane-1,1-dicarboxylate	3
Suberic acid	2
Diethyl cyclobutanedicarboxylate	3
Cyclobutanecarboxylic acid	2
Methyl hydrogen succinate	1
β-Methoxycarbonylpropionyl chloride	$1\frac{1}{2}$
Purification of thionyl chloride	$\frac{1}{2}$
Ethyl hydrogen adipate	4
Dry ether	1
2-Decanol	3
1-Naphthoic acid	3
Methyl 4-oxododecanoate	4
Toluquinone	3

Strengths
of Acids and Bases

III

	Specific Gravity	Per Cent by Weight	Molarity
Concentrated hydrochloric acid	1.18	36	12
Constant-boiling hydrobromic acid	1.49	48	8.8
Concentrated nitric acid	1.42	71	16
Concentrated sulfuric acid	1.84	96	18
Glacial acetic acid	1.05	100	17.5
Syrupy phosphoric acid	1.69	85	14.5
Concentrated sodium hydroxide	1.43	40	14
Concentrated ammonia	0.90	29	15

Atomic Weights
of Certain Common Elements

IV

Symbol for Element	Atomic Weight	Symbol for Element	Atomic Weight
Al	26.97	Hg	200.61
Ba	137.36	Ni	58.69
Br	79.92	N	14.01
Cd	112.41	Os	191.5
Ca	40.08	O	16.00
C	12.01	Pd	106.7
Cl	35.46	P	31.02
Cr	52.01	Pt	195.23
Cu	63.57	K	39.10
H	1.008	Se	78.96
I	126.92	Si	28.06
Fe	55.84	Ag	107.88
Pb	207.21	Na	23.00
Li	6.94	S	32.06
Mg	24.32	Sn	118.70
Mn	54.93	Zn	65.38

Index